# FROM SKY TO SEA
## A *Story of* **EDWIN A. LINK**

*by*
Susan van Hoek

*with*
Marion Clayton Link

BEST PUBLISHING COMPANY

*What is man, that thou art mindful of him...?*
*...Thou has given him dominion over the works of thy hands;*
*...the birds of the air and the fish of the sea, whatever*
*passes along the paths of the sea.*
                              *—Psalms, 1.8-3.9*

*Of all the wonders of the universe, the greatest is man.*
                              *—Aristotle*

FIRST EDITION
Designed by Carolyn Gibbs, Best Publishing Company

ISBN 0-941332-27-6
Library of Congress Catalog Number 92-74733


Composed and printed in the United States of America.


Best Publishing Company
2355 North Steves Boulevard
P.O. Box 30100
Flagstaff, AZ 86003-0100 USA

# Contents

# *Acknowledgments*

Ed Link is perhaps best known as the inventor of the Link Trainer, a flight simulator since modified and streamlined to serve land, sea and space. In oceanic circles he's also known for undersea inventions, including Harbor Branch Oceanographic Institution's *Johnson-Sea-Link* submersibles. However, the real story is in his character, in his remarkably stubborn will, and in his love for problem solving, exploration and discovery, which in turn made him a frontiersman in the realms of sky and sea. This work offers impressions of Ed, the spirit of genius playing in an ordinary world, who received over 30 patents in his allotted 77 years.

To help tell the story, Ed's widow, Marion Clayton Link, author of *Sea Diver, Windows in the Sea* and numerous articles, shared her memories and reflections, archives, and unpublished journals with me. My heartfelt appreciation goes to Marion, who long and patiently waited for this publication to become a reality, for the privilege of working with her.

Special thanks are also due Ed's younger sister, Marilyn Link, who was a mainstay; proofreader Else Hanover White, another mainstay; one-time Link Foundation Secretary, Anice Duriaux, for invaluable help in countless ways; Harbor Branch Oceanographic Institution, the marine research center that introduced me to Ed and supported me while I told its story; and all well-wishers who joined in informal discussions and otherwise enthusiastically contributed to this production. I'm particularly grateful to writer P. (Pat) Goodnow Thomas, formerly a Washington journalist with the Voice of America, who generously applied her editorial skills to the original manuscript. For sharing their computer expertise, I gratefully acknowledge Ed's and Marion's son, Bill Link, as well as my own son, Scott Adkins.

Finally, Marion Link acknowledges with me those many people who provided motivation by wanting to see Ed's story in print. These include underwater cinematographer, Al Giddings; author and diver-physician, Dr. Joseph MacInnis; and marine botanist and submersible technologist, Sylvia Earle; three famous figures in the world of oceanography who credit their own early inspiration to Ed Link and who in turn helped to inspire this work.

—Susan van Hoek
PUBLIC AFFAIRS DIRECTOR (RETIRED)
HARBOR BRANCH OCEANOGRAPHIC
INSTITUTION, INC.

# *Foreword*

*This is the poignant human paradox: a plastic brain
capable of endless self-transcendence, equally capable
of being trained into self-limiting behavior.*

> — *Marilyn Ferguson*
> — *The Aquarian Conspiracy*

On the surface, Edwin A. Link is remembered for placing the human race safely into the skies through proper aviation training and navigation techniques, for originating the simulator industry, for paving the way into the oceans with his cutting-edge ideas, for Link Trainers and *Johnson-Sea-Link* submersibles. However, it is his lifetime of bringing dreams into reality that inspires his admirers today. His story is a useful example of what all people are capable of doing if they strive to realize their largely untapped potentialities. Ed's rare ability to arrive instinctively at difficult solutions demonstrates an unusual faith in his "right-brained" intuition; something that is largely ignored in today's materialistic world. But intuition is surely a birthright of anyone who will take the trouble to learn natural ways to achieve alternate states of mind. As psychiatrist Carl A. Hammerschlag writes in *The Dancing Healers,* "To heal ourselves or help heal others we need to reconnect magic and science, our right and left brains."

Ed was a visionary. In 1980 he was presented with the Lindberg Award before 500 dinner guests at the American Museum of Natural History, and was designated "A truly renaissance man: engineer, inventor, explorer, philanthropist, businessman, pilot, archeologist, oceanographer, conservationist."

He was often called a "renaissance man" and no doubt he was, but, remarkably, he achieved that level of creativity without a formal education beyond his junior year in high school. He was no intellectual in the academic sense of the word, yet he was clearly a genius. Perhaps he was a prime example of how genius relates to a way of processing information rather than to how much knowledge is accumulated by formal education. Ed did not rely on inductive reasoning alone; he made quantum leaps of logic. As a mechanical engineer, he saw connections in apparently unrelated things, joined them in unconventional ways, and created dazzling new inventions. To do this, he evidently utilized the specialized abilities of both brain hemispheres.

Dr. Betty Edwards, in her book *Drawing on the Right Side of the Brain*, refers to studies headed by Roger Sperry, winner of the 1981 Nobel Prize in Physiology and Medicine, which says that highly creative people successfully integrate the two types of information processing that occurs in either side of the brain. On the other hand, research indicates that most people in Western society are one-sided, with the left-brain dominating the right. Though there may yet be some question as to the specific attributes of either side of the brain, and in some people these may be reversed, the fact of dual ways of perceiving cannot be denied. As Edwards observes, "Mankind has always sensed its own dual nature," and points out in *Drawing on the Artist Within*:

~ ...some inner acknowledgment of the duality of the brain seems to be harbored deep in human consciousness ...for example, philosophers through the ages have proposed two ways of knowing the external world, through the intellect or through the emotions; through logical analysis or through metaphorical synthesis. Dichotomous terms abound: Yin and Yang, rational and poetic, abstract and concrete, scientific and imaginative. ~

Hammerschlag goes so far as to say, "Mainstream America is a left-brain culture — we believe in rational scientific thought, causality, explanation," then adds:

~ The right brain is the home of magic, of intuition, emotion, creativity, faith, the irrational. Great discoveries in science or art are made through the nonrational, nonlinear insights of the right brain. It is the left brain that knows how to speak, but the right brain that remembers the lyrics to the songs. You need both to dance. You need both sides to remain healthy. ~

What if he is right? How can ordinary people get the cosmic dance of life right if they are only "half-witted?" What if the silent brain-hemisphere, empty of rationalizations, can perceive deeper insights while the other side habitually blocks such intuitive perception with a constant stream of learned and opinionated verbalization? What if the right-brain is attuned to higher aspects of the self, higher realities, parallel universes, or even a greater universal mind? Would this explain in some measure how an unlettered person like Ed Link could constantly take the ordinary and turn it into the extraordinary? I believe this possibility is worth considering as his remarkable story unfolds.

\* \* \*

FROM SKY TO SEA, Ed followed his unique vision. He followed it through a life of adventure to eventually serve on a Woods Hole Oceanographic Institution board with another adventurer on the high seas, J. Seward Johnson, Sr. Their relationship led several years later to Johnson's founding of an important oceanographic institution on the east coast of Florida at Fort Pierce.

The Johnson & Johnson executive and heir combined his oceanic interests with Ed's engineering expertise by turning Harbor Branch Foundation, already established by Johnson in 1963, fully to the emerging field of oceanography. He bought land and constructed new buildings at the snug harbor in Fort Pierce where Ed had docked his 100-foot research yacht *Sea Diver* and was building submersibles and operating a marine science center. He and Ed also attracted the Smithsonian Institution to establish a marine station on site. It was a dynamic combination of interests. Perhaps it was inevitable that Link and Johnson would come together since both were drawn irresistibly to the sea and both were concerned with the protection and wise use of its resources. Their joint insight finally led them to conclude that mankind must look to the oceans for ultimate survival.

It was this kind of insight that prompted Binghamton newspaper columnist Tom Cawley to observe in writing about Ed:

> ~ Ed Link had an eerie sense of probabilities, which in many ways, particularly in aviation, was prophetic. He [then] turned his attention to the sea (not as an expert yachtsman, but [to provide] a global source of food for the world's hungry), and was working hard at it when he died. ~

Just as Ed knew in the early twenties that the emerging field of aviation would be important to mankind, he later sensed that in the affairs of men, the earth — particularly the oceans — must come first, even ahead of space exploration. Both he and Seward Johnson concluded that since the planet is largely covered by water, to an average depth of two miles, oceanography was the critical field of endeavor to pursue and support.

Ed built a house on his parcel of land at the research center; Johnson did the same, and the two friends lived out their final years at the site of Johnson's not-for-profit Harbor Branch Oceanographic Institution. Cancer claimed Ed's life in 1981, and took Seward's in 1983. But their combined legacies live on in the laboratories at Harbor Branch, aboard the research vessels *Seward Johnson, Edwin Link*, and *Sea Diver* and in the famous manned submersibles, *Johnson-Sea-Link I & II*. Today Seward's commitment to the welfare of both man and sea and his great emotional and intellectual interests are apparent in the major financial investment he made in Harbor Branch, where he lives on as the very essence of the institution. Ed too lives on, through his inventions and pioneering discoveries. More importantly, a visit to Harbor Branch offers a clear testament to what the human spirit can achieve when it senses itself to be unlimited and learns to function with a fully integrated brain.

— Susan van Hoek

# Introduction

*"...Edwin Link is an inventor, businessman,
undersea explorer whose success story is a
20th Century Horatio Alger's tale."*

—Dr. John Furbay,

Occasionally a man is born who very nearly epitomizes the human potential at a particular stage of evolution. Edwin Albert Link, Jr., born to Edwin Albert and Katherine Martin Link in Huntington, Indiana, July 26, 1904, was in many ways such a man. Without the advantage of a "higher" education, he came to realize his potential through imagination rather than academia. He was an unsophisticated genius who stretched the human capacity to achieve to its outer limits.

Pilot and fiction writer Richard Bach (*Jonathan Livingston Seagull*) uses the adventures of a barnstorming pilot in an early book titled *Nothing by Chance* to indicate unconscious relationships between events that appear to occur merely by chance. In keeping with that philosophy, it is perhaps no coincidence that Ed Link was born in Indiana where one of Bach's barnstorming protagonists made his appearance in a later book titled *Illusions*. Like Bach's fictitious "hoosier" hero — a flying messiah/airplane mechanic — hoosier-born Ed Link was a real-life barnstorming pilot/mechanic who, missing out on higher education, failed to learn his limitations. Without that knowledge, like Bach's messiah, he routinely worked out new ideas and habitually did things that had never been done before.

But even though he rose above his fellow man in outstanding achievement he chose to be known to the world merely as Ed. Though Marion often called her husband Edwin, few others did. It has been said that Ed, who helped pave the way to space and designed entry into the oceans, invented as matter-of-factly as most people drive to work. Yet this genius of world stature, awarded and honored throughout his adult lifetime, apparently never intended to be anything other than "Ed," a man without pretensions. As reported by writer Fran Aller, when once approached for a story on his life, he declined, saying, "I think you need a better character to write an autobiography...My life doesn't deserve a story."

Binghamton publisher Harvey Roehl knew Ed well and described him in an article as deceptively modest:

> ~ He was always a very ordinary man, and to meet him you'd never know that he was world-famous not only in aviation but oceanography as well, and that he was at one time a captain of industry, founder of the whole field of simulation of flying and industrial processes. He'd been honored by world governments for his many accomplishments, and was known locally as a man who much preferred to be puttering in his [basement] workshop than to be on a public platform, being asked to make speeches. ~

* * *

I FIRST SAW ED IN FORT PIERCE, Florida where I worked at Harbor Branch Oceanographic Institution in 1980. I didn't know who he was when he walked down the corridor dressed like a railroad engineer with a little dog at his heels. He reminded me of some of my relatives in Indiana who worked for the railroad, or of an aging seafarer perhaps. He had a smile-creased, tanned, weather-beaten yet whimsical face. I could sense that he loved the shaggy dog, even as he mock-scolded her for refusing to wait outside in the golf cart. Surprised at seeing a dog in the hallway, I studied the interesting pair as they passed my office door, he with a spark in his eye and a lop-sided grin under a railroad engineer's cap, she wagging and prancing smartly; a short-legged mop scurrying to keep up with his long-legged stride. Hunching forward slightly, he moved on, lost in thought and looking perhaps a little weary.

Even though I had since met Ed and his Tibetan terrier, "Sherpa," when they came again, he still hardly seemed to me like the vice president of a major research center. But appearances to the contrary, he was an executive board member of Harbor Branch where research in the marine sciences and ocean engineering is pursued to this day in an atmosphere of prestige and academia. However humble he may have seemed, Link was by then a world-famous figure, successful in any number of endeavors.

When the man and his dog appeared on another day, he again gave her a command to stay in the golf cart. This time she dutifully waited until he was out of sight, but it was only a trick on her part. No sooner had he rounded the corner than she hopped to the ground and chased after him through the receiving department doors.

Though then a self-made multimillionaire, the image he projected of an artisan was not uncharacteristic; he was a hands-on mechanic and engineer through and through. Even after retirement from the Link company, along with other significant inventions he had built three vehicles primarily for scientific expeditions, the Perry-

Link *Deep Diver* and *Johnson-Sea-Link* class submersibles, and found time to rebuild with several cronies two Link theatre organs. In the engineering lab at Harbor Branch he also began and encouraged the development of an underwater, remotely operated vehicle (ROV) called CORD (cabled observation and rescue device), a prototype of today's unmanned submersibles. At home he also studied renewable energy sources, hoping to discover alternatives to nuclear energy (which he saw as only a partial and impermanent solution to a growing world need), and experimented with solar energy, steam and wind as supplements to diminishing fossil fuels. Until he died at 77, he worked at these interests, even while wearing a pacemaker and fighting cancer.

Among his other thoughts on energy, Ed wrote in 1974 while serving on President Nixon's National Committee on Oceans and Atmosphere (established in 1971) that though the country had large reserves of undeveloped petroleum resources, it was "not wise to hasten its runout time while it was still possible to import it from other countries." He recommended that, "Meanwhile our country should go on a crash policy of immediately developing solar and other energy sources to conserve what petroleum we still have." He said that automobiles would have to be smaller and more efficient, but he predicted (accurately) that the American public would be slow to give up "the present high-powered transportation which they love." He also said:

~ Development of solar power and other forms of energy should be encouraged meanwhile, and publicly financed where necessary. It should be remembered that nuclear energy is a non-renewable source of power, as is petroleum, and therefore should be utilized now while available, but with the realization that it is not the ultimate answer.~

A windmill towered over his house on the Harbor Branch complex. Nearby a half-life-sized, steam-driven train meandered through the mangroves, reaching the west bank of the Indian River lagoon and looping back again to the station, at times carrying Harbor Branch employees and their families, visiting tourists, or bus loads of school children. The train is now in operation at the Gold Coast Railroad Museum in Miami, but when Ed was alive, he and Marion would often steam out in the parlor car of The Little General to the lagoon for a picnic or a quiet drink at the end of the day. Ed also installed a scaled-down train station, complete with such historic artifacts as an antique ticket booth, an old-time Link nickelodeon player piano and a water tower. This edifice served as port of call for his "East Swamp and Gatorville Railroad."

\* \* \*

HE LIVED OUT MUCH OF HIS RETIREMENT with the same determination, the same restless energy that drove him throughout his career, which inspired him in mid-life to anchor on a reef in the open sea many miles from any shore, fighting wild weather conditions for days at a time, seeking historical artifacts and sunken treasure. That was just before he developed his own theory as to the first landfall and subsequent journey of Christopher Columbus through the Bahamas, and before he conducted the first underwater archeological survey of the sunken city of Port Royal at Jamaica, before he discovered the remains of an ancient city in the Sea of Galilee, and on and on. That same vitality had spurred him throughout his first career in aviation.

Ed was a man of action, scholarly only when he needed to do research or reflect on solutions to problems. His son Bill remembers him as a man who always worked, with little time for diversions. "The only television Dad ever watched was the news," Bill recalls, "and besides the daily newspapers he only read what pertained to his projects," though his younger sister Marilyn Link also recalls that he consistently read *Reader's Digest* from cover to cover.

Blessed with drive, stamina, curiosity, he pushed himself through his adventures with an enduring sense of excitement until he had seen the job at hand done and a new one begun. Fully living his life, he was motivated by a belief that a man's worth is measured by whatever he manages to give back to life, and he never stopped trying to give it all. Just days before he died he was occupied with redesigning the wheelchair for posterity, then, ironically, still working, he took his final rest on Labor Day, September 7, 1981. As hard as he had worked, work was never drudgery for Ed. As he liked to say, "I never worked a day in my life."

\* \* \*

LIKE AN ORIENTAL SAGE, Ed was deep yet simple. His closest allies say he was shy, modest, unassuming, yet he obviously sparkled with creativity to the last. He was known to stick stubbornly to his guns, and while slow to anger, he could get riled. At least late in life he was occasionally referred to by the younger men he worked with as a "hardass," but long-time submersible pilot Mike Adams recalls, "...you could get him to listen, though." Canadian author, diver and doctor of hyperbaric medicine, Dr. Joe MacInnis, called him "The Dreamweaver," but unlike most dreamers, Ed got things done. He could be summed up as "special," but never seemed to know it.

His wife Marion Link, an author in her own right, was Ed's helpmate, first mate, adventuresome companion, partner in historic adventures and lifetime love. She shared his attitude of unpretentious simplicity. Her husband led a remarkable life and did what he did because it was there to be done and he could do it; "and he persevered," she says, "stubbornly." Her husband worked and traveled and discovered and explored and went places no one had been before, and she went along, living her own remarkable life. Whenever he reached a roadblock, he merely removed it. If he needed a tool that didn't exist, he made it, and she came to expect that.

Perhaps it was again no coincidence that Marion — whose genius for journalism became devoted to Ed's spatial skills — turned out to be a perfect complement to his mechanical, intuitive genius. This, like many other coincidences along the way, makes a strong case for Bach's "Nothing by Chance" theory. Viewed from afar, it is easy to imagine an underlying pattern of direction, like Lao Tse's "something there is," unseen and elusive; perhaps an invisible hand guiding the innovator from airplanes and space simulators to deep diving submersibles for a sort of sky and sea coupling, like dancers moving to an arcane rhythm.

Another coincidence occurred when the space shuttle *Challenger* debris search and recovery work was accomplished in large part by the Link-designed *Johnson-Sea-Link* submersibles. While the lost space team had completed many hours of training in the Link-derived space simulator (which had once been used on the ground to work out a serious problem for an earlier team of astronauts in space), the submersibles, supported on the surface by Harbor Branch's research vessels *Seward Johnson* and *Edwin Link*, played a key role in successfully fulfilling the *Challenger* recovery mission.

If not quite Bach's modern day messiah, Ed Link was at least a quiet genius of heroic stature. I found him near the last with his beloved wife Marion, living in their home on the Harbor Branch complex, saying man's immediate future was in the oceans — before space; a great man working with steam, trying to improve on remotely operated vehicles, searching out geothermal ocean current and solar energy sources, riding around on a golf cart with little, fluffy Sherpa; an extraordinary man in the garb of an ordinary man.

And he saw himself as ordinary. In 1980 interviewer Fran Aller wrote:

~ Guided by an insatiable curiosity and quest for new adventure, Edwin A. Link has become one of America's foremost industrialists and inventors. Yet the 76 year-old Binghamton [and Florida] resident is more amused than surprised when he reads an article about himself. "I often wonder, who's that?" he said. ~

Perhaps inevitably, his life direction ended in oceanic work, as did Seward Johnson's. The two friends had found one of their final but enduring expressions in the not-for-profit Harbor Branch Oceanographic Institution, Inc., dedicated to research in the marine sciences and ocean engineering. In addition, Ed had charged The Link Foundation Board of Trustees at their last meeting before his death to consider supporting research related to the development and conservation of energy resources.

# CHAPTER I

# A MECHANICAL GENIUS DROPS OUT

## 1904–1922

*To sentence a man
of true genius to the drudgery of a school
is to put a racehorse to the mill.*

*— Charles C. Colton*

Edwin Albert Link, Jr. came into the world in the middle of the Industrial Revolution in 1904 at Huntington, Indiana, a small midwestern state rich in American history. Historian Frank M. Gilbert described the region in a treatise on southern Indiana as a once popular crossroad for great numbers of migrating Indian tribes, before a European invasion brought on the arrival of America's first French hunters. Gradually the territory was taken over by German, Dutch, Irish and Scottish pioneers who, making their way west by wagon train, recognized the rich soil for what it was worth and remained to cultivate the land.

Legendary trail blazers like Daniel Boone once wandered Indiana's meandering creeks and river banks. Abraham Lincoln's family settled for a number of years south of Huntington, just north of Boonville where young Abe is thought to have attended grammar school. To this day the people proudly identify with Lincoln's wit and humor, and they call themselves "hoosiers" just as Lincoln once labeled himself. Hoosier is an essentially meaningless word that in times past applied to vagabonds and mountaineers wandering from Kentucky to Southern Indiana. Walt Whitman, Hoagie Charmichael, Herb Schriner, Red Skelton and James Dean are only a few names on a long list of world-renowned hoosiers. Throughout his days Ed Link seems to have remained in many ways a hoosier, though just after his most formative years he moved away from the farming and industrial state to Binghamton, New York, where his father took up management of an ailing music company.

By then Indiana had very likely worked its way into Ed's young soul. He undoubtedly had memories of several big and lazy rivers that flow through the hills, woods and farmlands. And he surely remembered the seasons with their sudden and dramatic changes: summer, when insects sing and the countryside smells of dark, warm earth and deep-green growth; autumn, when an initial blaze of color fades to brown and leaves fall on the moist and waiting ground; winter, when cold fine mists mingle with wood smoke, and trees stand bare, tracing their skeletal silhouettes against a washed out sky; and spring, coming in March and April, when gray clouds heavy with rain give rise to a new cycle of budding daffodils, hyacinths, tulips, and crocuses, when migrating birds return; dogwoods bloom; wheat, corn and tomato plants eventually break through the soil; cattle graze on new grass; and children wait for the strawberries, apples, and peaches to come.

Cicadas and meadowlarks, crickets and mockingbirds provided a background melody to the small boy playing in the fields. He liked music and would listen to it all his life. Nearly every day his mother could be heard practicing her singing somewhere in the house. It's easy to imagine young Ed, even at play, concentrating, meditating, losing himself in whatever the center of interest might be, at least vaguely aware of the surrounding sounds. He liked to lose himself in the factory atmosphere, too, and was intrigued by the tools, instruments and unique sounds where his grandfather built pianos.

His older brother by seven years, George Theron, had interests of his own, but young Edwin didn't mind solitude because he liked gadgets and could spend hours amusing himself alone. From an early age he was preoccupied with how things worked, how mechanical things moved. Later on he talked about his early devotion to the electric train. He concentrated on it as a child, checking, probing, musing, trying it this way and that, already sensing an understanding of its machinery. Late in life he would look back and recall that in Indiana he rode on a scaled down model of a steam driven train and was fascinated with it. He vowed then to have one of his own one day, which he did at the age of 75.

Like other children, young Ed was driven by instinct, living in a timeless world of being. Brain researchers say that until approximately five or six years of age all children are highly intuitive and visually oriented. However, coincident with the onset of grammar school, this type of perception, thought to be located in the right brain hemisphere, seemingly gives way to the verbal, analytical thinking mode that today's researchers generally agree is located in the left side of the brain.

The first five years of Ed's relative freedom came to an end with the beginning of school even before he moved away from Indiana. Then it seems the walls closed in on him. He was prisoner to a clock, and boredom weighed heavily on his restless, creative mind. In the usual public school curriculum, it is only outside of school that the visionary, intuitive, mechanical, emotional or even spiritual interests of a child can be can be pursued. From the very beginning Ed wanted more than the classroom had to offer, studying whatever was required but also chomping at the bit for the freedom to focus on his own activities. As time went on he somehow managed to do both, learning the preferred skills without trading off his deeper insights.

Albert Einstein had a tremendous struggle with formal education. Years later, after equally tremendous successes in mathematics and physics, he concluded that his intuition had turned out to be worth considerably more to him than his academic training had been, and he postulated the maxim: "Imagination is more important than knowledge." If so, young Ed Link already harbored the seeds of imaginative genius when he speculated at school about future possibilities rather than paying strict attention to the subject at hand. He later spoke of how in the classroom his mind wandered off to the depths of the sea, though he lived far inland. He told submersible pilot Mike Adams that as a child he had dreamed of going deep into the oceans, wondering what he would see there. Just by holding a conch shell to his ear he could hear far off tides beating the shore; a prelude, perhaps, to his one day becoming the first human to conduct a saturation dive, spending eight hours under the Mediterranean Sea breathing a mixture of helium and oxygen.

His imagination was stirred when he gazed upward and visualized how it would be to fly. The times were ripe for boys who wanted adventure and knew how to dream. The flying Wright brothers were in their heyday. Other innovative people were cranking out ideas for new machinery that could extend man's capabilities almost endlessly. If he thought about it at all, he might have seen himself passing through invisible barriers, soaring into the future with nothing to hamper his lift-off but certain removable obstacles.

\* \* \*

THE EASY DAYS IN INDIANA ended abruptly for Ed and Theron when, after Ed's sixth birthday in 1910, their father was appointed to manage the heavily indebted Automatic Music Company of Binghamton, New York, in an effort to save the investments of a group of its creditors. These included the Schaff Piano Company of Huntington, a piano factory previously established by Ed's grandfather, George Theron Link, as an affiliate of Schaff Brothers Piano Company of Chicago.

Leaving their ancestral home behind, the hoosier family stepped immediately into the intricacies of Binghamton's commercial history. The Automatic Music Company, formed in 1899, was located in a building on Water Street that had once been occupied by Bundy Time Recording Company, formed in 1889 by A. Ward Ford, his brothers, and Willard Bundy, creator of the first punch type "time card." Historical records show that Bundy Time Recording moved to the Water Street address in 1894 from a rented grist mill on Commercial Avenue, but after merging with several other companies and renaming itself the International Time Recording Company in 1900, the business outgrew the building and moved in 1905 to larger quarters at Endicott, west of Binghamton. Following other mergers, this company in 1924 became familiarly known as IBM (International Business Machines).

Meanwhile, Ed's father took over as acting president and manager of the Automatic Music Company until it went bankrupt in 1913, at which time Link Piano Company was formed and housed in the same building on Water Street.

While the senior Edwin Link thus established himself in their new environs, he sent Ed to grammar school for what he thought would be a solid grounding in academics. He knew how to raise boys and meant to give his sons all of the usual advantages, and to prepare them to go on to high school and college, eventually to follow in his own footsteps.

Steadily making his way to success, Edwin Senior in 1913 filed for a certificate of corporation for Link Piano Company. City records show that a certain Armer E. Johnson then purchased buildings and land from the trustee in the bankruptcy of the Automatic Music Company, and on June 14, 1916, contributed the land to Link Piano Company in trade for a share in its ownership, along with stockholders P. A. Peterson, Edwin A. Link, Sr. and Ed's mother, Katherine. The company then employed a staff of 75, which eventually grew to between 100 and 125 people when the first automatic pipe organ went into production. This instrument later became known simply as the Link Theatre Organ, but was first marketed as the "Link C. Sharpe Minor Unit Organ."

Ed began early to show signs of independence. In school a headstrong battle against formal education had started, and it continued for years. All the while a well-meaning but relentless attempt was made to shape his creative energies into a common and acceptable framework, in much the same way that a child's preference for left-handedness was often forced to the right in those days. The schools were then uniformly and rigidly structured in an attempt to adapt to the industrial world, and as a result, learn-by-rote children were commonly manufactured and let off the assembly line when they got their diplomas while mavericks got lost by the wayside. All children studied grammar, reading, writing, spelling, history, and arithmetic. They memorized everything. They were not taught how to think, instead they were exposed to hard facts. Learning was accomplished by studying what was known, not by exploring or experimenting with the unknown, which was already appealing to the precocious youngster in Binghamton.

In the restrictive world of academia Ed showed early signs of being a congenial misfit. Quietly he began to defy authority by not conforming to the curriculum, either unable or refusing to step into the harness that was designed for him. Though certainly conforming to the rules of society on the surface, in retrospect he seems to have harbored the instincts of a true rebel. He was industrious and wanted to work hard and to learn, but he needed to do things his own way.

In grammar school his personality unfolded; he was somewhat shy, kind, fairly obedient, sometimes humorous and sometimes unusually serious, mischievous (he liked practical jokes), was adventuresome and as honest as Abe, but he was also as strong-willed. From his earliest days he had a determined, persistent, and stubborn nature. Sometimes he was even immovable.

While not overly studious, he worked single-mindedly at homemade gadgets and endless ideas, and though he often spent hours alone on his projects, he still managed to attract and fascinate his peers. He showed early signs of being a born leader, but with a hitch; his followers had to be interested in his ideas and accept him on his own terms. If not, he would choose to go on alone with whatever he was doing.

Usually his playmates at school and in the neighborhood chose to join him, because with Ed they could take part in activities like taking a clock apart, putting it back together again, and seeing it work. They could participate in a neighborhood circus complete with ringleader, trapeze artists, clowns, performing pets, magic, peanuts, cotton candy and pink lemonade — and earn a profit too with Ed designing and managing the show. They could witness boyhood schemes become realities because their leader had a habit of getting hooked on his notions and following them through to the end.

Weaving dreams and bringing them to fruition worked for Ed because, for all his stargazing, he had a strong sense of pragmatism. If flights of fancy took him into the clouds or beneath the waves, he thought like a mechanic, not a mystic, and matter-of-factly envisioned such excursions within the context of engineering. That way it was possible for anything to happen, given enough time. In his way of seeing things, if a person could think up a new idea they could also figure out how to make it work. It wasn't much to reach for the sky or even the depths of the sea if one studied the problems and then worked out safe and practical ways to overcome them.

His innovative genius began to find more tangible expressions in 1916 when he was only twelve years old. Ed saw himself deep sea diving not on the back of a dolphin but inside a snug underwater vehicle, and he designed the hardware and drew a plan for a very practical looking submarine. In the original drawing, now preserved at Roberson Museum and Science Center in Binghamton, a ripening capacity for thoroughness is evident in a cutaway plan that includes all essential details, though he would one day tell *Smithsonian* writer Michael Wallis: "Unfortunately, it wasn't very practical; it most assuredly would have sunk." (NOTE: photo on p.170, #1).

In his early years he drew on the environment and his imagination any way he could, often making his ideas visible by sketching them out on the drawing board. His first attempt at marketing is also preserved for posterity at Roberson in a comic strip drawn to advertise his father's business, in which he engages some hyperbole: "The Link Piano and Organ Company has already sold 40,000 organs."

Ed was obviously bright and innovative but ran into many roadblocks as he was growing up. Other people expected him to devote himself to textbooks, to their way of thinking, not to marketing musical instruments or to concern himself with the mechanics of submarines. Soon conflict in the family put a blight on his natural talents, and though born to be a doer, to look ahead, he found himself within a system that chained him to a desk, made him sit still and look backward in time through books. Perhaps he was already ahead of his time, wanting to take life in his own hands and choose what he wanted to do with it, even though others meant to turn his course.

Over the years Ed's father achieved an impressive level of success in business as well as in Binghamton society where he soon became a member of the Country Club. He was a conscientious parent who took a genuine interest in both of his sons, and meant to give them the best foundation for their futures. He was said to be a handsome man and a sharp dresser, a well-rounded role model, good at popular pastimes and even a winner of championship status at billiards, bowling and golf. But his was not the role that young Ed needed, and it soon became evident that Edwin Link Senior hardly recognized his youngest son's talents or his stunning potential. To further complicate matters, an ever-widening gap opened between himself and Ed's mother, which may well have advanced the boy's maturity in some ways but also denied him the nurturing he would have received from a more hormonious home environment.

Katherine Martin Link had come to the marriage from Tuscola, Illinois, near Chicago, established in her ideas, conditioned to a unique lifestyle, and differing in many ways from her dashing husband. She was evidently strong-willed enough to cling to her own sense of identity, which clashed with Edwin's ideas and personality. While he was socially oriented and business minded, she was artistically sensitive. Katherine's sensibilities perhaps gave her the greater insight into her younger son's personality, for unlike his brother Theron, who in many ways was like his father, Ed was more like his mother, with a passion for music, an interest in architectural design and a love for travel.

Though Katherine Link is described as "a woman with a rather stern and proper outlook" by biographers Kelly and Parke in *The Pilot Maker* — a book describing the development of the Link Trainer — she was also by their account "an accomplished singer and passive pianist." And in many ways she was an adventuresome and somewhat off-beat maverick who decidedly did not fit the stereotyped image of tea and parlor ladies in the early 1900's.

The differences between Edwin Senior and Katherine led to their divorce in 1918. Theron was by then away at school. Ed was deeply affected by the family split, but talked little of it except to one day tell his younger sister Marilyn that his father always respected his mother, though they were very different, and that his mother never loved any other man but his father. Ed was a fledgling teenager when, from the time of the divorce, his life became nomadic. He traveled with his mother across the country from the East Coast to the Midwest to the West Coast, to the Midwest again, back to the East Coast, back to the Midwest, and back to the East Coast again. It was his lot to struggle in and out of schools while his mother frequently moved around, augmenting her income as both a semiprofessional singer and a semiprofessional builder, designing and building the houses they lived in then later selling them for a profit.

In 1919, while his mother sang in Chicago and he stayed with her sister in nearby Rockford, Illinois, Ed finally developed a genuine interest in education at a vocational school, but this choice unfortunately turned out to be unacceptable to his father. Even so, Kelly and Parke report that at Rockford Training High he "took courses in mechanical drawing, foundry work, machine shop, and elementary carpentry." Night and day he threw himself into the activities offered by the school, they said, which Ed thought was a haven and a viable alternative to academia. "With the zeal of the damned," wrote his biographers, "he proceeded to steep himself in the world of the artisan in spite of opposition from his father."

While Ed thus discovered the joys of mechanics, Theron had already made it to the top of his class in academic standing at Hamilton College, and though he was said to have been painfully shy, he was popular with the girls and was even then laying the groundwork to become a college graduate, improve his social skills after marriage, and duly enter society in the accepted fashion. (Years later, in 1990, Theron's son-in-law, Dr. Joseph E. Murray, brought honor to the family in a way that would have pleased their father considerably by receiving the Nobel Prize for Medicine.) Theron's studies were geared to taking over management of the family business even while his younger brother was determining to buck both the family and the system. Ed discovered his gifts at vocational school, and from then on, he knew exactly what he wanted do. Nothing would stand in his way; he would study mechanics and energy, and some day he would fly.

* * *

THERE IS LITTLE DOUBT that young Ed Link had foresight, even prophetic vision. In designing his first submarine he demonstrated a youthful awareness that man would someday have need to spend long hours at work in the ocean's depths. Perhaps he had something as practical in mind when at about the same age he invented a system that lowered his bedroom window when the alarm went off, a bit of machinery devised from attaching together the clock, the window device, and the workings of a music box.

Seeing with his mind's eye, Ed from an early age was able to make startling connections, to rearrange existing hardware to make new things that would work in new ways. He was beginning to know himself, and to know that designing machinery and tools was for him the right thing to do. Conventional schooling was now out of the question; so he continued to press on in his own way, evidently not giving much thought to the social or intellectual pressures around him, not understanding or caring that his chosen field was looked down on in some ways. He was congenial, not aggressive, but he knew what he wanted and would have his way.

As a teenager he appears bright enough in an old family photo album; handsome like his father, looking every bit the college candidate with coat and tie, intelligent and obviously possessing a modicum of youthful self-esteem. But behind the shining, smiling demeanor a mechanic was definitely in the making. And he certainly would not have looked as dapper while pursuing his newly acquired hobby of building motorcycle engines. (NOTE:  photo on pg. 170, #2).

As far as his father was concerned, vocational schooling was not a viable alternative to an academic education at the right school, as was expected of people of their substance and social standing. Scholarship was, after all, fashionable. In their circle uneducated blue collar workers were thought to be little better than social outcasts.

At that time the information age was about to explode into being. Mass education promised to change the world. Almost everybody read. Newspapers abounded with muckraking journalists. The pen was proving to be mightier than the sword, or so it would seem. The publishing industry flourished. Textbooks made it possible for everybody to learn. Western society was plunging headlong into the development of specialized verbal skills, and, perhaps, losing some its insight in the process. Education was favoring the development of the left brain hemisphere over the right, logical, linear knowing over imagination and intuition. It was already considered shameful to be unable to read, even if an individual happened to be, as was said condescendingly, "good with his hands." The public schools, then as now, offered no regular training for such right-brained skills as art, dance, theatre, music, mechanical drawing, carpentry and engineering. These were electives for the few or alternatives for the dull if included in the curriculum at all.

In retrospect, it seems that Ed was oblivious to the times, at least in the sense of being clever with words. While he liked puns and mixed wit with corn in a "hoosier" style that became something of a trademark all his life, he wasn't socially glib. Though he was well able to read and managed to take advantage of the availability of information by educating himself, he was never a member of the intellectual in-crowd and did not choose to join the crowd.

Studies today indicate that many intuitive people give up, daunted by social pressures to conform. Even the most "right-brained" individuals often ignore that special way of seeing to be more like their peers, mistrusting and repressing that silent part of the self that seems to know without knowing, to sense without words.

Whatever the majority might do, Ed preferred to go his own way. Sensitive but not tender, he fought the system. Determined to attend vocational school, he was crossed. Each time he enrolled in a school of his choice, Kelly and Parke report that "his talents were recognized and encouraged," but he was moved back into the academic atmosphere by people who took an interest in his welfare from their own various and well-meaning points of view. Perhaps surprisingly, through a maze of changes he managed somehow to maintain his self-confidence, always knowing what he could do. In fact, years later he complained to reporters that the biggest problem with formal education was that "it teaches you what all you can't do."

The teenager thus went from city to city and from school to school being himself. Meanwhile, his brother Theron continued to excel as much in the academic environment as Ed did in the world of mechanics. Theron made Phi Beta Kappa while Ed was learning to take engines apart and put them back together again. It might be said that both of the Link children were geniuses, but Ed's aptitude for engineering was least understood or appreciated, and so he was forced to struggle.

\* \* \*

NOW 16, ED WAS IN CALIFORNIA with his mother in 1920 when he flew for the first time. He was enrolled at the Los Angeles Polytechnic High School where Kelly and Parke say he once again "flourished in the arts of science, mathematics, and machinery." He was making a little money working on motorcycles in a service garage and had begun to think almost constantly about flying. There were other projects as well, some of which caused concern to people other than his father. In the apartment where he lived with his mother, he built a radio, put up an antenna on the roof, then had to take it down because the tenants feared it would cause fires.

The desire to fly mounted as he followed the progress of famous pilots in the newspapers, his imagination fired by their barnstorming high-jinks until he could no longer contain himself. He borrowed a motorcycle, went to Chaplin Field, a little field operated by Charlie Chaplin's brother, Sidney, on Wilshire Boulevard where the Ambassador Hotel now stands, and saw for himself what it was like to fly. Spending a little of his father's money and his own meager savings for a single, fifty-dollar lesson, he did what he most wanted to do. The hair-raising ride included all the tricks the pilot could manage in a little, roaring, metal-framed, fragile-skinned Curtiss Jenny biplane. That day he was, as he often repeated over the years, "scared to death."

Describing that first ride as "fascinating all the same," Ed many years later told an interviewer, "When my father heard I started to fly he threatened to disown me, but I, like many youngsters, was stubborn." When he got down on the ground and realized that he had never even touched the controls, he thought, "that's a hellava way to teach someone to fly." Perhaps the germ was planted then for a new way to train pilots, but meanwhile, he had to be content as a passenger: "For better than an hour we did loops and spins and buzzed everything in sight," he said to Kelly and Parke.

Later he recalled his impressions. Wearing a leather helmet and goggles he sat in the open cockpit behind the seasoned pilot as they soared through the air. He felt the plane pull upward, heard the roar of the engine, saw nothing but blue sky above and the ground below. He experienced the death-defying joy of suddenly spinning downward, turning crazily, the ground rushing at his face, pulling out and reaching upward again, stalling, sensing with fear that a simple drop out of the sky would mean the end. Then the engine roared again and he was saved to fly again, with a memory that would last a lifetime.

Leaving the cockpit, Ed surely walked lightly on the ground, aglow with the conviction that he would be a pilot one day. There was no room for doubt in his mind. There was no practical way, no money, but still he knew he would do it. He went back a week later. Though he had some instruction in California, he would say, "I didn't complete it. I was just going to high school then. I didn't have enough money to continue, and besides, my father forbade me to fly at that time. So...." He told Wanda Wood in a community college radio interview that he flew two more times in a Curtiss Oriole he described as "a newly-designed Jenny," determining in the process that there was a future to flying.

Ed remained relatively happy attending the vocational school where he added photography to his growing list of abilities. His visual aptitude, his instinct for composition and balance, were already apparent in an early photo album documenting the move he and his mother had made to California. The artist within had recorded soft, white mists encircling dark, hard-edged mountain tops in perfect black and white contrast, while the pragmatist had methodically logged in the album the exact location, elevation, date, temperature and time of day.

Keen on airplanes, growing into his teens Ed worked as a mechanic and saved money for flying lessons. Often oil-stained, rebuilding a motorcycle, usually with grease under his fingernails, getting the education of an artisan and planning to fly, he was becoming anything but what other people wanted him to be. So in 1921, at the behest of his father, he was uprooted, shipped off to Bellefonte, Pennsylvania to a preparatory school meant to tame the maverick, prove his academic capabilities, and form the basis for college. Within four months, however, he left and went back to his own designs, this time in Chicago where his mother had moved once again. Ed simply wasn't interested in school. He could not get what he wanted at Bellefonte. He had decided for certain that he did not want a higher education, and it made no difference what his father thought about it. As he would later claim, he had no interest in college because he couldn't major in aviation.

Ed went to work in Chicago for Western Electric Company where Kelly and Parke report that his foreman soon recognized his unusual talents and recommended him for their machinist apprentice program. News of this development led to a last-ditch effort by his brother that sent him to Wheeling, West Virginia, where the young innovator was enrolled in the military-oriented Lindsley Institute. This time he found himself in a school that specialized in behavioral problems, though Kelly and Parke say, "While Ed wasn't a behavioral problem, he was an academic one."

To everyone's surprise and in spite of his own determination, he temporarily settled down and did very well scholastically for more than a year while living in a rooming house with his brother who had a job with an insurance company in Wheeling. Ed did not object to the military aspects at Lindsley. Perhaps this was because he had already become accustomed to the rigid discipline it took to stay at mechanical tasks for hours on end. However, his biographers claim that he "could not tolerate the dreary classwork" and so left school once again, returning in 1922 to his mother who had meanwhile gone back to New York to live. Considering that he was doing so well with his grades, perhaps he would have stayed at Lindsley had fate not intervened when his brother was transferred by his employers to Kansas City.

Katherine Link settled down and made Binghamton her permanent home. Through her influence, the returning prodigal continued to be exposed to design, music, and the sort of travel that encouraged his own interests. The rest of the time he haunted his father's piano and organ factory, developing a great appreciation for the organs in the process.

With little hope that her youngest son would ever acquire a formal education, Katherine was inspired to take him overseas for a matter of months and expose him to European culture shortly after he came home from school in Wheeling. Ed promptly satisfied his love for music in Europe by going around on his own to several countries, visiting the most famous pipe organs, introducing himself to players and choirmasters and arranging to attend concerts wherever he went.

Back home in 1922, enrolled in school again but still bucking the system, local legend has it that at Binghamton High School he one day jumped into the air, threw his books in a fit of frustration and stalked out of school forever. He had by then given up hope that vocational schools would ever be acceptable to his family. With that act of defiance he became his own teacher and continued to educate himself for the rest of his life.

At age 18, Ed firmly turned his back on formal education to apply his ingenuity and resourcefulness as he saw fit, taking full control of his life in the process. He did not know that by doing so he would eventually open numerous new doors for others, many of whom would stay in school to earn their doctoral degrees. Ed Link would one day offer much of his fortune toward scholarships for higher education, a value perhaps learned from his family. He himself got along without it, but still managed to earn university honorary degrees in addition to his more than thirty patents as well as a great number of awards and other honors.

CHAPTER II

# FLYING AGAINST THE GRAIN

**1923–1929**

*According to particle physics,*
*the world is fundamentally*
*dancing energy.*

— *Gary Zukav*
— *The Dancing Wu Li Masters*

inghamton, New York forms a triple-city with Johnson City and Endicott, famous in Ed's early years for keeping Americans well-heeled. The Endicott-Johnson corporation, then one of the most important shoe factories in the United States, provided work for large numbers of immigrants of all nationalities. The important commercial and industrial area was also the home of such well-known businesses as the old 1900 Washing Machines as well as Bundy Time Recorder Company, forerunner to IBM. The community has since developed into a center of culture, but when Edwin A. Link, Sr. and his family climbed into one of the early automobiles in 1910 and drove from Indiana to Binghamton, it supported a large population of relatively uneducated factory workers and offered little else.

Edwin, Katherine, George Theron and young Edwin found a climate in Binghamton similar to that left behind in Indiana; brisk in the fall under a persistent cloud cover, but with colder and shorter winter days. Over the years the children spent long evenings by the fireside, looking out from time to time on blue-white snow sparkling in the light of the moon. In spring they witnessed fragile, translucent maple leaves spiraling out from green twigs on long-barren limbs. Stately elms and chestnut trees budded back then, prior to the blight that all but eliminated both species. On a summer's evening, tall trees in dark green silhouette cast elongated shadows over the outlying hills. Biplanes could be heard droning over corn fields and cow pastures, exciting the children and often irritating their parents. Coming over the city, low flying pilots could see the heart of Binghamton divided in a "T"-shape by two deep-flowing rivers; the Chenango, running north to south and pouring

19

into the west to east running Susquahanna, only a few blocks away from where Ed one day made his permanent home on the banks of the Susquahanna.

Before the divorce that sent the creative teenager shifting across the country with his mother, the Link family had occupied a large two-story home on Riverside Drive. On his return to the area in 1922, Ed moved into another house of his mother's design, about when he dropped out of school and signed on as a full-time employee with the Link Piano and Organ Company. By then his father had contracted tuberculosis and moved on to California in search of a better climate, eventually to operate a route of coin pianos there while Theron managed the business back home.

With great diligence Ed stuck to repairing and tuning pianos and to repairing and rebuilding theatre organs. Ironically, this ultimately led him to success in the field of aviation though the job at hand had little bearing on his persistent dream of flying. From the beginning he concentrated on his work, evidently content for the time being with the novelty of the instruments, which fed to some extent his great love for music while the factory itself offered ample opportunity to experiment. Perhaps it was an ideal situation, for in the process of the work he could develop those special skills that had always seemed to be just out of reach during his school years. Meanwhile, through tuning pianos he discovered within himself a talent for perfect tonal recall.

During the time when he rounded the bend from his teens to his early twenties, when at least a few of his friends were already married and starting families, Ed became half-brother to a little sister in California. Marilyn Calmes Link, who grew up to idolize her brother and follow in his footsteps as a pilot and a consummate leader, was born in Glendale on February 20th, 1924, to their father's second wife, Maree Calmes Link.

This was an extremely busy and creative period for Ed, who was still living at home with his mother, working for his father under the supervision of his brother, and traveling extensively to make theatre organ installations and repairs anywhere from Long Island to Los Angeles. He managed at the same time to continue educating himself at the local library and with Popular Science and Popular Mechanics magazines, and had recently taken to trailing around from town to town after famous barnstorming pilots, collecting plane-ride tickets, helping airplane mechanics, washing planes, anything just to be on the scene. At the same time he extended his self-directed curriculum by building himself a makeshift darkroom and intensifying his interest in photography. On the side he developed an impressive collection of classical records; built and rebuilt radio sets; rebuilt motorcycles; found time to perform at silent movie theatres between matinees, entertaining audiences with his "amazing" wireless radio; and he once rode a motorcycle to California and back.

Though it wasn't what he thought he wanted to do with his life, Ed was using his creativity for the company in 1924, which led the following year to the company coming out with a new line of theatre organs under his direction and design.

A letter in the Link files at Roberson in Binghamton written by an organist known as "C. Sharpe Minor" praised these as having a beautiful tone and responding better than any organ he had ever played. The player further stated: "When I played on a LINK organ for an engagement...I fully realized that your organ, tonally and mechanically, was far ahead of any organ on the market today." By then Ed was extending the capabilities of the massive, fully complemented instruments, which could produce a wide range of music as well as silent-film sound-effects that simulated the likes of roaring thunder, galloping horses, and shrieking banshees. A lone player could in fact be a one-man band with such other instruments tied into the organs as flute, violin, drums, xylophone, carillon, glockenspeil, piano, guitar, marimba and many others.

With the concentration of a true artist Ed could easily lose himself in the rigging of these thunderous instruments, but however satisfied he might have been with the magic of theatre organs, he never gave up thinking about flying. All the while that he worked, he kept alive the dream of becoming a pilot, pondering how to acquire adequate training when there was no money for lessons, and how he might make such training easier and safer for himself as well as for others.

Like many other young people of his era, he had acquired a sense of social responsibility which strengthened through the years. Even as a young man he believed he was required to make a contribution to society, and when it came to flying, he had a very special concern for student pilots who in shocking numbers were not surviving their in-air training. In his opinion, such loss was unnecessary. He read in the newspapers about the dangerous job of flying mail for private contractors without proper training. He knew that in 1923, 31 of the first 40 airmail pilots were killed while flying. Flying lessons were available only to the very rich, and these lessons were inadequate in any case. Would-be pilots for the most part simply climbed into airplanes and tried to learn by the seat of their pants.

Ed gave all this deep thought while he worked, then concluded that there was no reason why something couldn't be done to teach flying on the ground. Knowing that he would not be the first to try, he began developing his own ideas for a realistic ground-flying instrument. He knew the French Penguin System allowed would-be flyers to get the feel of airplane controls, as did the Sanders Teacher and the Eardly-Billing Oscillator, but none of these were actually simulating real flight.

With his mind fixed on the idea of learning to fly before leaving the ground he began to increase his habit of following the barnstormers, observing their operations, willing to grease or wash their planes or do anything just to be around them. In between these visits he applied his unique way of seeing things to making an altogether different experimental instrument, which could be manufactured by the company, so that music could be heard over the din of skates at popular skating rinks. This involved attaching a Link Player Piano roll mechanism to a calliope.

Working, dreaming of flying, and meditating in the factory over ways to do things differently, making imaginative connections in his head while his hands and the analytical side of his brain remained occupied with more immediate concerns, Ed made a discovery that earned him a patent at the age of 20, in 1924 (said by others to have been his first, though Ed claimed that a patent for an automatic record player was his first). Defining a problem that had absent-mindedly annoyed him in his work for some time — the nuisance of lint sticking to player piano tracker bars — he found he could rearrange a bit of hardware and apply the principle of organ bellows to removing lint by transforming the bellows into a suction device. "It was a simple little thing," he later told Kelly and Parke in The *Pilot Maker*, "designed to make my job easier.... It worked fine and made me a little money, too."

"A little money" could be applied to flying, along with a certain degree of creativity. The year was 1926. For practice, he had taken to taxiing planes up and down runways while he continued to help out barnstormers in exchange for getting familiar with the controls. In turn, he applied this wisdom to his ideas about ground flying. At the same time he managed to get aloft by taking a few lessons from Richard "Dick" Bennett at Bennett Field in Binghamton, and obtained a few more lessons at Curtiss Field while making calls on the job in Long Island.

As the flying activities stepped up, accompanied by an increasing association with several pilots of questionable repute, Ed's disapproving father became so incensed that at one point he fired him from the factory. But this effort by Edwin Senior to rein in his son backfired, for without a job, Ed felt compelled to make his living as a barnstormer. Supplementing a small allowance from his mother, he continued to fly until his brother, after threatening to quit his father's company himself, got Ed hired back, Kelly and Parke say, "on the basis of his great skill at tuning and repairing the pianos and organs."

In a 1978 interview with Wanda Wood for a Broome County Community College radio show, Ed credited Dick Bennett with being the pilot who probably gave him most of his instruction. Other well-known aviators were flying in and out of Bennett Field at the time, as he reported, including Basil Rowe, Pan-American's first pilot, and Earl Southee. Lincoln Beachey was another early pilot who came to Binghamton, as was Ruth Law who Ed said had made a name for herself flying a Curtiss Pusher from New York to Chicago.

He went on to tell Wood that Ruth Law actually flew in the Binghamton area before he started flying, around 1916, using a horse training track for a landing strip at a time when, in his opinion, "the planes didn't look like much." They had little in the way of instruments, the earliest models even lacking compasses. The first instrument in the control panel was a tachometer in the cockpit giving the revolutions of the engine. Prior to foot pedals, early models were equipped with only a bar, called a rudder bar; the pilot would apply foot pressure on either end to guide the plane.

Ed spoke of some of the early women pilots, saying he thought that a few were a bit "noisy" but he respected the serious ones. These included Amelia Earhart, who later flew with Ed from Washington, D.C. to New York City while he gave her a demonstration of instrument flying when she acquired one of his trainers for her own flight school. He was "well-impressed" with Earhart, who in his estimation was, "one of the most retiring of women aviators." He said she was "a very nice woman, very modest, very quiet and very able." He also said he didn't blame Catherine Stinson, another early female pilot, "when she cracked up three times." Following two months of rebuilding the plane, for a second time, he said she took off and cracked up again, but when he was asked if she was a "typical woman driver" he replied: "Well, it was the airplane's fault, I think. She was pretty good to fly it."

Ed soon saw that the mounting interest in flying was bound to lead to greater numbers of people wanting to earn their wings. Men and women both were reaching for the sky even though it was still a dangerous proposition. He felt ever pressed by the need for a better training method. "It was just too dangerous for student and instructor. I wondered if it was possible to invent a plane that didn't fly. That was how it began," Ed told Arthur Herzog in a magazine interview, explaining the development of the first successful flight simulator in the December, 1964 issue of *True*.

Remarkably, the invention became a reality along with and even in spite of its designer's many other activities. Somehow Ed managed to do his job, still traveling; continue to follow the barnstormers from town to town; fly himself; educate himself; maintain his growing love for music; keep up with photography; and spend long hours — nights and weekends — alone in the basement of the red brick building on Water Street, developing what he called "the first primary flight trainer." Painted red originally, later blue when it finally emerged on the scene, this instrument would variously be called the "blue box" and the "pilot maker," before it grew in capabilities and finally became known as the "Link Trainer."

In spite of Ed's convictions, there were heated discussions among fliers at the time as to whether or not trainers were even needed. According to Ed, "Some people still believed that you could better learn by flying by the seat of the pants, the feel of the airplane," an argument which he then countered in his interview with Wood by saying: "Most of those pilots died shortly." He talked on to Wood about his early thoughts behind the trainer, crediting the idea, in part, to a man he saw at Wright Field, a certain "Major Ocker," who was trying to help people understand the problems with direction that are encountered in the air.

As he told the story:

~ ...[Major Ocker] took a seat and put it on a stool that would revolve. And then he'd blindfold the people and twist them around in this seat a few times, then ask them which way they were turning. They invariably said the wrong way, and that was one of the things that gave me the idea that you could make a whole airplane to train a pilot to do everything. He was merely demonstrating...that you couldn't tell where you were going by sight or feel. You had to have an instrument that told you where you were turning and whether you were flying straight or level, and so forth. ...We had no natural ability, like a bird, to do so; and even birds [can become confused], it's been proven ... they sometimes fly right into buildings and things by accident or at night when they scatter. ...That's the way early flying was. ~

Ed continued to explain that with the advent of a few instruments, he thought he could build a trainer that would teach pilots, as he put it, "...rather than their going out in the air, which was expensive and slow, and you had to have the weather to do it in; that you could learn most of it on the ground." Thus the entire simulator industry to come was germinating in the calm and determined mind of a one-time "hoosier."

Meanwhile at the factory he went on to advance with the company. The Capitol Theatre opened in Binghamton on September 23, 1927, and contracted a Link C. Sharpe Minor Organ, with installation directed by Ed.

In the factory basement he plugged away at his invention over a period of 18 months, until he had once more made the right connections with the materials at hand — primarily organ bellows — and successfully created a machine that could mimic the experiences of flying an airplane without ever leaving the ground. The first simulator resembled a primitive miniature airplane consisting of wings and fuselage that came complete with compass, stick, and rudder. The contraption could turn and bank, and revolve; simulating what a pilot might experience and thus enabling the flight student to acquire some command of his vehicle without spending countless hours and dollars in the air, and without endangering his life in the process.

The first trainer was later described in an article for a Link company publication, titled "The Story of the Link Orchestral Organ":

~ ...[It was] a stubby wooden fuselage with cockpit, mounted on an organ bellows that Ed had borrowed from his father's piano factory. The bellows were operated by an electrically driven vacuum pump, which caused the fuselage to pitch and roll as the pilot 'flew' the trainer. ~

It was a popular myth in the Binghamton area that the trainer was so realistic that some of its early users actually suffered from motion sickness.

Ed's engineering was direct, simple and highly practical. Perhaps as a carryover from his early days in Indiana, he also had a clear and simple sense of humor which surfaced many times during media interviews. Publisher Harvey Roehl once reported an occasion when Ed tested Roehl's aeronautical engineering expertise by asking him if he knew why the wingspan of the trainer was built to exactly nine feet, two inches. When Roehl admitted his ignorance, Ed replied, "Well, that's the biggest wingspan we could have and still get the trainer into the freight elevator in the piano factory." (Years later Roehl also told of a complete suit of armor that Ed had sitting at an organ console, which he referred to as his "Silent Knight.")

Though the little pilot training machine turned out to be difficult to market at the time, it was destined not only to save countless lives early in its career and throughout World War II, it would also evolve and continue to develop itself, proving to be the prototype to more and more sophisticated simulators, leading finally to a billion dollar industry. Eventually the Link Trainer would lead to instrument flight, new navigation techniques, jet-age computerized simulators, and training simulators for ship's pilots and for astronauts. But at the time, for Ed himself, the first simple model provided endless hours of practice on the ground. Others would have to wait for it, because, lacking insight, the world chose to ignore it. Ed's new pilot training device appeared to be, like so many other of his ideas, well ahead of its time.

At least the slowing economy made it more difficult to sell. Though certain members of the news media were quick to realize the flight simulator's potential, would-be users such as the U.S. Air Force just did not buy it. The designer was thus destined to suffer a long and sometimes humiliating period with his trainer, during which he alone, with characteristic perseverance, continued to believe in it. Evidently acting on blind faith Ed Link applied for what turned out to be only the first of a long series of training device patents. He received this patent on April 14, 1929.

* * *

IF THERE IS ANY TRUTH to new physics writer Gary Zukav's statement that life is dancing energy, then the dancing patterns of energy that wove the fabric of Ed's life did so to the accompaniment of music. At home his mother continued to study music and to play and sing. At the factory, Ed — who had as a child achieved one of his earliest inventions with the use of a music box — carried out his duties to the background of music, either from his own collection of classical recordings played on an old phonograph he had managed to salvage or by listening to his "wireless" crystal set.

Like a hidden refrain, music and energy seem to have commingled at the back of his mind, creating an esoteric tune that flowed throughout his life. As a young man, while he worked and dreamed of flying, thinking about the instrumentation of things, whether he worked on pipe organs and player pianos or fine-tuned the flight trainer, he listened to music. Music accompanied his efforts to organize and reorganize existing bits of hardware to move things efficiently, whether air through organ pipes or simulated planes moved by bellows. As Juliet Spall one day so aptly stated in an unpublished paper: "The music Ed heard...held the tonal quality of a finely tuned engine pushing through airspace at speeds unknown to eagles."

His habit of working to classical music eventually prompted him to devise a solution to the problem of frequent record changing, and he developed an automatic phonograph purely for his own use. This in turn led him to the creation of what he called "the Autovox, a coin selective machine," which was, perhaps, a forerunner to the jukebox. Little can be found about the device today, but it apparently worked much like the player piano. Although it is commonly accepted that Ed's first patent was for the device that removed lint from player piano tracker bars, he once claimed, during an interview with Harvey Roehl for an article by David Bowers (with Murray Clark), "An Interview with Ed Link" (located with Ed's papers at Roberson Center): "The first patent I ever had was the design for this." As he explained it to Roehl:

> ~ ...Rather than having a pneumatic mechanism, it was purely mechani-
> cal. ...It had two stacks of five records each on two spindles. The spindles
> divided in the middle; you could raise the spindles and slip the records in,
> and then select any one of the ten by push button. ~

Although what Ed described as "quite a few" Autovoxs were made at the factory, he failed to manufacture his phonograph further before Link Piano and Organ Company folded in the coming depression. Meanwhile, someone else invented a different automated record changer.

In spite of Ed's passion for music, his interest remained focused on flying, not on pianos and organs. And though he was a member of what was considered by all accounts to be a good family, he himself seems to have been unconcerned with the tarnished reputations airplane pilots had in that day. Obsessed with anything to do with aviation, he did in fact admire those people who regularly came through the area with their battered old biplanes, despite the fact that keeping company with barnstormers brought forth new quarrels within the family. Particularly distasteful to his father were the famous flying "aces," reported to be for the most part a boisterous, reckless, drunken lot of airborne gypsies who behaved as though they considered themselves national heroes, which in some circles they were. Believing in the future of aviation, Ed chose to remain loyal to these colorful pilots and got in his own flying time in the bargain.

Though the general school of thought is that many of these characters well deserved their reputations, it is certain that Ed admired them for their skill without becoming tarnished in the process. And though he himself was rapidly acquiring a reputation for being a daring, courageous and accomplished pilot, he never was considered to be a hard-living and glamorous star of aviation. On the contrary, World

War I ace, Col. George A. Vaughn, who knew Ed from his early flying days, later told Herzog for his *True* article, "I'd summarize Ed as humble, socially shy, gentle, kind and a country boy through and through."

But despite his own integrity and his father's opinions, Ed apprenticed with the rambunctious lot until at last he soloed with instructor and World War I ace, the famous Alfred "Al" Stanley. Stanley had made a name during the war years by going overseas, joining with the French and becoming a pilot of heroic stature with the Lafayette Escadrille. Returning to America after the war, his standing as an ace and his dare-devil skill carried him into the world of barnstorming where he quickly acquired a reputation for expert stunt flying as well as for liking his women and his drinking.

However, Stanley's lifestyle had no bearing on Ed's dreams because Ed was only interested in the future of flying. He evidently tended to live and let others live as they saw fit. Stanley was undoubtedly a great pilot, for which he was greatly admired by Ed, and Ed consistently kept company with him as well as a number of other pilots and mechanical engineers, including one Gunne Lowkranz who eventually became part of the engineering and development team in the simulator industry. Understandably, those years would stay alive in Ed's memory, and looking back, he would see his first solo with Stanley as his first real accomplishment.

Ed even kept quarters for a time with several of the barnstormers, sharing his mother's home while she was away in Europe for a matter of months. But in spite of this close association with the flying aces, Kelly and Parke make it clear that he "devoted himself to lending what credibility he could to the emerging field of aeronautics." With the development of the flight simulator, it is apparent that in his prophetic fashion he saw beyond the era of flying stunts and aerial theatrics to the greater potentialities of flight. Hard working, with a firm sense of ethics, not given to much strong drink, Ed, they wrote, "took aviation seriously and wanted to lend dignity to the field." As he told his biographers, "I wanted to promote aviation, not kill it."

Perhaps nothing during the twenties fascinated the American people more then the idea of flying. A certain element of the general public even loved the barnstormers, flocking to grass airstrips or open fields wherever they landed. They came like moths to the flame, eager to pay for the privilege of being scared out of their wits, to climb into open cockpits in wispy little machines that took them roaring off into the blue yonder, buzzing onlookers and often frightening cows in the field.

Joining the early pilots because he needed money to help develop the trainer, Ed later told Wanda Wood:

~ I used an airplane to earn a living with because one thing you could still sell was rides in an airplane, what we called barnstorming in those days. [We'd] go around to small towns in various places and fly over the town at about 50 feet and get everybody out, and then they'd come out to the field and then you'd sell 'em rides in the airplane... Most of [the fields] were just cow pastures. ~

The little planes could by then be seen over the countryside from western New York to northern Pennsylvania in numbers, hopping from field to field like buzzing insects. The pilots, including such well-knowns as Howard Bowen and Gardner "Peg" Nagle, seemed to be immortal, taking for granted their place above the horizon, flying into the sun, climbing and stalling, spinning and looping, defying gravity in irrational patterns across the sky. But there was no real night flying yet, not without instruments in the planes, though in some other areas beacons were put up every twenty miles to guide late-flying pilots. The job of selling airplane rides was surely made easier by the publicity brought to aeronautics by people like Charles Lindbergh who in 1927 captured the world's imagination by flying non-stop across the Atlantic from New York to Paris.

The number of earnest aviators was still small when Ed started flying; consequently, the name-pilots all knew one another. At the center of their comings and goings in Binghamton, he became acquainted with those who were best known.

Little did Ed know on the occasion when he met Lindbergh that one day in the years to come he would orchestrate the world's first, longest oceanic dive, in which Lindbergh's son, Jon, would be a principal participant. Ed met Lindbergh when the famous flyer was forced down in a nearby field (Choconut) in bad weather. (NOTE: photo on page 171, #3). He later described the episode to interviewer Wanda Wood without much fanfare: "He couldn't get his airplane started the next morning to get out, he and Major Lamphier, so I flew down with Dick Bennett to help him get it started, which we did. They got it started eventually and left." When Wood referred to other "old pilots" in the area, Ed stated:

~ Well, of course, I being the principal aviator around at the time, any new people that came to town, I would meet...some of them were well-known people of the day. Clarence Chamberlin was one of the first to fly the Atlantic; Billy Brock...was the first one to fly around the world in a land plane...and there were numerous others. ~

But in the midst of the excitement over aviation, a cause for gloom was creeping over the horizon. The world was gearing for an economic crisis. While Ed and Theron continued making a living at the factory, business began to go downhill, threatened by factors that included a declining stock market and a gradual phazing out of theatre organs by "talking" movies. Worried people were tightening their belts prior to the Great Depression, and they would soon have little use for the luxury of player pianos.

While events outside Ed's life had begun to shape his future, he was ready, having paved the way for a new direction by pursuing his mechanical and aeronautical interests in spite of persistent family objections. By the time the Link Piano and Organ Company was struck down in the Great Depression, he already had the trainer developed into a primitive but workable machine, ready for one of the world's first ground schools.

Meanwhile, he passed other milestones. He had already obtained his commercial pilot's license, No. 3582, in 1927, rated for "instrument, multi-engine, land and sea," but flying tests were not yet available then. He finally took his test in 1928. On February 28, 1928, he received delivery of his first airplane, a new Cessna Model AA (Cessna 4-120), "serial #114, with a 120 hp Anzani engine, DOC reg. 4156." He bought the plane, with help from his mother, directly from the plant. This purchase turned out to be one of many uncanny "firsts" for Ed Link, about which he said, "I bought the number one Cessna, the first Cessna that Cessna ever built that was eligible, that he could sell. He'd built a couple of haywire models before, but this was the first one that...was engineered through." The next year, 1929, the Link Aeronautical Corporation was established with Ed as chairman, president and founder.

Even though the trainer had not yet sold as he had hoped, the instrument would earn him, as he liked to say, "a little bit of money," first as a carnival ride that led to a few of the machines being sold to amusement parks, and then as part of a flight training package. As it turned out, the pilot trainer and circumstance helped Ed and several of his family members and friends to eek out a living during the years of bitter financial struggle ahead. That thread of "something else," whether it was serendipity or a genie on his shoulder, had programmed a fascinating future for the mechanic-come-barnstormer/inventor. Ed saw that with the invention of the pilot maker, something more than mere coincidence or even perseverance was working in his life, and he later told Kelly and Parke:

> ~ When I went to work in my father's factory, I started right at the bottom learning how to build pianos and tuning organs. It sure wasn't what I had in mind for a career, but it's curious how if a man puts his mind to what comes to hand, it often works for the best. I'm certain that if I hadn't had that experience, I would never have been able to build the first pilot maker. ~

Possessing good instincts, the persevering rebel knew how to trust life and let circumstances dictate, thereby successfully weaving himself into the fabric of the times.

# CHAPTER III

# DAREDEVIL FLYING
# THROUGH THE DEPRESSION

### 1929–1933

*"...They are saying ... you are a thousand years ahead of your time."*
*Jonathan sighed. The price of being misunderstood, he thought.*
*They call you devil or they call you god. "What do you think Fletch?*
*Are we ahead of our time?" A long silence. "Well, this kind of flying has always*
*been here for somebody to discover it; that's got nothing to do with time. We're*
*ahead of the fashion, maybe. Ahead of the way most gulls fly."*
*That's something," Jonathan said, rolling to glide inverted for a while.*
*"That's not half as bad as being ahead of our time."*

> — *Richard Bach*
> — *Jonathan Livingston Seagull*

As the industrial city of Binghamton braced for the coming Depression in 1929, Ed prepared to use his flightless plane for profit in the operation of one of the world's first ground schools — in the basement of the failing piano and organ factory. Even though the economy was in a serious decline, some people still yearned to fly at all costs, and he was ready with the right instrument at the right time. He planned to bring students to his basement classroom, put them in the ground trainer and teach them the feel of a plane economically while cutting their risks at the same time. Sure of himself and his simulator, for a total of $85.00 he guaranteed that every student of his would learn to fly by working in the ground-based machines until proving themselves ready to graduate to the air, eventually to solo.

Those who derided the process, deeming trainers unnecessary, called it "hangar-flying," while to others it was learning to fly the easy, safe, and financially feasible way. James L. Killgore wrote for *Invention and Technology*, in "The Planes That Never Leave the Ground," that Ed described his machine in an early advertisement as an "efficient aeronautical training aid..." and to prove it, he taught his older brother to fly in the trainer in a short time. "For six hours George [Theron] pitched, banked and whirled in the trainer," he wrote, then added: "To everyone's amazement, he soloed after just forty-two minutes of actual flying."

With perfect timing Ed and Theron had the school opened just as the factory began to fold. Later Ed told reporters that it was a good thing for him that it did fold, because he eventually did better with the trainers than he ever could have done with pianos.

\* \* \*

A MAJOR CHANGE WAS DUE TO COME in Ed's life, for at age 25, he was on the verge of meeting a girl who had a taste for adventure and a keen mind to match his own. Until then he had socialized primarily with barnstormers, mechanics and engineers — those who shared his immediate interests — and was otherwise not inclined to mix. He wasn't the kind to deliberate on his emotional needs or seek to establish lasting relationships. Those kinds of things would just have to take care of themselves or be ignored. Shy in any case, he evidently had little time or inclination to go out searching for a perfect mate, so he stuck largely to work and aviation and his cronies.

Meanwhile, he persisted in his interests and his genius developed steadily. He followed his instincts and learned to go with the tide. Apparently never trying to force results, he was more inclined to start things and stay at them doggedly until the right outcome unfolded naturally. In this way, even inventing was the logical outcome of something else, a project already underway, not to be thought of as a goal, a profession, or a specific direction to take. He didn't think there was anything special about inventing. As he said in any number of news media interviews: "Almost anyone can be an inventor if they find out what's wrong and then set out to do something about it."

But while there is some truth to Ed's statement, it is also true that he possessed unique qualities that made invention come easily. Fran Aller points out in an article, "If it Didn't Exist, He Invented it," for *Science Outlook*, that "Link speaks modestly about his inventions...," but, she adds, "Though he sees nothing special about his ability, he does admit it comes naturally to him."

For one thing Ed could look at a problem and make unusual leaps of logic, bypassing much analytical verbalization about what had been done in the past or whatever could or could not be done in the present or future. For another, he could focus his attention and concentrate indefinitely. He could live in the moment, working until he did what he set out to do, oblivious to the passing of time, often working all night long. Nothing pressing ever seems to have been waiting for him because nothing seems to have existed in his mind beyond the point of interest at the moment. He did not worry about the future, knowing he would meet and handle the next development when it occurred. In retrospect, he appears to have possessed tremendous faith in life and himself and whatever guided him along. And so it was in his private life as well. In 1929 Ed was concentrating on preparations for the flying school, losing himself in his work even as he unknowingly drifted toward a lifelong love affair.

In some ways it seems truly remarkable that their meeting ever happened at all. Working in the basement of a factory, content with machinery, music, and the company of his dog, Pat, the odds were decidedly against an intelligent, educated, self-motivated girl ever appearing in Ed's world, one who also loved music and who had even won a beauty contest on her college campus. Though he undoubtedly showed signs of genius, Ed was after all essentially a blue collar worker without a formal education at a time when most college girls expected to marry men with lofty degrees who fit within their own social sets, men more inclined to rub elbows with the elite at tea dances and cocktail parties.

Paradoxically, Ed seems also bound to have met this particular girl who, even with a higher education, had everything it took to belong in his life. Some would call it fate that they came together, though to psychiatrist Carl Jung that elusive element attributed to destiny might more rightly be defined as "synchronicity." Jung theorized that through the "collective unconscious" all people are universally attuned, while events affecting their lives are synchronized in time and space to one sort of universal rhythm. If so, then the meeting at hand was inevitable. Ed and Marion must gravitate towards one another, thereby disproving a whimsical theory credited to Einstein that "gravitation cannot be held responsible for people falling in love." But whether attractions of the heart can be attributed to synchronicity, movements of the stars, electromagnetic fields, destiny, divine guidance, all or none of the above, that singular element of coincidence which seems to have dogged Ed throughout his days was very much in evidence when he crossed paths with his future wife.

Marion Elizabeth Clayton, born November 15, 1907, in Ilion, New York — a small town in the historic Mohawk Valley where her parents were born before her — came to know Ed Link simply because she had a disagreement with her father and was consequently forced to change her mode of travel on her way to a new job in Binghamton, New York. The bright young reporter, just graduated from journalism school at Syracuse University, was on her way early in 1929 to her first full-time job when a series of unexpected events led to a blind date with Ed Link that did not take place until practically a year later.

Meanwhile, Marion had unwittingly and for some time been preparing herself to complement Ed's career. As a student, she was a campus correspondent for the *Syracuse Journal-American* and a part time worker on the *Utica Observer-Dispatch.* She was a serious student, had joined Pi Beta Phi Sorority, and was elected to Theta Sigma Phi, national honorary Journalism society, and Phi Kappa Phi, national honorary all-university scholastic society. With a number of accomplishments already behind her, she was ready for a writing career and eager to start work as a cub reporter for the *Binghamton Press.*

She had made arrangements to live in Binghamton at the YWCA, as was the custom for single girls on their own during the twenties. Her father originally planned to drive her there in the family car. However, plans went awry when, still in Ilion, she switched a work schedule at the family grocery store with her brother to go out on a date without obtaining her father's consent. Such approval was generally mandatory at the time, when most people recognized the father as supreme head of the household. Because Marion had not followed the appropriate chain of command,

her father refused to help her move. Instead she must carry all her worldly possessions with her from Ilion to Utica by trolley, and from there take the Chenango
Valley Railroad to Binghamton.

During what was expected to be a tedious train ride, a young man by the name
of Gilbert Giles turned out to be Marion's seat companion. The topic of conversation
made this unexpected meeting all the more pleasurable; Giles talked almost exclusively about a fascinating friend of his, one Edwin A. Link, an inventor with a number of interests including flying. Marion had twice had the opportunity to go up in an
airplane and wanted to become a pilot herself, but was held back by lack of funding
and by parental disapproval. Now that she was to be on her own with a full-time job,
she thought how fortunate it was to be riding through the countryside, hearing
throughout the trip about this unique person who had his own airplane and was organizing a "ground school."

Even though Marion was intrigued by the thought of the unknown pilot, she
might have forgotten all about him in the excitement of her new job but for another
coincidence; Gilbert's fiancee Isabelle Moore also lived at the "Y", on the same
floor and right around the corner from her own quarters. She and Isabelle became
close friends, and Marion quite naturally continued to run into Ed's friend Giles
from time to time.

Meanwhile, Marion was soon caught up in a life of her own, making friends,
dating, enjoying her career as well as her new-found freedom. Writing news became
an all consuming passion as the novice reporter turned professional. Her hopes and
dreams seemed to be more or less fulfilled already when, during her first Christmas
Holidays in Binghamton, as the world tottered in 1929 on the verge of economic disaster, Isabelle and Giles arranged for the 22-year old old Marion to go out on a blind
date with the 25-year old Ed Link.

That first date was a revelation for Ed; suddenly there was more to life than
airplanes and engineering. At first glance he was aware that something had been
missing in his life, and it is perhaps safe to say that he was smitten by her beautiful
smile. Meanwhile, the instinctive reporter lined up an article from her evening's
encounter with the pilot, who had entertained her with stories about his friend, Pat,
the wirehaired terrier. As Marion later recalled; "Ed billed Pat as his 'flying companion,' and that intrigued me." He told her that Pat loved to fly, knew the sound of
his airplane from any other, and liked to run outside and bark any time the Cessna
flew over the house without him. *The Binghamton Press* ran her story, which is now
in the archives at Roberson Center, with a picture of Ed by his plane and Pat standing proudly out on the wing.

The meeting for the interview further developed their casual relationship. They
went out together again a time or two, but Marion's active social life otherwise
remained the same. She dated another young man on a regular basis and continued

to see other friends. Eventually she moved out of the "Y" to share a place with three other women who were also making careers for themselves. But while she went her own way, not knowing how Ed felt about her, Ed was admitting to himself that he was interested in her in more than a casual way. His mind was becoming set. He began to think often about the reporter and how to court her in earnest.

Binghamton's Capitol Theatre manager indirectly took the role of Cupid by asking Ed to teach the musical genius, twelve-year-old Searle Wright, how to handle the Link Theatre Organ for a series of live recitals. This child prodigy, already popular for his piano performances, had accepted an invitation to perform between films, the only hitch being that he had never before played a theatre organ. Once the training task was undertaken, Ed was surprised at how little it took to instruct the prodigy, who showed an amazing capacity for the instrument. Searle was already playing smoothly through a medley of Victor Herbert tunes, and was playing one of Ed's favorite pieces, "Ah Sweet Mystery of Life," when the two looked up to see Marion Clayton standing at the front of the empty theatre, having been sent there by her editor to cover the story of the upcoming recitals. It was a significant day of coincidences for Ed; a lifelong friendship sprang up between him and Searle Wright, and he was provided with an unexpected opportunity to resume and build the relationship with Marion.

Ed began to see her more often, at one point appearing on her doorstep just as she was on her way out with another date. This somewhat awkward development prompted him to tell Marion at their next meeting that if she was going to continue to see him, he thought it ought to be to the exclusion of all others. To his surprise, she instantly agreed. Furthermore, she let him know that she was pleased and relieved to realize at last that he had a serious interest in her. From then on Ed claimed the right to monopolize her free time, wrapping his world of airplanes, barnstormers, and classical music and photography — seasoned by his own brand of humor and adventure — around the lovely and intelligent young writer. They flew in his Cessna, spent long evenings listening to records, and gradually merged their talents to produce Ed's flight school manual. (NOTE: photo on pg. 172, #6).

For what is thought to be the world's first flight manual, Ed had already prepared page upon page of instructions, which were, to Marion's dismay, spread about in an order of his own that amounted to an endless and chaotic array of stacks of papers. She took up the role of organizer and editor, patiently pulling together the stacks of paper in book form. The result was Ed Link's "Ground School Instruction Book," a mimeographed affair meant to supplement the flying school he was preparing to run with the use of his new invention, the flightless airplane.

According to the uncanny way in which things seemed to work for Ed, Marion was turning out to be his perfect match, applying her business organizational skills and her journalistic talents to his work, attending his flight school, going on dare-

devil flights with him, and loving his music and his dog as much as he did. Her natural place was at his side, in his self-created world, while at the same time he
admired and respected her interest in journalism and her wish to keep a steady pulse
on the world economy and the marketplace of ideas through the newspaper job.

For a quiet girl from a sheltered home in a small town, life for Marion became
more exciting with each passing day. She thought it unbelievable that she was
involved with Ed's work at the frontier of world aviation, at a time when she was
also reporting news that was almost always in an uproar, during the heyday of prohibition when the underworld inevitably made its infamous rise and when the economy was sinking daily toward the Great Depression.

Her once predictable life would never be the same. Typically, on a cold
October day she found herself driving upstate to meet Ed at a border town where he
intended to fly her to Canada to spend the weekend at his friend Bill Morris's place
on Perch Island in the St. Lawrence Seaway's Thousand Islands. But by the time she
arrived, the temperature had dropped to an unseasonal low, a blinding snowstorm
had developed, and she was grounded with Ed on the mainland. They sought refuge
for the night with friends in Clayton, New York, and were picked up by Morris in
his boat the next morning.

It wasn't long before she learned to accept adventure as a way of life. A full
year had passed since her first blind date with Ed and she was learning to cope with
his surprises as well as his constant state of being busy with serious pursuits, all at a
time when world affairs hung in a constant state of suspense. It was at that critical
moment in history when, as everyone stood helplessly by, Wall Street took its fatal
and resounding crash.

The failing Piano and Organ Company ground to a final standstill. The Link
family declared bankruptcy during the Christmas Holidays in 1930. Ed's father in
California left his coin operated piano route in favor of selling real estate while in
Binghamton Ed and Theron turned in desperation to the trainer and ground school.
Ed picked up what he could by barnstorming, chartering flights and ferrying passen-
gers in his airplane. Soon he would be helping his father to survive the depression.

Even with the bankruptcy the year marked a number of milestones for Ed. He
had grown to know and love Marion Clayton. He met young Searle Wright. The
Link Flying School was established. Before the weekend in Canada with Marion, he
had flown a group of business men to Canada for a fishing trip at Perch Island,
which would one day be his own. By the end of the year, he had acquired close to
500 hours air time, nearly 170 of which were cross-country.

The Link Flying School was in full operation by the time the plant closed
down and its assets were liquidated. The school then found a new home at the
Chenango Bridge Airport on the outskirts of Binghamton where Ed kept his planes,
and remained in operation in spite of the fallen economy. Ed's students spent one

night a week on the trainer until they were "checked out," at which time they flew with him in an Eaglet he had managed to acquire for practical air time. He later reported to Wanda Wood on the initial use of the trainer for ground school:

~ Actually, one of the reasons I was so interested in teaching flying was because I felt that it was a good proving ground, more to learn how to build a trainer...I took them up in the air and found out what they hadn't learned on the ground. ~

Afterwards he used his discoveries to modify the trainer. More than one hundred students managed to solo before the Depression deepened and the flying business dwindled to a minimal operation.

Ed continued to supplement his meager income by servicing airplanes and chartering flights. He also flew for Binghamton's first airline, Martz Airline. He and several other pilots located along a Buffalo to New York bus route flew the Martz Bus company's customers in to places not serviced by ground transportation. "The eight-passenger Bellanca was the same type [of plane] that Clarence Chamberlin and Ruth Elder tried to fly across the ocean," he told Wood, pointing out also that at the time, "there was nothing but grass fields lighted by beacon lights for runways and the only real criterion for an airstrip was if it sold gasoline or not." (Sometime after Lindbergh's cross-Atlantic flight to Paris, also in 1927, Chamberlin successfully made a non-stop flight from New York to Germany in a Bellanca.)

Marion had another taste of adventure after accompanying Ed on a trip to New York City where he had conducted business and she had encountered both the City and a "speakeasy" for the first time. On the way home his plane developed engine trouble, and they had to make a forced landing on a baseball field in the Pennsylvania countryside. A game was in progress at the time, and as they circled to land, people and cars scurried off in every direction. Ed then coolly touched down, made his repairs, and took off again.

During this period he briefly experimented with glider flying. He worked at the airport, flew parachute jumpers, did stunt flying, and continued barnstorming, scraping in whatever money he could. Many others found themselves out of work entirely. Marion remained employed by the newspaper, even asking for a raise at one point, only to be reminded that she was lucky to have a job at all. For almost everyone it was a time of tremendous hardship. The government had not yet organized a welfare system and it was left to those who were best off to do volunteer work, primarily by operating soup kitchens to help feed an ever-growing stream of the poor and hungry.

Ed and Marion chose that unlikely time to officially announce their engagement, thereby taking the first step for a new life together in the midst of the oppressive and pervading sense of hopelessness that was felt throughout the nation. They knew that Marion would have to leave her job after the wedding — in those days it was unheard of for married women to work — but that would not hinder their decision. They took their vows on the 6th of June, 1931, and afterward drove through the Adirondacks to the Canadian border and on to Quebec City for a honeymoon cruise to Montreal up the Chicoutomie River.

When they returned, the newlyweds moved into a quaint cottage by the Chenango River close to Binghamton Airport, which was then yet another "cow-pasture" where Ed operated his business. Their first home was a rustic little summer cabin located at the edge of farmland on the riverbank. The cabin had been decorated by Ed's mother with wicker furniture from her attic while they were in Canada. The place was trimmed outdoors with flower-filled window boxes, and consisted of a living-room, bedroom, kitchen, screened porch, and outdoor bath facilities, all of which had been made fresh with new paint.

On September 29, 1931, a patent was issued to Ed for a "Combination Training Device for Student Aviators and Entertainment Apparatus." His struggling pilot-maker business had moved with the flight school from the closed factory on Water Street to its first home inside an airport hangar, the trainer taking its place beside flying planes for the first time. These now included Ed's Cessna and the Eaglet, a Travel Air and a small conglomeration of oddities belonging to other pilots. Ed's barnstorming phase was essentially over by then, except when his cronies turned up to amaze people with wild stunts and to drum up airplane rides. At times he would still join in for a little stunt flying himself, but more often took parachuters up as his contribution to the immensely popular "air-shows" he and his friends put on.

Still among his friends were Al Stanley, Gardner "Peg" Nagel, Frank Hawks, and Harold Bowen. A good number of the era's flying aces would appear on the scene and disappear like migrating butterflies, while others stayed on to drum up work more or less permanently. Many of the latter would become involved in the future simulator industry, including the well known barnstormer, "Slim" Emerson, and the brilliant young engineer, Gunne Lowkranz, of Swedish background.

Ed was still doing whatever he could to survive, including teaching flying whenever he had students. Although he was generally safety-conscious to the extreme, as the Depression wore on and work became more scarce, he took commissions regardless of inherent dangers. When a government contract to conduct an aerial photographic survey came his way, he accepted it even though he lacked the oxygen needed for high altitudes and could not afford to buy the necessary equipment. In what Marion describes as "the little old Travel Air," without an extra air supply, Ed went aloft daily, flying high over the Appalachians, discovering that he could work at altitudes of over 10,000 feet by taking very long and very deep breaths. In this way he saw the contract through, even though he was violently sick after every flight.

As their first summer by the river came to a close, when evenings grew short and the nights turned cold, Marion came down with an illness and the honeymooners abandoned their uninsulated cabin, moving in with Ed's mother in Binghamton at 10 Avon Road. One day this would become their own homestead, while the little cabin was destined to be washed away by a flood soon after they moved out.

Marion gradually took over the responsibility of running Ed's office, keeping books, managing the paperwork and helping to keep the ground school going. Even so, their financial situation worsened. Jobs continued to dwindle at the airport. To anyone but Ed, working for himself might have seemed hopeless. The pilot maker was on hold, though to his mind there was still a real need for ground school training. Plane rides were not selling, and flight school was out for almost everyone; for others, it was barely affordable. Marion wrote in a journal she had begun to keep:

> ~ The depression got well underway and the next years were hectic ones during which I spent two winters in bed with chronic colitis, and the Link family piano and organ business failed. We struggled along trying to make a living from the flying school and an aviation repair shop. The trainer, which had shown such promise, sank back into obscurity. ~

Ed and Theron had already tried to interest a different group of people in the trainer by piggy-backing it on a borrowed model-T truck to Saint Louis, where they intended to put it on display in a National Aircraft Exhibition, but Kelly and Parke report in *The Pilot Maker* that officials there "refused to enter the 'gadget' as an exhibit," someone even suggesting that they use it for a carnival ride. As times grew bleaker, Theron, in the Link pragmatic fashion, finally talked Ed into agreeing to the next best thing to selling airplane rides; they would put the flightless plane to work at county fairs for a quarter a ride. Through this initiative Theron managed to sell the first few models to amusement parks, thereby helping to keep the business struggling on. A November, 1930 article in *Science and Invention* said of the now patented trainer: "...the device is a center of attraction at the Mayfair Miniature Golf Course in Los Angeles, California, where it was first installed."

Eventually almost 50 pilot-makers sold to amusement parks. Only two had gone to the aviation industry, without instruments, at a cost of $450 each. One of these went to the Pioneer Instrument Company of Brooklyn, to be used for demonstration purposes. The other was bought by New York State University's Museum of Arts and Industry.

Next, Ed followed a lead and flew to Pensacola, Florida, with his friend Bill Morris, proposing to teach trainer usage and sell it in numbers to the Pensacola Naval Institution, but this effort turned out to be yet another disappointment. He had already sold one model for $1,500, with instruments, to Naval officials at the Institution who were impressed enough to want to order five more, but Navy brass in Washington said, "no."

According to local legend, Ed was so desperate for cash to get things going that he offered half the business to anyone for the amount of $500, but got no takers. Another popular story in Binghamton is that he offered stock in those early days in place of payments he owed, and only one person accepted.

Eventually Ed moved his entourage to the airport at nearby Endicott where he established a government licensed airplane repair station, continued with his other freelance endeavors, and worked at all hours of the day and night, producing a few more flight simulators in the new hangar. He had meanwhile moved with Marion into rented rooms in nearby Vestal, while his mother, giving in to the pressures of the Depression, rented her house out to strangers and went to stay with her sister in Illinois.

Following a lead to possibly connect with the Army Air Corps for more sales, Ed and Marion trailored a demonstrator south to Newark, New Jersey, at the suggestion of one of the most noted pilots in aviation history, Charles S. (Casey) Jones. Jones was known as an ace pilot, for holding the 13th pilot's license ever issued, for learning to fly with Wilbur Wright, and for holding the world's speed record in 1931. For years he had operated the Casey Jones School of Aeronautics in Newark, making in the process a number of important contacts with famous private citizens who came to him as student pilots, and he had already made important military contacts while serving with the Air Corps.

This well-seasoned pilot, recognizing the importance of flight simulation, bought six of the trainers, and contracted Ed to fly to Newark on occasion to teach and demonstrate "blind-flying" at the school. Jones was preparing to take over the complete responsibility of marketing the trainers through the JVW Corporation (Jones; Col. George Vaughn, America's second leading World War I ace after Eddie Rickenbacker; Dick Watham and Lee Warrender), a partnership corporation owning the Casey Jones School and managing its sales efforts.

Ed and Marion's trip to Newark was undertaken during the fateful winter of 1932. Lacking funds for a hotel room, they were staying at a nearby rooming house when news came that President Roosevelt had closed the banks because of a run of withdrawals. Ed had to get back to his operations at home as soon as the trainer marketing agreement was signed with the JVW Corporation, but was stuck in Newark short of enough funds for the return trip. That night his subconscious mind went to work. He woke Marion in the middle of the night to tell her about the dream he had just had of designing and building an "electric sky sign," which was, he said, "made up of a grid of light bulbs under the wing of an airplane, with lights that could spell out messages in the dark." But in the cold light of day, the stranded couple had to place a call to Ed's mother asking her to please send them enough cash to get home.

Back at Endicott, still barely eeking out a living, things appeared to be status quo. The *New York Herald Tribune* reported on the still largely unsold pilot-maker, saying "...it promises to revise completely the meaning of the once disparaging term 'hangar flying,' since for the first time it affords airmen an opportunity for improving their skill."

Theron fell victim to the times and took work elsewhere. Fortunes were lost all around and the future looked dismal. People despaired, occasionally to the point of suicide. Greater numbers than ever were reduced to lining up in the streets for free handouts from soup kitchens. Ed wasn't doing much better when he made a decision to act on the dream he'd had in the rooming house at Newark. Trusting in his intuition, he put his ingenuity to work and built the world's first "electric sky sign," stubbornly staying at it even after an initial failure. The first model was mounted on his Travel Air biplane, but it turned out that the engine wasn't powerful enough to handle the load. Undaunted, he set about mounting it on a Stinson monoplane with a Wright Whirlwind, J-6 engine, and on July 24, the system got up into the air and was a success. Ed had already been out selling the idea and was immediately ready to begin aerial advertising for Spaulding Baking Company, proclaiming across the night sky in bright lights that "Spaulding's Cakes are Fresher." Several other planes proved able to carry the load as well. Marion later wrote about the device that helped them through the Depression:

> ~ An ingenious invention of Ed's, a changeable message Sky Sign from which a future Goodyear blimp sign was patterned, carried us through this crucial period. But it was a dangerous business. Racketing through the night over the hills and mountains of New York and Pennsylvania in a one-motor Fairchild plane burdened with a heavy frame beneath the wings which flashed messages, Ed had many close calls. Often I was with him. As the business expanded, the smaller sign was supplemented by a large one on a Tri-Motor Ford. ~

But while the publicity was good, any sense of security and stability was an illusion. Without a word of warning, Ed was suddenly told he would have to move his operations once again. This upheaval came about at the whim of George F. Johnson, of the Endicott Johnson Corporation shoe business, who had taken a particular dislike to flying and didn't want his sons — who were sneaking off to buy rides with Ed — to fly. As Ed later put it, "George F. didn't believe in flying." The wealthy and powerful Johnson forced him out of town simply by deciding to close down the city-owned airport, which happened to be located on Johnson's company-owned field. According to Ed's later version, as told to Wanda Wood:

~ I went to see Mr. Johnson and said, "Well, one of the difficulties is, I've got about ten or twelve men working out here and if you close the field down it puts me out of business and it puts about ten or twelve people out of business." And I said, "There is a possibility I could move to Cortland, but that's going to cost me some money, five or six hundred dollars that I don't have and can't afford to bear it." He says "How much is it gonna cost you"? And I said, "Five hundred dollars." And he sat down and wrote me a check and gave me five hundred dollars to move. ~

But as Ed had already learned, seeming setbacks often work out for the better. As a result of the shoe magnate's action, his situation actually improved when he next became an airport manager, even though from the start he had to pay a sum of fifty dollars a month rent for the job. In place of the little wooden hangar at Endicott he moved into an unused airport at Cortland, approximately 50 miles north of Binghamton, with a larger, brand new hangar capable of housing his entire operation, including the newly acquired, oversized Tri-Motor Ford called a "Tin Goose." He named the new business "Link Aeronautical Corporation," and went on with his work. In a later interview with Wood he remarked: "Usually the Chamber of Commerce pays people to come to town, but this time I was paid to get out of town, and I took most of my employees with me."

He settled down again to lovingly grinding out still unwanted trainers, picking up whatever living he could by teaching, ferrying planes, repairing engines, chartering flights, sometimes sponsoring airshows, and running the more lucrative business of aerial advertising. But what he really needed was a large contract to pay for the production of his pilot trainers, which remained, essentially, unsold.

In addition to running the office, while still at Endicott Marion had made her contribution by operating a hot dog stand at the airport, which supplemented their income and provided what was too often the only food they had to eat. "The air shows," Ed would later say, "were always an idea to get a crowd out, but Marion made more money selling hot dogs to the crowd than I did flying airplanes." Now at Cortland she continued to run the office and took on a job as a part-time hostess where she and Ed had taken an upstairs room in a house that doubled as an occasional tea room, serving dinners for fifty-cents apiece on Wednesday evenings.

But their greatest relief came with Ed's creation of aerial advertising, which not only helped them out and sold products for others, it lifted the spirits of area residents who were deeply discouraged by the Depression, sounding an optimistic note in a time of utter pessimism. Brightly lit planes in the dark of night were like an omen of good fortune. People ran outside when they heard the planes coming to see this latest aerial wonder; brilliant lights spelling out messages overhead, spectacular in the night sky. They marveled at the pilot who had thought up the scheme. At no time in the history of the world had anyone seen anything like words beaming messages across dark space, upstaging even the moon and stars.

Ed later described the sign to David Bowers, Murry Clark and Harvey Roehl in an interview, carefully explaining in detail that he had a piano mechanism in the plane and would punch out the rolls for different messages. "The holes would light up for 'Spaulding Bread,' 'Enna Jettick Shoes,' and others," he said. "I put a venturi tube in the slipstream of the airplane and that created a vacuum. It was a player piano in the air!"

Operating the signs from three planes over a period of three years, Ed and company pulled out of the worst of the Depression, but not without a number of harrowing experiences. Pilot George Bevins once made a forced landing in a field outside of Philadelphia aboard a Fairchild cabin monoplane owned by Ed's company, which, among other things, broke a wing of the plane and landed Bevins in the hospital. After that the plane was further damaged by vandals in the night. ["They wrecked] the ship completely with stones and clubs, and [carried] away with them valuable pieces of equipment which had escaped damage," according to a Camden, New Jersey newspaper account recorded by Kelly and Parke.

Marion found the entire "sky-sign" venture terrifying, but often flew with Ed anyway. To make sure that people came out to read about the virtues of Utica Club Beer and other products they promoted, Ed came up with yet another innovative installation, what he called an attention getter; a 10-note pipe organ. With a big wind-driven air compressor under the Ford's wing, the organ was played by rolls, and "it had to be loud," he told the trio of reporters, "or nobody could hear it." Meanwhile the daredevil pilots, who had become nearly forgotten has-beens during the Depression, were heroic stars once again. They took off and landed in the dark with nothing to guide them but two little rows of smudge pots, and roared through the night at low altitudes — under 1,000 feet, sometimes as low as 200 feet — "too low to bail out at night, and in country too rough to land," Ed and the others would often repeat.

Ed later received what is now debated as either his fourth or fifth patent for the electric sky sign, called an "Illuminated Aerial Display," issued December 4, 1934, though he never manufactured or marketed the device. These advertising flights were the means to tide him over until the advent of World War II, which brought its own solution to the problem of economic woes and paved the way for the world's first major simulator industry.

Still, it was the sky sign business that provided enough income for Ed to bring three other pilots in, first to Endicott and then to Cortland. Al Stanley and George Bevins flew with Slim Emerson and Ed throughout the adventure. These four men had a decided advantage over any other pilots in the world; they grew wonderfully adept at night flying by diligently practicing instrument flying in Ed's little flight trainer.

The flightless plane was the true hero of the day, making night-flying possible and certainly helping to preserve four human lives. Even so, this pilot-making "blue-box" had yet to prove itself to the military, which was to come about through a dramatic encounter between Ed and the United States Navy.

CHAPTER IV

# THE SIMULATOR INDUSTRY
# TAKES OFF

**1934–1947**

*I know as an inventor that really good
inventions tend to grow and evolve. Only weak
inventions take a single step and no more.*

— *James Lovelock*
*The Ages of Gaia*

*T*he stock market plunge was forerunner to a far worse blight on human
history than economic woes. Economic disaster indirectly brought
mass support to Germany's failing Nazi party, leading to the unifica-
tion of Germany, Japan and Italy in a war destined to bring the world closer
together by reducing its diversified cultures to one common state of suffering.
Ironically, the gristmill of world war would also increase the fortunes of many,
including those of Edwin A. Link.

While the majority of Americans had little sense of the coming Holocaust, rest-
lessness had prevailed throughout Europe and the Orient ever since the end of World
War I. The resulting rise in tensions were to be experienced firsthand by Ed and
Marion in the coming years, within the context of journeys abroad prior to the out-
break of World War II. Meanwhile, orders from overseas for the ground trainer had
begun to trickle in as a prelude to the coming conflict.

Born during the Seedbed Era, raised through World War I and the Booming
Twenties, honed by the Great Depression, Ed matured through the early thirties just
as America entered the Roosevelt Era. Having endured battles with formal education
as well as personal and economic hardships, he had come through as an accomplished
tuner and builder of pianos and organs; a barnstorming, fully licensed pilot; a government licensed airplane mechanic; an already several times patented inventor; an
accomplished photographer; and a happily married man. Now, the tool he invented
almost before its time was destined to be manufactured from the original rudimentary
instrument it was into more and more sophisticated models, while Ed himself evolved
from a struggling innovator into a major figure in the great Industrial Revolution.

But in 1933 and 1934 dark events far-reaching and profound were coming over the horizon. One can only wonder what Carl Jung's "collective unconscious" had in mind when German history culminated in the strangest and most destructive behavior that civilization had yet bred.

Even while Ed Link developed his trainer, stirrings of anti-Semitism were dovetailing in Germany with a devastating interpretation of Darwin's theories of natural selection, fostering a deliberate and audacious attempt by the nation's leaders to take over and manage the process of human evolution. In so doing, this nation would destroy much of Europe and thoroughly devastate itself, take the lives of countless Allied soldiers, and wipe out between five and six million Jews as well as millions of European Christians.

Elected in 1933, Franklin D. Roosevelt was coming on the scene at home, assuring Americans in the wake of the Great Depression that "the only thing we have to fear is fear itself." Repairing economic damage and facing the coming wars years, he was to prove himself a consummate leader. Out of office at the time, Sir Winston Churchill in England had begun to issue unheeded warnings of the threat of Nazi Germany. He would later replace the hopelessly optimistic Neville Chamberlain as prime minister and rise to the role of allied spokesman for Europe. Mussolini and fascism were in control of Italy, to become third member of the Axis powers with Germany and Japan. Already Japan was in the process of brewing its own suicidal bid for the world, which would, on December 7, 1941, result in an attack on Pearl Harbor.

But in 1934, while nations balanced precariously, Ed Link went on, an honest, creative, unpretentious man struggling in New York to get someone, anyone, to recognize the value of his trainer to would-be pilots. Ironically, while Hitler was preparing to stir mass hatred, to destroy the lives of millions, Ed was manufacturing a gift to mankind, an invention for individuals, regardless of race, ethnic group, nationality, or religious or political ideals. What he did not yet know was that history would remember him because of this invention, that Churchill would praise it as playing a vital role in winning the war, and biographers Kelly and Parke as well as countless reporters would immortalize him by writing: "At least a half-million pilots, from thirty-five countries, owed their lives to preflight training on the 'blue box.'"

But in 1934, Ed was still struggling to make ends meet. The aerial advertising business had grown and become more widespread. Pilots flying the 'sky sign' necessarily continued to sharpen their skill at instrument flying, motivating Ed to enhance the trainers to some extent, though the most sophisticated instrument panel was yet to come.

Early that year, while seemingly disassociated tensions around the globe continued to build, the U.S. Army Air Corps, which had taken over airmail contracts, lost five planes and pilots within one week. Ed, his followers, and the newspapers lost little time in attributing this disaster to a lack of night and instrument flight experience. The marketing man, Casey Jones, who continued to make use of the trainer at his flight school in Newark with impressive success, began laying plans to bring Ed together with military representatives in New Jersey.

It was a time of delicate balance in world affairs. Like barely perceived rumblings hinting at an earthquake to come, like distant heat lightning in a far off night sky, vague rumors of war drifted westward across the Atlantic. A thing nebulous and as evil as a hidden cancer was about to spread its corruption over the globe. Responding to stepped up inquiries, Ed applied himself ever more diligently to selling the trainer, along with Charles S. Jones and the JVW Corporation, now his exclusive sales agents.

Due to Jones's efforts, the pilot maker began to receive more publicity, a job made easier by the fact that the media liked the instrument. Even before buyers and users, reporters and editors had the foresight and imagination to fully appreciate the trainer and its significant potential. That year the *New York Daily News* reported that "by blind flying on the trainer, one could shorten essential air training by more than 50%."

Working in concert, Ed, Casey Jones, and JVW Corporation members George Vaughn, Dick Watham, and Lee J. Warrender continued to spread the word, reaching out for possible customers the world over. Far-ranging marketing efforts first took root in Germany, Japan, and Russia, while, failing to recognize a prophet of their own, Canada, England, and the United States were last to respond.

Though future customers were indeed beginning to take notice, Ed still plugged away in Cortland, building a few trainers almost by hand. Not yet out from under the cloud that seemed to plague him during the earliest developmental stages of the trainer, he was still trying to run his government-approved repair station and build trainers in a hangar without heat, even though he thought he had an oral agreement from the start that his landlords would furnish heat once manufacturing began.

Meanwhile, with more new orders trickling in, the trainer was finally "on the line" to some extent. SUNY Librarian and biographer, Martha Clark, writes:

~ By 1934 the aviation industry had become a recognized feature of American life and began to prosper. Link's fortunes followed suit, aided by events in the United States and the world which caused military personnel to recognize the potentials of the Link Trainer for teaching instrument flight. ~

The country continued to show signs of economic improvement, indicating that Ed's prospects surely would improve. In light of the Army Air Corps' catastrophes and the paralysis that all pilots other than Ed and his immediate cohorts experienced in inclement weather, Jones moved on his important Washington and military contacts, arranging for Ed to give a demonstration for a select group of representatives in Newark. He called Ed the day before to say that he had chosen February 11, 1934, which appropriately turned out to be dark and soupy, for Ed to fly some 200 miles from Binghamton to Newark. From a slippery runway in Binghamton, the same man who late in his teens motorcycled round trip between New York and California, who during the Depression dared to fly at altitudes of 10,000 to 15,000 feet without an air supply, who logged many hours of madcap night flying at low altitudes to advertise Spaulding Cakes, took off into the gray soup.

A more eloquent argument could not have been made for ground training and instrument flying than the sound of Ed's engine as it faintly hummed through the clouds at Newark. At that very moment, as reported in *The Pilot Maker*, Casey Jones and Air Corps representatives, shivering in the cold rain, certain that Ed would have had to turn back, were just leaving the runway when the sound of his engine stopped them in their tracks. "He had made it on instruments," wrote his biographers. Hunched against the weather, the group waited while the faint hum increased in volume to a steady drone and the little plane gradually materialized out of the heavy clouds. They could barely perceive the pilot waving as his plane came down through steady rain on a gentle angle for a smooth, effortless landing. Washington was immediately notified of the urgent need for flight trainers.

Ed's wife later wrote: "It was not until after a series of fatal crashes following the decision of the Army Air Corps to take over the flying of the mail, that the Link Trainer won recognition." Biographer Clark recounts Ed's skill at flying on instruments:

~ ...[It] was reflected in his constant tinkering with the trainer, which led to new models with advanced instrumentation. ...the dramatic landing in Newark eventually led to the U. S. Army Air Corps' first order for six fully-instrumented trainers, at the purchase price of $3,400 each. ~

A new, billion-dollar industry was born, but not before Ed and Marion underwent yet another downward spin. Still dead broke and heavily in debt, relying only on uncertain financial improvements, Marion suddenly fell ill with an intestinal disorder and had to be hospitalized at John Hopkins in Baltimore. Ed was in a tight spot, at this point not yet knowing how the Washington military brass reacted to his instrument landing at Newark Airport, uncertain of the trainer's future, and anxious over his wife's health. But relief was in sight. First came word that Marion was indeed recovering; then the big break came and he was able to rush to her hospital bed with the news: the United States Army had at last placed their order.

With Marion back at his side, the only fly remaining in the ointment — other than the unheated hangar — was a governmental lack of funds that held up the first order. This sent Ed and Casey Jones to Washington to visit Congress, and eventually an appropriation was passed by both Houses of Congress and signed by President Roosevelt, March 28, 1934, which led to the Army's taking delivery, June 23, 1934, of their first six, Model "A" Trainers. Ed was now fully committed to the manufacturing business. The pace of events picked up momentum. A month after delivery to the Army, with the approval of the United States Government, ten trainers were sold to the Japanese, the first of these delivered in July, the remaining to be sent throughout the year.

On December 4, 1934, he won a patent for the electric sky sign, called the "Illuminated Aerial Display." But that same month, the award of the patent was overshadowed by an entirely different matter. His landlords at the city-owned airport still had not provided heat at the hangar, claiming that Ed had agreed to pay additional rent whenever heat was needed. Ed said no such agreement had been made. Then, in Marion's words, came a "big impasse" and Ed "virtually slunk away" though his rental contract was still in force. The planes were already relocated at Tri-Cities Airport in Endicott. Marion had found a new place to live on Helen Street in Binghamton. It was Christmas night. Carolers could be heard in the distance, along with a barking dog. Silently treading new-fallen snow, Ed and his cohorts systematically moved the entire operation out of Cortland to a small factory on Gaines Street in Binghamton. The Cortland landlords sued him for back rent. Four months later, the court ruled against Ed and he had to pay the landlords $875. In a complete about face, the City of Cortland many years later sponsored an elaborate testimonial dinner for Ed and dedicated a bronze plaque at the airport in his name. The plaque has been read since by countless numbers of people. It bears the legend:

### EDWIN A. LINK

~ On this site in the early 1930's, the "Link Flight Trainer" was perfected and resulted in the first sale to the Army Air Corps of ten trainers. This heralded a new era in aviation safety and progress. During World War II, Link trainers were used to train more than half a million airmen throughout the world. The citizens of Cortland County are proud of this historic association and grateful to this inventive genius for his dedicated service in behalf of his fellow Americans. ~

Once again proving the "blue-box" to be a universal instrument, late in 1934, four more Model "A" trainers were shipped overseas, these to the Soviet Union. At last the trainer was taking its rightful place of prominence in world aviation. Ed's sincere and practical desire to help would-be pilots safely into the air was realized, bringing peace of mind to the long frustrated inventor who knew all along he had created something the world badly needed, but had, in its ignorance, systematically rejected over the years.

Link Aviation Devices, Inc. was fully established by 1935, with Ed as president and his brother, George Theron, who had rejoined the operation, as treasurer. The business of manufacturing trainers and other aviation devices was now a reality at Gaines Street in Binghamton. Link Aeronautical Corporation continued with the flight school, an airplane repair service, and charter flights at Tri-Cities Airport at Endicott. (NOTE: photos on pg. 171, #4 and #5). Things seemed to be going well. Then in 1936 a major spring flood occurred in Binghamton, plunging Ed into yet another tailspin and prompting Marion to comment: "Business was going well until fate intervened and got even for the Cortland episode." The factory at Gaines Street was left under six feet of water and silt. Fire broke out in one of the buildings, wreaking more havoc before Ed and his helpers could get to it by rowboat and put it out. In the aftermath, file cabinets were so badly soaked they fell apart, all company records were lost, and the remaining machinery was coated and clogged with mud. Ed was devastated. Anyone else might have given up. Marion's father, heretofore a staunch admirer of his indomitable son-in-law, began to wonder if Link shouldn't give it up and look for a secure job.

But the invincible Ed Link was building and selling trainers again within the year. By 1936 the flight simulator had grown from a primitive machine to the now popular Model "A," equipped with compass, air speed indicators, rate-of-climb and turn-and-bank-indicators, volume control for the pilot within a preselected range, and instruments allowing an instructor to transmit simulated radio signals to a student during flight. This model was soon followed by a slightly more advanced "B" series. Then, vital to instrument flying, a new "C" series trainer came on the line; a more sophisticated device featuring a full-scale instrument panel and desk assembly for an instructor.

Meanwhile, the British responded to growing unrest in Europe by ordering Link Trainers in 1936 for their Royal Air Force training centers, on condition that they be built within the British Commonwealth. Plans were then made to open a new Link factory in Canada, at Gananoque, Ontario, not far from Perch Island in the St. Lawrence Seaway's Thousand Islands. Ed and Marion later purchased the Perch Island cottage from their friend Bill Morris for a summer home.

Late that summer Ed received an invitation from the Japanese Navy asking him to reside in their country for several months and teach Naval flight instructors about the pilot training device. His initial reaction was to turn down the invitation, but when the United States government heard of it, they urged him to accept, just as they had previously encouraged him to sell Trainers to the Japanese so that he could be on the alert for signs of military buildup. He then accepted on condition that he could bring his wife along, after flatly declining a Japanese offer of a surrogate wife to keep him company during the several months he was to be there. Prompted by the government to accompany Ed, Marion then made the decision to resign her job with Link Aviation, which she had already considered doing in favor of more community involvement, and go to Japan.

They traveled by rail to California, stopping for a brief visit with friends and family in Chicago. Marion began recording events of interest in her journal, in which she stated on November 4, 1936: "Awoke in New Mexico, interesting desert scenery - Navajo Indians - Roosevelt carried the election with a landslide of votes." She saw the countryside race by her window as she thought about world events, then picked up her pen and added, "...Would hate to see this great country of ours follow the lead of Fascist Europe."

On arrival in California Ed and Marion faced a whirlwind of social activities. These included a visit with friends to the Ambassador Hotel on Wilshire Boulevard in Hollywood, which, coincidentally, was located on the old airstrip site where Ed had made his first flight at age sixteen; a visit in San Diego with marine pilot and future Link operations chief pilot, "Pete" Dougherty; and a reunion in Glendale with Ed's father and his young sister Marilyn, whose mother had died of breast cancer in 1929. They also met his father's third wife, Lillian Monberg Link, formerly of Los Angeles.

Ed was still only 32 years old as he and Marion began this voyage of world-wide significance. They sailed for Japan on November 12, 1936, departing from San Fransico's Golden Gate Harbor aboard the Japanese liner, *Tatsuta Maru*. They were on the Japanese ship only because all American lines were on strike, and found themselves unwitting participants in a "first" celebration. The *Tatsuta Maru* was the first vessel ever to sail under the brand new Oakland Bridge.

"Colored flags were flying, battleships filled the harbor, hundreds of planes flew overhead, cannons were fired and whistles blew," Marion wrote of the Grand Opening, noting: "The bridge is tremendous, a fact scarcely evident until compared with the *Tatsuta* which glided beneath it with plenty of room to spare."

They would have taken an American liner were it not for the strike, but as Ed had often said, "If you follow the events at hand, things seem to work out for the best." He made valuable new acquaintances on *Tatsuta Maru*. Among other notables aboard were the American Ambassador, Joseph Grew, and his wife, and coinciden-tally, Baron Okura, owner and director of the company through which Japan had purchased its first flight trainers. Baron Okura was considered then to be one of the five most outstanding figures in the Japanese Empire.

\* \* \*

"AT THE CRACK OF DAWN I peeked from the porthole to see the shore of Tokyo Bay, and soon after, a fairy fleet of silent sails - hundreds of fishing boats in the early morning haze," wrote Marion as they entered the Bay. After a formal round of intro-ductions and a brief glimpse of the land, they were settled into a temporary home consisting of a third floor apartment overlooking beautifully arranged Japanese gar-dens. Other English speaking families lived nearby.

Shortly after Ed arrived at his headquarters he was confronted with a carefully dismantled Link Trainer, as well as a line of polite hosts who requested him to reassemble it as they watched. Suspicious of their motives, he refused on the grounds that the tools he needed were at home, and the only way he could reassemble it was to pack up the pieces and send them back to Binghamton. In fact, he was certain that their motive was to learn how to build trainers themselves, which he now suspected was a major reason why they brought him to Japan in the first place. However, he soon settled into his new routine, doing only what he had been cleared to do by his own government: teaching a small group of instructors, with the help of a translator, how to use the trainer for Navy flying classes.

When Ed's mission was over, he and Marion availed themselves of the opportunity to tour Japan, but were free to travel only in areas where there was no evidence of the coming war. Everywhere they went he took scores of photographs while she hurriedly jotted descriptive entries in her journal. Signs of wartime preparations were masked by beautifully arrayed Geisha girls on promenade, a rare, New Year's day event. Families in colorful native regalia could be seen leaving calling cards at the homes of their friends and relatives, another New Year's Day custom. Marion wrote of hairpin curves on misty mountains; visits to temples and shrines; endless meticulously manicured gardens: tea tables, floor cushions, and unmanageable straw slippers. Had they not known better, they might have been deceived by so many signs of peace and prosperity.

A formal farewell dinner party in Ed's honor at the famous Maple Club contributed to the illusion of utter tranquility. But in the morning, when he and Marion boarded a ship for Shanghai, they reminded themselves that the trip to China was being undertaken in spite of intense objections by the Japanese government, who had already invaded distant Northern China. Signs of war were to be more obvious to them in Shanghai than in Japan, while contrasts between the two countries would be overwhelming. Even weather conditions on the Chinese coast seemed a forecast of the dreadful events to come. On their arrival Marion wrote:

~ Aboard *Shanghai Maru,* January 5, 1937. It was pouring rain when we woke up this morning, and later when we went on deck a fog hid nearly everything. As we neared the coast of China the water changed from a greenish paste to muddy brown. At lunch time in Yangzte Bay we soon began to see picturesque Chinese junks - most of them carrying sails so patched you could not make out the original materials.

As we entered the mouth of the river and the shore line began to take shape it was seen to be flat and yellow-brown - a continuation of the color motif of the water. The skies overhead were low and drab and leaden-colored. Not once during the four days we were in China did we see

the sunshine, and I had an impression of dull monotones of landscape.
...Out in the river and up and down the harbor were gunboats from Japan,
Great Britain, and from all over the world. ~

In spite of the bright lights of Shanghai, their first dismal impressions of pre-
war China were deepened by gloomy newscasts as well as a sense of fear and suspicion that seemed to permeate the atmosphere. Marion jotted in her journal that
Chinese Nationalist leader Chiang Kai Shek had been kidnapped and that two
Curtiss-Wright American pilots were taken as prisoners. Soon they were subjected
to a mysterious attempt to keep them in Shanghai after an old friend of Ed's, Sam
Irwin, who headed the Curtiss-Wright Intercontinental Corporation, invited them to
visit his plant in Hangchow. In utter cloak-and-dagger style, three sinister men in
dark suits — complete strangers with no apparent reason to know them or their plans
— approached them one after the other while they waited in the hotel lobby for their
ride, and warned them not to go to the Chinese holy city of Hangchow. Even as they
went, the cold, rainy day increased their unease and further deepened their early
impressions of a poor and dreary land. Marion wrote:

> ~ The dirty, darkened garments of the people were much contrasted
> by the bright prints of Japan, and the landscapes were an equal con-
> trast, brown fields dotted with mounds of earth, the burial places of
> the dead.   Our road followed the old sea wall north along the coast,
> and through murky haze the flat landscape blended into the ocean bot-
> tom where the tide had gone out. It was almost impossible to distin-
> guish the breaks between land and water and sky. After dark, we were
> the only car on the road and we made a steady pace interrupted now
> and then by soldier guards who stopped us to see where we were
> going and why. ~

The next morning in the pouring rain Marion went sight-seeing while Ed
demonstrated the trainer to Chinese officers at the Hangchow airport. He then visited the Curtiss-Wright plant. Both events remained free of incident. In spite of the
Japanese objections to their trip and the unexpected warnings before leaving
Shanghai for their side trip to Hangchow, the only mishap that occurred in China
was in Shanghai. One day on a shopping trip, standing before a vast sea of rick-
shaws whose runners all wanted the fare, Marion was suddenly whisked away from
Ed into the thick of traffic in a runaway rickshaw. She discovered to her horror that
she couldn't give the runner directions to turn around and take her back because he
didn't understand a word of English, and she was well into the city before Ed at last
came rushing through the traffic to her rescue in a second rickshaw.

* * *

IN FEBRUARY, 1937, the couple returned home to Binghamton where the simulator industry was expanding in a big way. Ed, Theron, and Casey Jones began to pull in many of their friends and acquaintances to help establish the fast-growing organization. Soon Ed set to extending the capabilities of the trainers, constantly designing new instruments, and working on ideas for what he called a "Visualator."

Another trainer model, the "D" trainer, designed for European Air Forces, was next on the line. The varied business interests continued to grow and at last became consolidated. Ed and his brother were officers of Link Aviation, Inc. Link Manufacturing Company, Ltd., fully established in Gananoque, Ontario, was building trainers for the British. The family was growing as well, for Marion was carrying their first child. She settled for the summer in their cottage on Perch Island, while Ed commuted between the island, Binghamton and Gananoque via his single engine Consolidated Vultee.

Then came another of what was becoming a line of "firsts" for the Links. In 1938, on the first of January, their son Bill (William) Martin was the first baby born in Binghamton. As the celebrated "New Year's Baby," he and his parents were showered with gifts and an excess of public attention.

Ed's fortunes were on an upswing. On May 31, 1938, yet another patent was issued for the "Aviation Trainer." Increased contracts drew him to foreign countries, and in September, leaving the baby with Ed's mother, he and Marion traveled overseas together once again. This time Ed was scheduled to meet in London with Air Commodore Peregrine Fellowes, English representative of Link Trainers (who remained so throughout the coming war). With his camera and Marion's journal they had planned to tour England together, but when they arrived in London they found the country to be in an unsettled state over recent movements of Nazi troops, and as a result, his time was taken up entirely by Fellowes and the Air Ministry.

Marion spent her time touring London with Peregrine's wife, Eleanor Fellowes, and in the process sensed first hand the powerful feeling of impending disaster that permeated the land. She was shocked to see street signs designating the location of bomb shelters, in spite of Prime Minister Chamberlain's famous "Peace in Our Times" statement and his current presence in Germany to negotiate peace settlements. Marion's first journal entry in London read:

> ~ September 13 - 23, 1938. All summer the Nazi cauldron has been brewing trouble in Czechoslovakia, and since the start of our trip it has reached such serious proportions that another great war is feared. Here in England, there is no other topic of conversation, and wireless broadcasts of the situation are frequent and much listened to.

On Sunday we went to the Vesper service at Westminster Abbey which was called as a prayer for peace. The whole Abbey was packed, the aisles crowded - and during the prayer one could feel the feverish thought of the congregation set upon that one objective - peace.

We chanced upon a vitally interesting time for our visit, but so great has been the confusion and panic in the government offices that Edwin's business has been very much slowed up.

We were told direct from the War Office that the Air Force stood by one night this week with engines warmed up, ready for the air attack from Germany. To me the whole thing seems like mass hysteria and I cannot make myself believe it, but all England expects war, prepares for war, and prays there will not be war. ~

From the onset, their much anticipated holiday was fraught with warnings of things to come. On September 23 Marion wrote:

~ In spite of the crisis, Eleanor and Peregrine and Ed and I started in the Fellowes' car for a trip to France. We crossed the Channel at New Haven for Dieppe and then drove that first day to Cannes ...The next morning we learned that France had mobilized part of her Army. We visited a beautiful old Cathedral in the midst of an impressive funeral service accompanied by the soul-stirring notes of a lovely organ that brought tears to my eyes as I thought of war and these poor people of France subjected to fresh carnage.

...Steadily the crisis is deepening. Chamberlain has gone to Germany. London and Paris are being evacuated in case of air raids. At our inn there are refugees from Alsace and Paris and the atmosphere is one of deepest gloom. Today outside our window the village crier rang his bell then read a summons for more units to be mobilized. M. Jeudi, our host and chef, expects to be called any moment, and his pretty little wife goes about with bated breath and teary eyes. The London Times arrives with gloomier and gloomier news. We wonder whether we should start back for London but decide to take the chance — I couldn't bear to miss Paris. ~

That night on the way to Paris their car broke down. They also feared they were lost. Peregrine and Eleanor Fellowes set about trying to determine their whereabouts while Marion stood by with a flashlight and Ed tinkered with the engine until he at last got it started again. Not until the next morning did the overdue party arrive at their hotel in Paris, just as a cavalcade headed down the street with England's

Prime Minister Chamberlain in the lead car, smiling and waving his misguided reassurance to the French before he made his way home from Germany.

Yet again the touring party's car let them down, this time with a blowout on a Paris street during a blackout. Groping in the silent and ominous darkness, without even the benefit of a flashlight, Ed and Pergrine managed to change the tire. Then they cautiously picked their way back through the darkened streets to the hotel, without the use of headlights.

Still another sign of the times surprised the tourists when, on their return to Paris from a side trip to wine country, they visited Chartres Cathedral just outside Paris. Ed had tried to photograph the magnificent stained-glass windows from a view on the cathedral stairs when a gesticulating gendarme appeared and abruptly confiscated his camera. Ed and his party could not have known that only that day the French had issued an edict saying no public buildings were to be photographed. Meanwhile the officer took off on his bicycle with Ed's camera, with two outraged English-speaking women running down the narrow streets behind him, until they caught up with him at his precinct. The officer proved kind enough to hear their story as told in halting French by Eleanor; then he removed the film and returned the camera to Marion. He also took down her address, and to her surprise, after they returned home he mailed Ed's film, with a friendly note, back to her in Binghamton.

It was a trying holiday during which the Americans found Europe to be in a state of turmoil. Already there was civil war in Spain. Italy began to move into Africa. Winston Churchill tried hard to convince the British of the peril Europe was in. Perhaps the majority of Americans, physically removed and complacent on the other side of the Atlantic, had no notion of what was at hand, but Ed and Marion would never forget the heart-rending service at Westminster Abbey as the participants prayed together for peace. They took home to Binghamton the sad memory of a deeply frightened people.

* * *

NEW TYPES OF TRAINERS CONTINUED TO APPEAR with regularity. In response to a request by the British Royal Navy Air Force for help with celestial navigation training, Ed went to Annapolis to prepare himself for a new invention by studying celestial navigation with one of the world's most noted authorities, Captain P.V.H. (Philip Van Horn) "Van" Weems. Thus began the plans for what became known as the renowned Celestial Navigation Trainer.

Weems was a retired naval officer who ran a navigation school in his stately home, one of Annapolis's old showcases. In the coming war, he was to return to duty and serve as captain of the lead ship and commodore in command of an escort convoy. His duty was to see fleets of US ships carrying supplies and military personnel safely to England. But in the meantime he became the famous airman's navigation instructor, and he became a lifelong friend and an important associate in many of Ed's future endeavors, including the development of aviation instruments and his later seagoing missions.

With Weems as a tutor Ed discovered that he had a natural talent for navigation and soon became himself a leading expert in the field. If there was any one item on his list of varied interests that he identified most strongly with, it was navigation, and in later interviews he often told reporters that he was essentially a navigator. After mastering the subject he began co-authoring with Weems a small book, the first simplified version of celestial navigation, which was published in 1940. Weems in turn worked with Ed on his Celestial Navigation Trainer (CNT).

Among the Link papers at Roberson Center in Binghamton is an unidentified mimeographed sheet titled "Link CNT," which gives a brief history of the CNT, including a paragraph describing the invention:

~ [The CNT] had a flight deck of a bomber at the center to accommodate both pilot and navigator, and a canopy of stars overhead - like that of a planetarium - which could be rotated and tilted to correspond with the location, hour, and time of year anywhere in the northern hemisphere. When the flight started, the stars moved automatically in accordance with the speed of the bomber and allowed for the changes of latitude and longitude and coming of daylight, etc. ~

The unknown author went on to say that the CNT was received by instructors and pupils with great enthusiasm, and that they were particularly taken with an "exciting facility" it had which allowed them to "advance aviation by several years with the mere turn of a knob." By doing so they could "fly" at speeds far in excess of any aircraft yet designed at the time; and furthermore, the writer stated, "they could fly it anywhere, including over and around the North Pole."

In addition to the CNT, the above mentioned paper describes another popular navigation aid of Ed's:

~ Another interesting side-product of the [CNT] was something dreamed up by Ed Link to help pupils learn the names and positions of the main stars on which their navigation depended. Aided by a good camera and a team of lovely young models he combined his knowledge of psychology, astronomy and anatomy to produce a series of "Star Identification Charts." In these the models, wearing nothing but two or three sparkling stars strategically placed, posed in appropriate attitudes to produce the correctly shaped constellation. Their popularity was enormous. Few RAF navigators thereafter forgot the position of the stars they needed to aim their sextants at... ~

Ed also designed a "Star Globe" to complement his simple and enticing method of teaching celestial navigation with the female form as a chart on which to locate heavenly bodies.

* * *

IN 1939 HITLER INVADED POLAND. War in Europe had gone from an anxious rumor to a hard reality. Ed, once called a country boy by George Vaughan, soon became a hardworking industrialist running a wartime factory. On November 7, 1939, he received a patent for "Means and Methods of Instrument Indication in Airplanes and the Like," essentially an aircraft integrated instrument display. Then another patent, simply registered as "Recorders" was issued a week later on the 14th of November. Meanwhile, with the onset of war, orders for the trainers increased. Marion, who was obviously impressed with the CNT, wrote:

> ~ The little business was now a big business...and Ed spent the next few
> years with his nose to the grindstone. Many new models were developed
> to keep up with the rapid progress being made in the design of fighting,
> bombing and transport planes. A tremendous celestial navigation trainer
> [CNT] was devised to simulate the stars in the heavens, with a cockpit
> large enough to contain the entire crew of a long-distance bomber.
>      Ed also developed a bubble sextant to be used in aircraft, which he
> manufactured for the Air Services by the thousands. His advice was
> sought extensively by the various branches of the armed forces. ~

In an article called "The Planes That Never Leave the Ground," James I. Killgore indicates that he too was impressed with the celestial navigation trainer. He wrote that the CNT, "designed by Link with the help of P. V. H. Weems," was "perhaps the most interesting simulator built during the war." "The British requested this colossal machine in 1939 to train flight crews carrying U.S. aircraft across the Atlantic," he said, and then gave his more detailed description:

> ~ A forty-foot silo housed a simulator fuselage held aloft on a tall steel
> frame. Seats were provided for a pilot, navigator, bombardier, and radio
> operator. Suspended above the fuselage was a large dome lit with 379
> points of light representing stars, by which a navigator, using a sextant,
> could track the aircraft's position. Over the course of a "mission," the

star dome crept and slowly rotated on a steel track, reflecting changes in time and position.

A projection screen flashed a reproduction of passing terrain to give navigators practice picking out landmarks during daylight flight. Instructors could introduce cloud cover to obscure the terrain and could turn a rheostat to dim the stars for simulated overcast nights.

As the war progressed, the CNT became valuable as a trainer for bomber crews making forays deep into Europe. Trainers were outfitted with the then top-secret Norden bombsight. Bombardiers practiced lining up cross-hairs on factories, airfields, and other targets passing on a movie screen beneath the fuselage. ~

(A 1943 Hollywood movie starring Pat O'Brien had wartime bombardiers training on such simulators, then putting their new expertise to practice by bombing Tokyo.) More than five hundred of these miniature planetariums were built in the U.S. and Britain during the war. To add to Ed's growing fame, the Royal Air Force publicly estimated that the CNT's reduced by half the actual flight time needed to train bomber crews.

Despite the praise being heaped upon him by world leaders, Ed maintained all the personal qualities, including humility, that endeared him to many people. Though he achieved fame and met any number of military celebrities during the war, he remained the modest character that he had always been, with the same simple tastes that he'd had as "hoosier" child in Indiana.

Writer Harvey Roehl once asked Ed for his reflections on the many great aviators and military leaders of the war whom he had met personally, and from that interview he wrote:

~ He always tended to like particularly those he considered 'regular fellows,' and perhaps he'd think the best characterization of this would be a person with whom you could sit at a bar over a couple of beers and have a pleasant conversation. For example, I recall that General 'Hap' Arnold (the commander of the US Air Forces) was one he regarded in that manner. ~

In 1940 Ed and Marion made a permanent move from a house at Crestmont to the family homestead at 10 Avon Road in Binghamton. At that time his mother moved out to live in an apartment while she built herself yet another, smaller house. During the year a new factory was established to accommodate the growing industry, at Hillcrest in Binghamton, even as more complex simulators were developed. Ed's planes now consisted of a Cessna, an Eaglet, a Curtiss Jenny, a Tri-Motor Ford, a Vultee, and a Stinson.

By 1941 the CNT was completed and sold to the British Royal Air Force at a cost of $85,000. On June 3, a patent was issued to Ed for a "Signal Controlling Means." That year an addition was built on to the house, and Ed and Marion became surrogate parents to his 18-year old sister, Marilyn, who moved from California the following February. That same year Ed's father died, in May, in California. More milestones were passed. Marion gave birth to their second son, Edwin Clayton Link, on November 30, 1941, just one week before the Japanese attacked Pearl Harbor. She and Ed, young Bill and Marilyn had spent their summer in Canada that year. Ed worked at the factory there, and made the acquaintance of Air Marshall Robert Leckie, wartime Chief of Staff of the Royal Canadian Air Force. After the war Leckie make this public statement: "The Luftwaffe met its Waterloo on all the training fields of the free world where there was a battery of Link Trainers," as quoted by Kelly and Parke in *The Pilot Maker.*

When Japan entered the war on December 7, 1941, while Link Aviation developed gunnery, radar, and automatic pilot trainers, Ed began to concentrate his attention on his new "Visualator," an all-in-one instrument that reduced the amount of scanning a pilot had to do and provided everything needed for instrument flying. Kelly and Parke report it as, "...one of the first attempts to collect in one basic instrument most of the information necessary for a pilot to fly on instruments." Ed's Visualator has since been described by admiring engineers and biographers as a "monumental breakthrough," but like some of his other ideas, it was a bit ahead of its time for the military and was not accepted. Even so, his Visualator was a forerunner of similar devices in use today, and though never recognized, he had once more demonstrated his remarkable capacity to anticipate needs. In any case, it can truthfully be said that all of Ed's earlier efforts led to instrument flying.

Meanwhile at home in his basement he built himself a darkroom and studio, took up photography ever more extensively, and built a workshop where he spent countless hours working on projects.

The war brought forth new planes with new needs, and the trainers, first modeled on a composite, general airplane, had for some time been simulating particular planes. In 1943 Bell Telephone Laboratories came out with the first all-electronic flight trainer. Curtiss-Wright introduced another model. Link Aviation had begun to build its own electronic simulators. As progress continued in Ed's operations, many others besides himself had become so involved in the development of trainers that they threatened to be out of his hands altogether. He found himself forced more and more into the role of businessman rather than engineer and mechanic, and liked it less and less. Even though he quietly accepted his place behind a desk, he never came to terms with no longer being a hands on man.

George Vaughn told Arthur Herzog for his *True* magazine article: "Link never was really happy in business. That he had a growing, prosperous company was entirely secondary to him. He likes developing." To Marion: "Ed never really cared about being a businessman, but when he was called on to do it, he put his nose to the grindstone and did it very successfully. There were many times when his supper awaited him at home until far into the night." Throughout the war he traveled and acquired contracts for building trainers, handled foreign operations, became a consummate diplomat, and grew in stature as an industrialist, while his creative side had to take a back seat and become more or less dormant.

During those years Marion made her contributions to society through church and community organizations, working as a volunteer with a number of groups, including the Blind Workers Association, officiating at meetings of the county Planned Parenthood program, and serving as a member of the Syracuse University Board of Trustees. (With these and many other of her activities, she qualified for a listing in *Who's Who of Women in America*.)

Then Ed once again began to project future needs. Before the advent of workable aircraft carriers, he visualized whole armies of seaplanes, an amphibian fleet operating from the water's surface. He developed an "Aqua Trainer" to simulate landings and takeoffs to and from the water. The Aqua Trainer's lower section was submerged in the water while the upper section, resembling a small airplane like the Link Trainer, floated on the surface. Once the engine was going and the vessel got up on a plane, the whole thing rose to the surface and simulated takeoff.

Though the Aqua Trainer never went into production because efficient aircraft carriers came along soon after it was developed, it was (and still is) considered by many to be an elegant, remarkable invention, which, according to The Pilot Maker, incorporated several important firsts: It was the first instrument known to utilize a snorkel device on its engine, and it had a thin, high speed wing and a manageable hydrofoil. But Kelly and Parke report: "While the device was an astonishing achievement and made use of several new concepts, it was expensive and tricky to operate." In fact, Marion tells a hilarious tale of Captain Weems trying it out near their Perch Island summer cottage, and washing away downstream with the wind and currents, finally to be rescued by Ed in a boat. The original model, still operable, can be seen today at The Antique Boat Museum located on the St. Lawrence Seaway in Clayton, New York.

In 1942 Ed came out with yet another extraordinary device. Liking to hunt and fish in the remote Canadian wilderness, he designed and built a sectional canoe compact enough to be folded up, stored in a canvas bag, and transported by car or small plane, one that was also light weight enough to be carried through the bush. He called this boat the Linkanoe, and hoped it would help see the simulator industry through the lean days that he saw coming both with the end of the war and the inevitable increase in simulator production competition. Chiefly worried about the future of his employees, he wanted something to fall back on when and if simulator sales began to drop.

Later Ed began a publicity campaign by flying with Marion and the Linkanoe in his Grumman Widgeon on a hunting and fishing trip to Cuba, toting the gear into a remote swamp for a bass fishing excursion and then back to the beach for publicity shots. From Cuba they flew on to the Yucatan and the lagoons around Acapulco for more news coverage. Whimsical though it may seem today, the Linkanoe was a highly practical device in its day, and sold well enough to make a difference in company revenues for a time.

The Link Marine Division was established in Canada to manufacture Linkanoes, as well as another sectional boat, the Linkboat, which was designed next by Ed on the same principles. Both vessels found a market temporarily, and were particularly popular with the Canadian Mounties. However, sales would gradually decline with the advent of new, light weight aluminum canoes that could be easily portaged.

Another not-so-successful plan began in 1942 when Link Aviation introduced flight training on a domestic level through what they termed the School Link Program. With Link Trainers and Ed's sister Marilyn as a key figure, Ed believed they could go into the schools and by introducing the idea of flight and the sense of accomplishment attained by pilots, broaden the horizons of school children. According to Kelly:

> ~ ...We held a series of seminars at schools and colleges for teachers at all grade levels, explaining what we hoped to accomplish and what we thought the benefits would be. We made appearances at hundreds of teacher groups, always striving to interest and to train teachers in the use of aviation materials and, of course, in our School Link Trainers. It was tough going...
>
> We were aided and abetted during this period by the addition to our staff of Ed's half-sister, Marilyn. She was assigned to our education Department along with Edmund Carmody, Paul Dittman, William Konicek, Norman Potter and myself. We worked under the general guidance of Philip Hopkins, the vice president who had volunteered to put Link in the education business. Marilyn was a graduate of New York University, with a B.S. Degree in Education and was particularly adept at working with teachers.
>
> In addition to her education training, Marilyn had her commercial pilot's certificate. We were all pilots and each of us had his own idea of how she should obtain additional flight proficiency. With all the conflicting advice, it's a wonder she continued flying at all. G. W. "Slim" Emerson, Link vice president, was a former barnstormer and wanted her to learn some of the less formal techniques of his day, as did "Pete" Dougherty, who was then the Link company pilot. Carmody, Dittman

and I were military oriented and felt a more disciplined approach was best. Of course, Ed Link was her constant mentor. Perhaps in spite of our efforts, Marilyn progressed and received the twin-engine and instrument ratings. Her flying ability gave her a unique status in the teaching community, but our School Link Program continued to meet stiff resistance. After two almost fruitless years, we agreed that Marilyn should seek a Master's Degree and gain some experience teaching. Accordingly, she enrolled at the University of Illinois, and after receiving her M.S. degree, she went on to teach in the New Jersey Public School System, and later at the University of Nebraska. ~

Marilyn also worked part-time for the Nebraska State Department of Aeronautics as a pilot and in the summer worked for a private concern in the Canadian brush country flying people and supplies in a Grumman Widgeon amphibian aircraft as far north as Hudson Bay.

The need to make a contribution to society, an ethic religiously practiced by both Ed and Marion, was ingrained as well in Marilyn's character. She went on to a notable career as a school teacher, making such an impact on her students that she continued to hear from many of them for years to come; some of whom had taken her "pre-flight" training courses. (As late as March, 1987, Marilyn received a letter from a mother in Short Hills, New Jersey, who recalled driving with her son, Rod, to take Marilyn from school to Morristown airport. Marilyn had told the woman on hearing of her fear of flying: "The two most dangerous times in a flight are at take-off and landing." The woman wrote that she was able to fly with some ease after that, by praying hard on the way up and down and relaxing in between, then added: "The little boy you inspired many years ago is now a successful sculptor in Ketchum, Idaho, and I want to thank you for your dedication.")

Knowing the war was coming to an end, Ed's concern for company employees mounted. On November 8, 1944, he issued to the Binghamton employees a three page bulletin titled "The Future of our Company," in which he addressed the matter of future employment and tried to relieve anxieties. He told workers of his plans to remain in operation and reassured them that everyone would be included in those plans. The opening paragraph, in appreciation of his employees, sheds light on his way of thinking:

~ The loyalty of Link Employees, to me personally and to the Company, has been one of the finest experiences of my life. That loyalty, coupled with a patriotic devotion to our country has, during these past few years of intense, abnormal war production, resulted in a major contribution to our military achievements. ~

Biographer Juliet R. Spall later wrote: "Ed Link never lost sight of his own humanity, nor that of his employees." Throughout the years of growth and achievement, Ed's reputation as a "very ordinary man" who cared about others also grew. Binghamton's Harvey Roehl pointed this out:

> ~ It was no secret around here that as he succeeded in the business world, he always remembered those who helped him achieve that success, and that he assisted many folks through their times of need in later life — but you would never learn this from Ed. It represented a type of personal loyalty all too infrequently seen in this day and age, or any age, for that matter. ~

And yet, another Binghamton reporter once quipped: "He's typical of this part of the world, the man's generous to the extreme about big sums of money but try to gyp him out of 50 cents and he'll make a federal case."

A series of patents was issued in 1944, for a "Recording Navigation Instrument," (sextant) May 23; "Aviation Trainers," issued to Ed and co-inventor, Karl A. Kail, September 12; "Navigation Instruments" (sextants) granted to Ed and co-inventor, Harold A. Marsh, October 3; and for the "Celestial Navigation Trainer," December 5, Ed's patent.

In 1945, Ed received yet another patent for the "Training Device." That same year he was awarded the Howard N. Potts Medal for distinguished work in: "Science or the Mechanical Arts", by Franklin Institute, "for valuable contributions to the Field of Training Devices for Aviation."

The sectional boat business lasted only long enough to allow the Canadian organization to coast for a short while when the simulator industry ground to a halt after the war ended in 1945. The British at last gave up on Link Trainers, which brought production to an end. The factory at Gananoque had to be closed down, including the production of the now slow-moving boats as well. Ed was very upset. Marion wrote that he became badly depressed, finding it practically unbearable that the Canadian employees had to be given final payment and let go.

He received three more patents in 1946: on February 26, for another sextant, "Navigation Instrument Including Horizontal Attachment"; on April 30, for a device for teaching astronomy and celestial navigation, the "Star Globe;" and on August 20, for the "Sectional Canoe or the Like."

Now Ed was at a loss, having most recently kept his creative fires burning with the development of the sectional boats. When the boat business failed, he turned once again to photography and the darkroom for solace. Meanwhile, a revamped simulator industry was due to boom once again, this time exclusively with advanced electronics and computer technology. Consequently, it went on essentially without Ed. The hands on man would gradually remove himself from the operation and begin an incessant search for a new source of inspiration. Though his trainers would continue to evolve, even without him, his own relatively simple instruments had already saved untold numbers of lives; half a million of his trainers had sold in thirty-five countries during World War II.

When asked by Harvey Roehl years afterward which of his many accomplishments he took the most pride in, Ed answered:

> ~ I think that what I am proudest of is the fact that Winston Churchill, in a speech to Parliament during the height of the Battle of Britain, gave recognition to our trainers as having made a significant contribution to winning the battle. He didn't mention us by name, but it was very clear to what he was referring. ~

In 1947, Ed began to serve as Director of Mohawk (originally Robinson) Airlines. That year he was awarded yet again for his simulator, with the Sir Charles Wakefield Medal, Institute of Aeronautical Engineers, "For His Invention of the Link Trainer." It was time for new horizons.

# CHAPTER V

# YONDER IS THE SEA

**1947–1951**

*Yonder is the sea, great and wide,*
*which teems with things innumerable, living things*
*both small and great.*

*— Psalms 104:25*

Ed Link wasn't interested in energy in an abstract or theoretical way. He was an applied engineer who wanted to make things work. Canadian author and doctor of underwater medicine, Joseph MacInnis, who worked closely with him on his later undersea projects, wrote for *Sea Technology* magazine that in some ways he was like the quintessential Yankee tinkerer, one who "...saw beauty in tools — in wrenches and drills and lathes — and what they could fix and fashion." But had Ed pursued the mysteries of energy and matter through the study of particle physics, mastering the likes of electrons, photons, quarks, gluons and neutrinos, he might have found whole new ways of doing things. Who's to say what a genius without an appropriate sense of his limitations might have done with a new understanding of the secrets of the universe.

By dealing only with the tools at hand he had already fulfilled more of his potential than most people do in a lifetime. He was a successful and brilliant mechanical engineer with many patents to his credit and with an even greater number of inventions for which he never applied for patents, all covering a broad spectrum of needs and applications.

In an attempt to pull together the threads of his diverse interests he claimed to be essentially a navigator. However, it appears to his followers that he was caught up with the mechanics of motion, using navigation only as a tool to be applied to flying, sailing, exploring and discovering. By the end of the war, he had already experimented across the board with differing modes of transportation, from an early fascination with model trains, to motorcycles; from flight training methods, to airplanes and amphibians; from a childhood submarine design, to building canoes and boats that could be collapsed and portaged.

If he was primarily a navigator, surely a fascination with locomotion was at least a rival thread of continuity that wove its way throughout the fabric of his multifaceted life. While still involved with aviation he had already become familiar with the water, for years ferrying to and from Perch Island in a 30-foot Chris Craft, called *Picadoodle,* when he wasn't flying there by seaplane. He flew his amphibian to fishing lakes where he liked to paddle in a canoe for hours on end, away from civilization, deep in the Canadian wilderness. Who knows what thoughts crossed his mind as he drifted with the wind, watching sun-sparked ripples dance over the water's surface. Perhaps he thought about the sea. Perhaps it was a natural outcome of his interests that he would take up sailing; if so, it would seem that nothing was really changing with Ed Link but his point of view, from sky to sea, initially with the wind powering his course.

Sailing became a serious interest after pilot and crony Slim Emerson, then vice president at Link Aviation, and engineer Gunne Lowkranz, another company vice president, purchased with Ed a second hand, over 50-foot wooden sailing vessel called *Python.* From *Python's* original hailing port at Long Island, New York, the aviators, to varying degrees green at sea, sailed their newly acquired sloop up the Hudson River to cross the Mohawk, through Oneida Lake to Rochester, and across Lake Ontario to the St. Lawrence and Perch Island, apparently learning to sail as they went.

The sailboat came at a time when Link Aviation was becoming too big and impersonal for Ed. "The post war years proved to be a period of team building at Link Aviation," wrote biographer Juliet Spall. "No longer was Ed able to run a one-man show." It is true that he had to have a handle on the work being done. For his way of working he had to spend time alone, focusing and concentrating so that new ideas could work their way through his layers of consciousness. In an article about Ed appropriately titled "The Dreamweaver," Joe MacInnis observed this tendency and took it one step further, saying, "He loved working alone, late at night, gnawing at a problem until he had mastered it. Not for him the committee approach; he was guided by the light of a singular flame, burning brightly within his head."

The advent of electronic technology at Link Aviation didn't inspire Ed. Instead it left fewer and fewer opportunities for him to roll up his sleeves and work like a mechanic. The past, with all of its hardships, challenges and creative solutions, was over and done with. Gone was the piano factory basement and the cold hangar where he had often worked alone all night building the first trainers. The days of rigging theatre organs for special effects and biplanes with electric lights to spell out messages in the night sky were gone. The war was over, along with the pursuit of wartime contracts in foreign countries. A new, easier era had set in, but Ed's life seemed less of a challenge. He became restless to the extreme. Remaining bound to a desk was surely as unappealing to the still highly imaginative and mature man as it had been to the schoolboy some 40-odd years before.

Ed began to spend more time at Perch Island, where Marion and the boys had spent their summers throughout the war years while he flew back and forth between the Canadian factory and Binghamton as required. *Python* turned out to be a temporary challenge, trying his ingenuity and patience. He worked hard at learning the mechanics of sailing, growing fond of the vessel as he mastered her quirks and peculiarities. At one point he learned an important lesson in secure anchorages when gale-force winds ripped through the waterway and broke *Python* loose from her moorings, leaving her relatively unharmed but nevertheless shipwrecked on another shore. Eventually he would take leave of *Python*, but not before acquiring a model of her to scale that sits in Marion's den today.

Sharing ownership of the sloop did not allow enough freedom for the Link family to roam at their leisure, so they began a search that ultimately ended in the purchase of their own vessel, a blue-painted, streamlined wooden yawl designed by Sparkman and Stephens, aptly named *Blue Heron*. With this development, a barely noticeable turning point had come for the 43-year old Ed, after he had already fulfilled himself in the aviation industry, after several years of using the Link Trainer for a national school program, after the publicity tour with the Linkanoe, after the demise of the short-lived marine business interests, and after he had tired of flying and lost interest in the day to day workings at the factory. It came at a time when nothing satisfied him. He wasn't interested in the pursuit of so-called worldly pleasures. He would just have to wait and see what came next.

Ed's transition came before he understood where he was going with it, or that it would mean a major change in his life. Continuing his vague search from the decks of his sailboat was like looking for the ox while riding on its back. MacInnis had an apt description for Ed and his situation:

~ A vagabond at heart, but one with a purpose, he took off into the Caribbean with his wife Marion — the pillar of his life — and his two young boys. Although he may not have known it then, he was in pursuit of another dream, of probing the ocean's uttermost depths, and staying there to work. ~

Ed was at sea, but the initial infatuation with sailing could not last. Cruising alone would not satisfy him for long, a reality which he must have known intuitively from the start. Yet not until sailing led him to other interests did he even begin to see the deep ocean realm as his place of ultimate fulfillment, although his first open water cruise to Havana with Marion certainly made a profound impression on him, in spite of the sort of obstacles that novice sailors must endure.

* * *

IN A DECEMBER 1947 *Rudder* magazine article, titled "An Airman Goes to Sea", Marion began a vivid description of their first crossing, from Key West in Florida to Havana, Cuba, with an admission that they didn't really know much about what they were doing:

> ~ We were new at saltwater sailing. We had owned *Blue Heron* less than a month, and our only experience to date had been the trip down through the keys from Miami with two friends who had left us the day before. In short, we were fliers, not sailors, and although we had spent a good share of the past twenty-five years in airplanes, this marked our first attempt at ocean sailing, and also our first try at cruising alone without a crew to assist. ~

She wrote of storm warnings prior to the cruise that filled her with fear. At first she was against starting the 90 mile crossing to Havana, but decided to put her trust in Ed, reasoning that since he had years of reading weather maps and judging conditions as an instrument pilot, it was worth a try.

Motoring out of Key West Yacht Harbor at 2:00 a.m., Ed and Marion passed the anchorage of the *Williamsburg* where President Truman lay sleeping while on a brief vacation, then moved along a seven-mile lane of markers and lights leading through the reefs and out to sea. Ed set the sails. Whatever weather conditions had kicked up the sea the preceding day had disappeared. Gliding out under the stars, they both were overwhelmed with the wonder of night sailing in the open sea. Marion continued her narrative:

> ~ ...Overhead the sky was bright with stars, and a waning moon had already started its descent of the heavens.
>
>    It was my first experience at sailing under the stars, and it will always be one of the highlights in my memories of sailing. Until that night the stars had always seemed cold and impersonal. Now I found Ursa Major and Polaris as welcome as old friends. ~

Although the seas continued to rise during the first few hours of the crossing, the wind dropped off and the sea was calm by dawn. The novice sailors were forced to motor, in spite of only carrying *Blue Heron's* limited capacity of 40 gallons of gasoline. A little bird landed on the vessel and made itself at home all the way to Cuba, usually sitting on Marion's shoulder at the tiller. After a day of motoring with a raised sail catching a scrap of breeze now and then, they at last spotted headlands east of Havana. Ed spent the remaining hour of daylight taking sights of the sun. When the vermilion orb sank below the horizon, leaving them once again shrouded in darkness, a northeasterly wind began to blow. Ed trimmed the sails and cut the motor. Looking for something to show them the way, they recalled being told that the light atop Morro Castle at the entrance to Havana Harbor could be seen for eighteen miles, and that it was the first thing one could see at night, sailing toward Havana. Then Marion wrote:

~ So we foolishly picked out the biggest and brightest light, said "That must be it," decided that the little row of twinkling lights extending out from it to the right was the Malecon from our recollections of Havana, and changed our course to carry us toward the lights. It was a bad error. ~

They were close in to shore by the time they realized their mistake. By then *Blue Heron* was traveling swiftly off course with the wind and the current. At last they could see the glow of the city in the night sky. To their disappointment, Havana was miles up the coast. They came about and sailed seaward again in order to clear the reefs along the shore, then turned around and headed in again. It was 2:30 in the morning when the anchor was dropped in Havana Harbor, with precious little fuel to spare. Ed dropped the sails and the worn out sailors went to sleep. The next morning they were saddened to discover that the little bird, so much a part of their first seagoing adventure, had become caught the night before in the falling sails and had died. Marion wrote of their haul into Cuba:

~ That was a long five hours, for we were both dog tired and spelled each other off at half hour intervals. I recall one hour-long period when a certain little town on the shore scarcely moved ten degrees. It was most discouraging. We finally had to start the engine once more in spite of the fair breeze to pull us past this place. I learned afterward that this section of the Cuban coast has very strong currents, perhaps due to the depth of the water which drops off quickly from the shore to 738 fathoms.

It was while we were making such slow going that the firmaments treated us to a most beautiful spectacle. As we sailed along, suddenly in the dark skies over the Cuban shore a brilliant star shot across the heavens, trailing a blaze of light in its wake. The meteor was gone in an instant, but the memory of its passing lingered. ~

On the way to Havana, their high hopes had been dashed when the expected northerly wind refused to blow and instead they were treated to a dead calm. On the return to Key West, Marion noted that their expectations were again reversed:

~ Instead of the pleasant night's sail with a fair wind from the southeast upon which we were counting, we ran into a gale blowing out of the east and northeast, and before we saw the warning, yet heart warming, lights of the Florida keys we were two very weary sailors.

On our previous trip we had left Key West at 2 a.m., expecting to make landfall in Cuba before dark the same day, and had missed our calculations by at least eight hours. This time we left Havana at four in the afternoon expecting to strike the keys somewhere to the east of Key West after daylight the next morning. Instead we spotted our first lighthouse about 3:45 a.m. Navigating a boat is quite different from navigating an airplane. ~

With the graceful eloquence that stamps all her writing, Marion described the crossing from Cuba back to Florida:

~ ...We were on our way. The sails were set and trimmed, *Blue Heron* heeled over until water ran in foaming floods through the scuppers on the lee side. Occasionally her bow would dig into a big one, breaking green water over the forward decks and sending it back along the deck on the windward side. It was beautiful and awe inspiring.

I was at the tiller, my usual station while the skipper was setting sails and readying ship. And I was worried. The strong wind and heavy seas were putting so much pressure on the tiller that I did not see how the two of us were going to struggle all night with the ornery stick. I had both feet braced on the far side of the cockpit, and was using all my strength to battle the waves which broke against the bow. Had it been my decision, I would have turned back. But not Ed!" ~

Here she wrote of the confidence she placed in their boat:

~ I have felt before that a boat is a living thing. The transition at the moment when the motor is cut and the sails fill never fails to impress me. A static thing of wood and metal suddenly frees itself from its bonds and assumes a temporary but delightful life of its own. And now, *Blue Heron* took us into her care, seeming to promise us if we would stick by her she would deliver us safely at our goal. ~

But even with so much faith in *Blue Heron*, enough happened on their return journey to discourage less hardy souls than Ed and Marion from ever putting to sea again. Two hours out from Cuba they realized that they had filled the gas tank too full, to the brim, and when the boat heeled over gas spilled out of the fill pipe and into the bilges. The cockpit reeked of the smell of gasoline, and fumes overpowered the cabin below. The seas were violently rough and both of them were seasick. Neither Ed nor Marion could eat, and both were constantly deluged with cold spray. Then the jib sheet parted near the bow:

~ So the unhappy skipper got himself up, fastened the lifeline around his waist, attaching the other end to the bitt on the stern deck, and dragged himself forward on the lee side, his feet frequently buried in the swirling water that rushed through the scuppers.

Somehow he managed to get hold of the two ends of the line that had parted, and after a superhuman struggle, interrupted by a session or two at the rail, made them fast. Crawling still farther forward, clutching at every projection that offered him a handhold, he reached the bow and somehow fastened the sail which had whipped loose. Then he slowly worked his way back and collapsed for another interval.

Time wore on. We became wetter and colder, and I learned something about myself that I would not have believed. I, who am a very light sleeper at home, went to sleep on a slippery wet deck sloping at an angle of forty degrees, my clothes soaking wet, my hair dripping salt water, my toes squishing in my shoes, and water running down my neck. And I slept. ~

Before dawn the benumbed crew thought they almost hit a red light seeming to loom out of nowhere, marking a dangerous reef. Marion woke up with a start, staring in horror at the light then quickly screaming a warning to Ed at the tiller, who immediately brought the boat about. But scanning the horizon afterwards, they realized that the only light around was the morning star, which had by then risen high enough above the horizon to lose the brilliant red color they had observed when it first appeared.

With the return crossing behind them, finally at an anchorage recommended by the Coast Guard as being good in anything but a south wind, Ed and Marion slept, only to be awakened by southerly waves rolling in from the ocean straight at them, over the shallow ocean floor, rolling the boat, tossing and crashing dishes, canned goods, cooking utensils and cutlery in their cabinets and drawers or loosening them altogether to freely fly about the galley. When everything was finally under control and this new trial over, thinking themselves to be out of harm's way as they moved up into the keys, they were confronted by yet another sailor's dreaded dilemma, for inside a "secure" channel, during an exceptionally low tide, located directly between the red and green markers where they belonged, as they entered Angel Fish Creek, *Blue Heron* went hard aground! Marion summarized her saga with irony:

~ So ends the tale of two airmen at sea. Our conclusions:

That you can't get places as fast with a boat as an airplane, but you can have more fun. That navigating on the ocean requires quite a different technique from navigating in the air. That things may get a little rugged at times, but it's a wonderful feeling to know that you can handle the situation. That for pure adventure and sheer beauty, there is nothing like a cruise. ~

* * *

ED WENT ON RECEIVING AWARDS and honors. In May, 1948, he was issued yet another Training Device patent. Meanwhile, his next challenge at sea came by taking part in a major sailing race. Marion mentioned it in her notes:

~ When Ed became interested in ocean racing, I worked with him to equip and ready ship for the arduous contests. The first time *Blue Heron* was entered in the St. Petersburg-Havana race, Ed brought her in first in her class and second in the fleet. ~

This milestone was another first for Ed, and a serious victory. Not long a sailor and hardly a racer, he was up against seasoned participants who spent a great deal of their time, energy and even money on trying to win cups. While his opponents applied themselves to the perfection of their vessels and securing expert crews, Ed simply thought it over and made the right connections, the same way he always did when challenged by obstacles. This time, in spite of Marion's observations on returning from Havana that navigating in the air was not like navigating at sea, he applied principles learned in the air to offshore navigation. By using air navigation charts and a radio direction finder, he sailed an odd course and won, even though he was a completely unknown newcomer in the field of ocean racing.

Arthur Herzog described the event for *True* magazine:

~ The other boats headed south, the normal route to Havana around the Florida Keys, but Link sailed due west, 90 degrees in the wrong direction and was soon reported lost, with search planes sent to look for him. Link, though, had decided to navigate by aeronautical rather than Coast Guard weather reports because the former gave the weather over a larger area. Link plotted his route by figuring the prevailing winds over the whole course, and sailed into Havana first in his class and, only because of his handicap, second in the race. (Herzog then quoted Ed, who normally didn't like competitive sports, as telling another reporter, "I took up golf once and put it back down very gently." ~

In spite of his dislike for paperwork and his growing infatuation with the sea, Ed continued to maintain an office at Link Aviation. The simulator industry had survived the post-war slump, revived, and was on an even keel. Although after the war in 1945 it had faced cancellations of orders, complicated by a glut of trainers on the market, the hoped for rebound was taking place. Reporting on the history of trainers, writer James Killgore said that next to the all-electronic trainers, the "wheezing Link Trainer was antiquated," but that in 1949, "Link unveiled the C-11, or Linktronic, the first flight trainer designed to simulate flight in a jet-powered aircraft." Killgore said of the evolution from trainers to space simulators:

~ Machines like NASA's giant vertical motion simulator, designed for advanced air and spaceflight research, hardly seem to be descended from the small, whirling trainer with which Edwin Link started it all some sixty years ago. ~

Lloyd Kelly, *The Pilot Maker* co-author, who had joined Link Aviation in 1945, was now playing a major role in the development of more sophisticated, digital (from mechanical to electrical) simulators. Under the management of capable directors Link Aviation grew more and more into sophisticated technologies, which left its founder betwixt and between. The jet age was upon Ed, having opened in 1939 when, independently, Germany's Hans J.P. von Ohain and England's Sir Frank Whittle built the world's first turbojets. Flight had gained speed and lost its romance for Ed. Sailboat racing could not hold his interest, either. Lacking motivation, unchallenged by merely winning or losing cups, he continued to search for more meaningful directions. Even Perch Island lost its lustre, and Marion wrote in her journal:

~ Meanwhile the little island in the St. Lawrence suddenly seemed very tame, and in 1949 we secured a lease on 156 square miles of Quebec wilderness which could be reached only by amphibious airplane or by portaging many miles of lakes and trails. We chose a lake just big enough for the Grumman Widgeon to land, and from an old broken-down log cabin, set about reconstructing a comfortable (though rustic) hunting and fishing lodge. Everything that went into its making came either from the forest, or was carried in the limited space of the Widgeon, with the exception of a refrigerator and a generator, which were hauled in by dog team when the lakes were frozen over. ~

Ed was a 45-year old millionaire. With that kind of success he could think about retiring early and taking it easy, but wealth, coming as it did only after years of bitter struggle, was never in itself a source of satisfaction for him. To his way of thinking, he had not proven himself by acquiring riches, and he was in no way a big spender who could sit back and enjoy the "good life." Solidly practical about money, he once told an interviewer, "I've never been much interested in money, though you have to have it to survive."

In December, 1949, Ed was issued a patent for the "Aquatic Device." Now he needed to keep up the momentum in his personal life. To be fully retired in Florida with a stress-free life of golf and cocktail circuits was no panacea for happiness to a mechanic who, though tiring of modernized airplanes, perhaps remained a barnstormer at heart. Ed liked doing things the hard way. To work at and solve a problem was something worthwhile; Time could not nag at his soul or wear him down with boredom. The genius must be occupied; he still had contributions to make; he had to have a dream beyond the mundane. Work, even if it was only play to him, was necessary.

* * *

FOR YET A WHILE LONGER Ed remained a guiding light at the factory, though more and more often taking off to sail in Florida or to rough it at the lodge in Canada. But even the log cabin got a little tame after he and Marion and the boys labored to bring it up to date. A new porch, a kitchen, a bedroom and an outhouse were the first additions to the original single-room dwelling, and it still lacked a road. They drew water from a nearby lake and carried it to the lodge until Ed built a water tower, allowing for running water and an indoor toilet. Oil lamps provided their only light until the new generator arrived by dog sled.

If Ed wanted adventure at the 156 acre wilderness retreat leased from the Quebec government, he got more than he bargained for on at least one occasion. He, Marion, and Clayton suffered several days of extreme anguish when 16-year-old Bill went out on a windy, rainy day, on his own, to explore some nearby cliffs and do a little hunting, and got lost. When Bill failed to return to the cabin on the first night, Ed put out a call for help over his radio. The Royal Canadian Mounted Police, Ed, Bill's brother Clayton, and several rugged Canadian bushmen and their guides carried out an all-out search on foot and by canoe, with a helicopter standing by waiting for the weather to clear so that it too could join the search. When Ed was not with the search party on the ground, he was flying overhead in spite of the foul weather. By the second day high winds were tearing branches out of some of the trees and uprooting others. A radio report indicated that a hurricane was in the vicinity. Tension mounted when by the third morning Bill was still missing, but he turned up at last that same day.

When it was all over Clayton turned his brother's misadventure to his advantage by writing an award winning story for *Boy's Life* magazine, which included a description of Ed's search by air:

~ ...Even though this was no weather for a plane to be flying in, Dad just had to fly. ...He roared over the cabin at about a hundred feet and skimmed over the small lake back of us, just above the treetops all the time. He skimmed above the forest on the edge of Miller Lake... Every time he passed near the cabin it looked as if he would hit the trees in front of us. ~

By the third day the weather had worsened. Clayton said the fog was so bad that as he watched his father and several guides walk out the door they disappeared from view. He continued with his story:

~ About eleven o'clock Dad couldn't stand waiting around any longer for the fog to lift. He just had to do something, so he decided to take the airplane up again to have another look around.

...The fog had lifted, but clouds hung heavy on the hilltops and it was raining again. ...We heard the engines going back and forth across the woods. Perhaps a half hour later Dad returned. He had seen no signs of Bill. He and mother were terribly worried because they knew that Bill could not survive many more days of exposure to the wet and cold without food or shelter.

We were all sitting around gloomily wondering what to do next when my mother gave a cry of joy and ran to the door. Dad and I both jumped up and looked out of the window to see Bill coming toward the cabin with two of the guides, looking very tired, wet and dirty, but very happy. My mother ran out and threw her arms around him and we were all crying out of sheer joy. Boots [the dog] was prancing around trying to get attention from someone, but finally gave up and retired under the table. ~

Bill later told of how he had wandered lost through the woods to a lake he had no recollection of ever seeing before. When he realized he was not going to make it home that first night, he applied his knowledge of wilderness survival to finding shelter in a crevice, made a rustic bed of cut boughs, and slept as best he could beside the dying embers of a fire he had started from a few salvaged matches. The next day, after hearing his father's plane some distance away, he struck out, got more confused, and ended up sleeping that night under a soggy fallen tree. He ate nothing during the three days he was lost but a raw partridge he managed to shoot but could not cook because he had run out of matches. His father's plane was never near enough for him to draw attention to himself from the ground. When he heard the distant drone of the engine, he drew a huge arrow on the ground at the edge of a lake, but it was never seen from the air. He was finally rescued by two guides who heard him firing shots from his rifle at regular intervals. The guides returned his fire, then signaled back and forth with Bill until they gradually closed in on him.

Both of Marion and Ed's boys were keen on adventure, and, as might have been expected of boys, they loved the wilderness as much as their father did. What was perhaps not to be expected was that their soft-spoken, gracious and refined mother loved the rustic life as much as they did; even as she enjoyed every new, unexpected challenge that Ed constantly managed to bring into their lives. "I was an adventurer too," she now reminisces. "I had to be. I loved life with Ed because he was always dreaming up something new to do."

Still looking for something new, Ed was in the process of phasing himself out of the business. E. Allan Williford became General Manager of the Link company in 1950, bringing to the organization a background in administration with Union Carbide and Ansco. Williford may well have been shocked to discover Ed's familiarity with the employees, and seems to have thought that he had been too informal in his operations. He reorganized the company, and in the process, appointed Lloyd Kelly (co-author of *The Pilot Maker*) as general sales manager of marketing.

It was true that the business had grown too big, too computerized for Ed's style, and it was time for a change all around, even though he always remained in touch with certain of his favorite projects. In 1950, yet another patent was issued in his name, for a helicopter device described as an "Air Speed Indicating System for Rotary Winged Aircraft."

Even though his fertile mind lingered in the shops at the factory, Ed knew he was becoming an outsider in many ways, just as he knew that the company could forge ahead without him. The pilot, mechanic, industrialist; the creative innovator who had started it all, was fading from the picture but he was too young and dynamic to retire. He needed to change his direction. It was only a matter of time until he finally turned to the oceans, but only after undergoing certain rites of passage; two life-threatening events within a single year had yet to be conquered.

The first occurred on a hunting trip in Canada. Ed and Stuart MacLean, a friend from Louisville, Kentucky, flew by Grumman Widgeon to MacLean's hunting lodge at Hudson Bay, where MacLean hoped to shoot a polar bear. Armed for the kill — MacLean with a rifle and Ed with a camera — the two men spent hours on the ice, searching the horizon for their prey. At last they spotted a polar bear swimming offshore, nearly within their range. The magnificent animal drew closer to the hunters then began swimming past their position on the ice. Ed began to shoot a quick succession of photographs. MacLean took a shot at the bear, but the bear, only aggravated by the bullet, kept swimming. MacLean continued to fire, and though he found his mark, the bullets failed to penetrate the bear's hide deep enough for a kill. Finally the wounded bear became enraged and changed its course, suddenly swimming directly toward its tormentors. Ed was reluctant to lose the opportunity of photographing the oncoming bear and hesitated a moment too long, until it was too late to run. Still he continued to shoot pictures as the bear reached the edge of the ice, hove its great hulk onto the surface, and began swiftly lumbering towards him. Without a moment to spare, another shot rang out from MacLean's rifle. This time the bullet went all the way through the bear's neck, and the great animal crumpled into a heap within a few feet of the unarmed photographer.

Within the year, after summering in the Chesapeake Bay, Ed determined that it was time to sail *Blue Heron* down the Atlantic Coast to winter in Florida. With two other friends and his nephew-in-law, Dr. Joseph E. Murray, he set sail in the open ocean early in the fall, soon enough, he reckoned, to reach Florida before the northeasters started to blow. But his forecast turned out to be a miscalculation. On the way down the coast the wind freshened and began to kick up the seas unseasonably early. The little ship pounded southward, at first progressing slowly and then making little to no headway at all. Soon it was tossing violently in a full-force storm.

To an observer in another boat, *Blue Heron* would have seemed to turn to mist and disappear in the driving rain, then perhaps to reappear from time to time on the crest of a wave only to drop out of sight again in the wave's trough. The staunch yacht took a beating, but even so she held her own as the stormy sea rose and spun and dropped her again and again. Then a giant rogue wave caught her broadside and knocked her down. The stunned crew barely had time to realize what had happened before the reliable little vessel righted herself again, and in so doing, scooped her storm sail so full of water that it split under the weight. The cockpit too had filled with water. Ed was on watch during the knock down, seeking protection from the weather as best he could by sitting on the step at the companionway hatch just inside the galley, bracing himself on either side and constantly poking his head out to look around. As a result, when *Blue Heron* righted herself, he watched helplessly as the uncontrolled sea poured through the open hatch and into the cabin below.

At last the storm moved on, leaving in its wake a soggy, bedraggled *Blue Heron* bobbing at sea in the deepest darkness somewhere off the coast of South Carolina. The crew had lost their bearings, knowing for certain only that they were somewhere in the vicinity of a stretch of treacherous reefs known as the "Frying Pan Shoals," where ships far sturdier than the fragile, wooden-hulled *Blue Heron*, had had their bottoms torn out. At that point, weighing one danger against another, Ed decided to take a chance. He slopped below decks and rigged the radio into working order just long enough to contact the Coast Guard for an exact position to reset their course by, then he cautiously disconnected the radio again.

Back at the tiller he eased his vessel into its reset course, and the crew relaxed as *Blue Heron* got under way. Little did they know that the greater danger was yet to come. With the first streak of silvery morning light, a plane began to circle overhead. Ed soon guessed that it was the Coast Guard trying to make contact. On recon-

necting the radio, he learned to his horror that he had been given the wrong coordi-
nates the night before, and as a consequence, they had sailed not towards Florida,
but directly into the Frying Pan Shoals. As the wet and eerie morning light gradually
spread over a now dead calm sea, they were able to make out the shocking truth: By
some miracle, *Blue Heron* had managed to safely pick her way into the thickest part
of the treacherous reefs, where she would remain until an embarrassed and apolo-
getic Coast Guard team came to rescue her.

Ed, it seemed, had passed his trials. He was learning the hard way, and in the
process, becoming a seaman, though he and his family still went off to the Canadian
wilderness from time to time. Marion recorded the activities leading to the change to
come in her journal:

> ~ So for several years we flew north in the summer and fall to that beauti-
> ful land of lakes and forests, and south in the winter to the idyllic life
> aboard *Blue Heron*. Then one winter, Ed's attention turned to the under-
> water. He was a little bored with ocean racing, now that he had conquered
> it. Before I could believe it, I found myself embarked on a new adventure.
> We were members of an expedition which had gathered to dive on the
> wrecks of three ancient sailing ships on the reefs off the Florida Keys. ~

The year was 1951. Still a responsible citizen and growing in stature, Ed was
appointed to Binghamton's First City National Bank board of directors (and
remained so until retiring in 1974). Meanwhile, the coming era was rapidly
approaching. His and Marion's troth with the sea had its real beginning in the spring
of 1951, when *Blue Heron* pulled into Bill Thompson's Yacht Basin at Marathon in
the Florida Keys. Coincidentally, Ed was ready for what he would find there, having
stowed a heavy metal diving helmet and a crude hand operated compressor aboard
his vessel, which he and the boys immediately experimented with in Thompson's
swimming pool. In her first book, *Sea Diver*, covering their diving and cruising
adventures, Marion immortalized the moment:

> ~ I should have realized right then that one of those crucial times had
> arrived in Ed's life when it was essential for him to progress on to a new
> enthusiasm. ~

And so it began. Herzog wrote for his *True* story:

> ~ Link and his wife Marion were aboard the *Blue Heron* in Florida, ready
> to start on a Caribbean cruise. A friend mentioned that he had spotted
> what looked like an old [ship] wreck off the Florida Keys. Link, who

happened to have some untried diving equipment in his locker, went down to investigate and came up a changed man, having found a Spanish cannon dated 1617... .

Overnight the Links became treasure hunters, scudding about the Caribbean and bringing up pieces-of-eight, ballast and other cannons — finds they would probably think fairly commonplace today; in smart skin-diving circles an old cannon, unless it happens to be an English bronze or a rare Spanish gun, coated with platinum and worth its weight in income tax, is not a very sophisticated find. Link, however, was just getting started. ~

"When Ed sets his mind on an objective," Marion said, "every other consideration fades into the background." Though those first finds may not have been sophisticated, they led Ed to develop highly innovative tools for underwater work, most of which are now used matter-of-factly by divers the world over. When he began diving, wanting to gain practical, real-time working access to the underwater realm, he found himself to be at an entirely new frontier. The sort of tools needed to work in that alien atmosphere hardly existed, and so, taking up a new quest, he would make his own.

# CHAPTER VI

# TRACKING TREASURE & CHRISTOPHER COLUMBUS

**1951–1958**

*If I take the wings of the morning and dwell
in the uttermost parts of the sea, even there thy hand shall lead me
and thy right hand shall hold me.*

*—Psalms 139.9.10*

Ed Link the aviator had found a turning point from sky to sea. His journalist wife, Marion, made the transition with him and immediately began documenting his new endeavors in notes and journals, which ultimately led to publication of her first book, *Sea Diver*. The book was titled after the ship they were yet to purchase and redesign to suit their diving needs, and was published by Rinehart in 1958, reprinted by Rinehart again in 1959, and released yet again by the University of Miami Press in 1964.

Though her book, *Sea Diver*, written in a popular style, was in great demand at the time, it eventually went out of print and is now not easily come by. However, there can be no story on the life of Ed Link that does not encompass those years covered by Marion in her first book. Her descriptions of that era are important not only because they provide a record of how an aviation engineer found himself eventually creating new tools for undersea research, but because they describe his activities in detail as well as some of her own early underwater diving experiences.

Marion's book also documents Ed's still valid theories on Columbus's first landfall and his important tracking of Columbus's first journey through the Bahamas. It tells of her discovery of an anchor thought to be from the *Santa Maria*. It vividly describes the Links' extensive diving experiences in a remote area at sea still thought by many to harbor a vast amount of sunken treasure, the Silver Shoals. This region, densely populated with reefs and located far from shore between the Bahamian Turks Islands and Hispaniola, is of great interest to true treasure seekers the world over. Pleasure diving companies as well hope to one day find a safe means for conducting underwater tours there.

To clearly link the past with the future, this era must be retold, and so, much of Marion's material, both published and unpublished — from her notes, journals, and now out-of-print book — is combined and produced here along with new material gleaned from conversations between Marion and the narrating author. The important historical highlights of this period are best seen through Marion's own eyes; but even so, an exciting segment written by Ed himself is also included. It all began after Ed, Marion, Bill and Clayton had grown accustomed to sailing aboard *Blue Heron*.

* * *

## Part I - Tracking Treasure

WHEN THE BINGHAMTON COUPLE first took a seaward direction, took up racing, then moved on to cruising, Ed the barnstormer/inventor-come-industrialist still remained somewhat involved in aviation engineering, often traveling between his simulator industry at home, the Canadian wilderness and his sailing yacht in the sunny tropics. Though some might thrive on what could have been the life of the idle rich, it was anathema to Ed, and definitely not the way he had imagined he would spend his time now that his presence was no longer in great demand at the factory. The truth is, he simply was not adjusting well to success and the easy life that came with it. He was no longer a hands-on leader, which left him at loose ends. And so it was that in 1951, with Marion and "Vital," a French-Canadian deckhand recently recruited from their lodge in Canada, he joined the "Looe expedition" aboard their sloop, *Blue Heron*, off the coast of Marathon in the Florida keys.

This followed an earlier cruise with the boys, who were on Easter vacation, aboard *Blue Heron* to Bimini in the Bahama Islands. (NOTE: photo on pg. 172, #7). After learning of the upcoming expedition, they all left for home, but they would be back. Ed was hooked. He was ready to satisfy his curiosity and learn what he had wanted to know as a child: what it was like under the sea. He looked after business interests at Binghamton then flew to Marathon again at the end of May to ready ship for the Looe expedition. Marion got the boys back in school and saw to other family affairs with one of the several warm-hearted "housemothers" who helped out over the years, and cared for the boys when they were home alone. When school was out, Marion and the boys joined Ed on June 6, arriving at Marathon in time to celebrate their 20th wedding anniversary. She wrote in *Sea Diver* that all the divers gathered around an outdoor grill that evening to broil fresh caught barracuda and talk of the coming mission, then of starting out the next morning under a hot summer sun:

~...[with] three ill-assorted craft — a cruiser, which was used for sport fishing the remainder of the year; a sturdy LCP boat with two decks, which had been chartered for the expedition; and *Blue Heron*, whose sleek lines and delicate grace were never designed for hauling heavy cannon from the ocean floor. ~

The Smithsonian Institution's Mendel Peterson was with the company of nearly thirty men, women and children on this hunt for sunken treasure, the first of its kind for the Links. Also present was the well-known professional diver, Arthur "Art" McKee, owner and chief supplier of The Museum of Sunken Treasure on Plantation key, and Bill Thompson, a diver from Marathon who had discovered the three ancient shipwrecks they were heading for. Thompson was accompanied by his "vivacious" wife, Ethel, as Marion described her in her journal.

Mendel Peterson was to figure largely in the coming era. Marion wrote in *Sea Diver* that with this acquaintance, Ed had "formed a connection with the Marine Archeology department of the Smithsonian Institution in Washington, for which he set out to provide artifacts and exhibits." Peterson was an acquaintance of the couple that had organized the Looe expedition, Dr. Barney Crile, medical doctor and son of the founder of the Cleveland Medical Clinic, and his wife Jane (who became lifelong friends of the Links). Peterson was then acting head of the Department of History, and would become officially chairman of the department of the Armed Forces Museum of History and Technology, Smithsonian Institution. And he would, as was customary with many of Ed's initially casual contacts, become another close friend for life. Years later, in 1965, Peterson dedicated his scholarly publication, *History Under the Sea*, to: "Edwin A. Link, Inventor and Underwater Pioneer."

Many years later Peterson visited the widowed Marion at her home at Harbor Branch to catalogue and put a value on the Link artifact collection, a formidable task leading him to at last comment: "Anything Ed Link ever touched is precious." But in 1951, Peterson was, as Marion described him, "a good-looking young man with rather bold brown eyes and a heavy shadow of a beard on his mobile face," who was preparing to dive with the Links and their new-found diving associates in the Looe expedition.

Planning to search the waters off Looe key in the Florida Straits, the skippers first anchored near two other wrecks, where cruise organizers Barney and Jane Crile had the year before joined Thompson in salvaging an impressive cache of ivory. Shortly after their arrival on site, almost everyone in the group was geared up and in the water, but not Marion. Afraid of diving and not much of a swimmer, she remained aboard *Blue Heron* as an observer while the others spread out in search of further signs of ivory. The day's foray ended with the discovery of an old cannon, which the divers with some difficulty managed to recover. Marion wrote in *Sea Diver* that with makeshift equipment and the well-intentioned but awkward efforts of the amateur crew, it was hours before the cannon was finally raised and secured to a spot in the curve of *Blue Heron's* bottom and keel, where it was made fast for the journey to shore.

Ed had provided substantial help in raising the cannon. Seeing no signs of progress as the party struggled with the heavy object, he had taken action, assessing the situation underwater, surfacing to fetch steel cables as replacements for the ropes they were using — which had gotten hopelessly frayed on the coral — going back underwater to sit astride the iron barrel and rig the cables around the cannon, all the while "plunging up and down with the motion of the boat as if he were riding a bucking horse," Marion commented in her book, and eventually getting the job done.

Success at retrieving the cannon came with Ed's first underwater salvage attempt, and he recognized its significance at once, for unlike pleasure cruising, this was something he could do at sea that required ingenuity. His foremost objective then quickly became to convince Marion to learn to dive. In spite of what she described as "almost a phobia" against putting her head under water or even getting water up her nose, she finally agreed to give it a try.

They had no wetsuits as yet, and Marion wrote that to protect themselves against stinging jellyfish, heavy diving weights and corals on the bottom, the full complement of divers plunged into the water fully dressed. She reported that the veterans wore black ballet tights or long ski underwear with bright-colored, long-sleeved jerseys, while the novices were in ordinary long-sleeved shirts, dungarees and shoes. Shaking inside but "outwardly calm," she wrote of how she prepared for her first dive:

> ~ ...I donned jersey and dungarees over my swim suit, tied on my deck shoes and bathing cap and waited to have the diving mask adjusted — not the clumsy metal helmet which Ed had experimented with earlier...but a Desco mask, a triangle of glass edged with black rubber, equipped with intake and exhaust valves and connected to a hundred feet of hose. Air, cool and comforting, poured in through the open valve as Ed tightened the fastenings of the mask about my face. ~

Ed was trying out the new "Aqualung" for the first time at sea after diligently practicing with it in the swimming pool. The gear consisted of a face mask and a separate mouthpiece, with a regulator and air hose attached to a tank of compressed air strapped to his back. The scuba (self-contained underwater breathing apparatus) gear, only recently developed overseas by a handful of Frenchmen, would prove to be practical for underwater searches, though he continued to work for longer periods with the less limiting use of "hookah gear," consisting of a full-face mask with an air hose leading to an air compressor on the deck of the ship.

The aqualung, first tested in 1943, had came about from a combination of ideas in wartime France, when Jacques Yves Cousteau and others were conducting strategic underwater experiments. Undersea author and diver Hillary Hauser noted its most crucial development in her book for young readers, *Call to Adventure*:

~ Cousteau needed to devise a method that would enable a diver to inhale and exhale, through the same mouthpiece, without breathing back in the carbon dioxide that is emitted during exhalation. ...Air Liquide engineer Emil Gagnon...had in his laboratory just the device Cousteau was looking for — an automatic shutoff valve designed for use on automobiles that were running on natural gas. ...In three weeks Cousteau and Gagnon produced a prototype of an Aqualung. ~

According to a list compiled by an unknown author found among Ed's possessions at the Link Foundation offices, *A Brief History of Underwater Events* (*333BC to 1974*), an aqualung dive, conducted in France by Frederic Dumas at a depth of 203 feet and lasting one minute, was the world's first scuba dive. The second experimental dives took place in Sweden in 1947, conducted at 297 feet by "Cousteau, Tailluz, Dumas, Georges, Fargues, and Morandiere," then in 1948, at 307 feet, Dumas made an aqualung dive on compressed air.

Within three years of the French experimental dive in 1948, novice diver Ed Link, wearing an aqualung, escorted his wife under the sea. Though sustained diving was not yet practiced universally, others in the 1951 Looe expedition were to differing degrees already old hands at it, and with her own husband and sons so willing and eager to experiment, Marion could no longer find an excuse for holding out.

Well aware of her anxiety on that first dive, Ed hovered close to her side as she descended through a sea she described as populated with innumerable jellyfish, not taking her eyes off "the outline of *Blue Heron's* keel as it took shape in the pale green light" above her head. In spite of the presence of her underwater guide, she soon experienced trouble from "an unexpected quarter":

~ My feet, in their canvas shoes, insisted upon floating. As I descended the rope, I had great trouble keeping them lower than my head. When I reached the bottom, I could not get my feet down; they seemed determined to go off on an exploring trip of their own. Ed, seeing my predicament, surfaced and soon returned with extra weights, which he put in my dungaree pockets. That helped some, and I was able to put my feet on the bottom, but my efforts at walking were unsteady.

I stood on the white-sand bottom twenty-five feet below and looked around me. A beautiful sea garden stretched out on every side, a world of waving sea grasses, fantastic coral formations and lacy traceries of sea fans. Here were cool caves from whose crevasses undulated the feelers of giant crawfish; beneath the sheltering ledges lay broken bits of coral and shells.

Ed touched my arm and beckoned me to follow him. He led me to a pit in the sandy bottom where lay a cannon crusted with coral and covered with sea growth. Scattered in the sand lay dozens of purple-tinged, porcupine-like sea urchins, forming a protective ring around the cannon. The spiny creatures frightened me, and I backed away, lost my precarious balance and wavered helplessly toward another pit, which was liberally dotted with more sea urchins.

It was only by a tremendous effort that I saved myself from tumbling among them. In my excitement I gulped great quantities of air and then found myself gasping for breath. The hose could not conduct air fast enough to satisfy my urgent requirements. My heart pounded. I felt stifled in the small confines of the face mask. Then, my feet once more safely on the bottom, I regained control of myself, and my breathing slowed to the point where the air hose could take care of the situation again. ~

After taking another good look around, she slowly inched her way up the life line, determining to learn more about diving and to explore the bottom for herself. Meanwhile, from within the safety of *Blue Heron's* cockpit, she learned that sea urchins, members of the echinoderm family, are relatively harmless to man except for possibly leaving a patch of needles in the skin of divers who come too close, and are common in seas the world over.

That night at dock an inscription was found on the cannon Ed had rigged to bring up from the Ivory wreck, which read "anno 1617." (NOTE: photo on pg. 174, #11). Perhaps this was the hook for the Links, who studied with reverence this piece of weaponry from a ship that had lain beneath the sea, lost, for more than 300 years. It was "...a real find, from a ship which must have sunk," Marion thought, "at about the time the Pilgrim Fathers first came to the New World." She wrote that Mendel Petersen had already identified the Looe key wreck they were heading for next — from a coin brought up the year before — as an English warship, but he assumed that the Ivory wreck had been a vessel in the slave trade, of uncertain age and nationality.

Off Looe key, Ed's concentration was now focused on the depths of the ocean, his imagination triggered as much by the beauty and endless mystery of the sea as by the wreck itself, which in turn inspired Marion to investigate its history for inclusion in her book. As it turned out, both Ed and Marion had stumbled across new beginnings from this single adventure; Ed to take up ocean navigation and engineering and Marion to conduct extensive research on the history of this wreck and other events which had taken place over the centuries in that part of the world.

Finds on the Looe expedition included a 2,000 pound cannon bearing a crowned rose (insignia of British Royalty) and coins dated as late as 1720. Peterson had been inspired to search in Washington through the casualty lists of the British

Royal Navy of the 18th-century, eventually to learn that the vessel was the *HMS Looe*, which sailed from England in August, 1743. The entry in the British Royal Navy records reads: "1743 [*sic*] Looe 44 guns, Capt. Ashby Utting, lost in America," as quoted from *Sea Diver*. Further research revealed that the vessel was patrolling the waters adjacent to Cuba and the Florida keys when, on February 4, 1744 it was shipwrecked with a captured vessel, the Spanish *Snow*, which had been following the *Looe*. Though both ships were lost, the crews made it safely to shore. Meanwhile, Thompson's discovery had opened the way for a whole new world for the Links. In her book Marion had written:

> ~ By the time that expedition was over Ed and I were confirmed divers and treasure seekers. We had been afflicted with a contagion which was to lead us on strange and unexpected adventures. Following its onset we found ourselves unable to resist tales of treasure-laden ships lying upon the ocean floor, their contents still untouched. We felt sure that they only awaited our coming to surrender vast quantities of riches. ~

Treasure seeking quickly became addictive. Marion continued:

> ~ ...[It was] a virtually inescapable malady [that] was to lead us to risk our boats and equipment many times, and even our lives, in treacherous reef-strewn waters, oftentimes far from sight of land. Before the disease had run its course, we had visited every part of the far-flung Bahamas, had followed the lure of sunken treasure clear to the Silver Shoals, a forty-mile square area of scattered reefs lying between the remote Turks Islands and Hispaniola, shunned by every mariner since the time of Columbus. And off the shores of Jamaica we found ourselves battling the wind and tides which constantly assault the long, lean line of Banner Reef, scarred with the wreckage of many a ship headed across the Caribbean. ~

But first Marion had to overcome her fear of diving, which she accomplished on the *Looe* wreck on her second dive. Determined, she entered the sea that time on her own:

> ~ I lowered myself slowly along the life line until my feet hit the edge of a wire basket placed on the bottom as a repository for the divers' finds. A heavy black air hose hung from the boat above; it was being used to clean away coral chips and sand from the objects on the bottom. I paused and looked around.

Towering high above the narrow valley on either side were coral cliffs and caves, from which grew beautiful sea fans and other branching Gorgonia. In my ignorance, at the time I thought the animal-celled Gorgonia was vegetation.

Tiny, bright-colored fish swam about my feet. A huge pinkish-brown hog snapper hovered nearby. As I watched, three large, beautiful, black-and-gold angelfish sailed majestically past, waving their fins in slow and perfect rhythm, while just beyond, a single brilliant-blue angelfish shyly looked out from behind the pinnacle of coral rock on the valley floor.

This time, with the aid of the flippers, I was able to swim about this strange undersea ravine, floating up the steep sides of the coral rocks, peeping into eerie chasms and then gliding down to examine a nearly buried cannon, scarcely distinguishable under its disguise of coral. It was then I saw the giant anchor of the sunken warship, coral-covered and almost hidden under a jutting shelf of rock. Its huge ring was large enough to swim through. The shank, half buried in the coral, still revealed a section longer than myself. It must have weighed more than a ton. I hovered over it enthralled.

For more than an hour I explored this lovely spot, getting tremendous satisfaction out of playing fish. And the fish didn't seem to mind at all this clumsy, strange-looking creature from the world above. They swam about me, scouting out food from the bottom, playing tag with each other, completely oblivious of me. With startling suddenness the realization came to me. I was no longer fearful of this strange environment. I was at last at home on the bottom. ~

Ed already knew that treasure diving alone would not satisfy the desire building within himself to know and work uninterrupted in the sea. The greatest portion of the surface of the earth was yet to be conquered, and it had to be done responsibly. He and Marion together had what it took to make a valid contribution. Predictably, he was full of curiosity, both about what he would find in the ocean's depths and what it would take to fully explore them. He was already experiencing the enormous limitations encountered in the retrieval of underwater objects, while at the same time sensing the tremendous potentialities of the ocean's resources if only man could master its alien environment.

Just as Ed had foreseen the vast future of aviation in the early flying days while others were satisfied with barnstorming and the exhilaration of stunt flying, he now began to realize that the sea offered much more than hidden treasure or even the pure joy of deep diving in its sapphire depths. He was already wondering about evidences of history lying hidden beneath the surface, even about Plato's legendary Atlantis, while his limitless imagination told him that here also were vast new resources to be tapped. So, while becoming an expert diver in search of gold, he studied the sea and made connections that would take him far into the future, realizing the need for new tools to gain greater access to this realm that covered so much of the earth's surface.

Marion credited Mendel Peterson with channeling her husband's developing interest in the underwater world into the field of marine archeology, "for it was impossible," she wrote, "to discover these ancient artifacts without feeling a tantalizing curiosity as to their origin." What had started out to be merely a "new sport," she said, "soon resolved itself into a consuming and enthralling interest in the past history of that part of the New World."

Ed's tendency, long discerned by Marion, to wander on his own path until it led to fulfillment could be seen in his past, as she pointed out in *Sea Diver*, when a number of his former major interests finally resulted in the "booming enterprise" of Link Aviation during World War II. Now multiple new interests at sea were vaguely coming together, promising to culminate again in something substantial. "His entire life pattern," she said, "had been one of following his own interests, his inventive mind and creative thinking carrying him along from one new project to another."

But for the time being, life settled into a new routine, and she wrote in her notes for *Sea Diver*:

~ While Ed organized and developed equipment and planned new forays under the sea, I studied the historic background of the areas which we searched, seeking stories behind the shipwrecks which we dove upon, and plotting out possibilities for further search. From my first exciting and rather frightening dive off the coast of Marathon, Florida I had progressed to a point where I looked forward with eager anticipation each time to my next visit to the ocean floor. ~

They were now old hands at diving themselves; Marion following Ed's lead after overcoming her fears and working through an awkward stage of handling underwater equipment and becoming familiar with the strange new environment. The greatest drawback in their growing dedication to underwater work was that along the way they had given up on *Blue Heron* and had taken instead to cruising in a 75-foot twin-diesel cruiser, *Eryholme*, which Ed had borrowed (for nearly a year) from Lee Warrender. Though the Link family neglected their beloved *Blue Heron*, Ed exercised his craftsman's expertise and constructed a model of the graceful little sloop before relegating her to the region of fond memories, to be loaned on occasion to friends and replaced at last with another boat.

As Ed and his wife and children grew committed to this new life, he found that he could apply himself to a whole new set of problems, which led to acquiring and renovating a larger, more stable workboat. Ed had learned that if he was to continue with his new interests, he would need more equipment above decks as well as on the sea floor. He needed a crane, winches, and work space, however much he and his family remained attached to their beloved *Blue Heron*. The new vessel turned out to be a wealthy man's yacht built on the lines of a shrimper that he had seen in Miami. Marion wrote of the change: "*...Blue Heron* was replaced by a 65-foot shrimper-type trawler that could accommodate the equipment needed for salvage diving on wreck sites along the coast of Florida, the Bahamas and the Caribbean."

*Blue Heron* had been out of the picture for over a year when, on May 7, 1952, supplies were laid in the new ship, gear was transferred from *Eryholme*, and *Sea Diver* was ready for her first cruise. Fully redesigned and renovated by Ed, she was powered by an eight-cylinder Caterpillar diesel rated at 150 to 300 horsepower and carried four large fuel tanks with a capacity of 1600 gallons. He had also designed a number of other changes to improve her versatility, including the addition of a crow's nest 35 feet up the mast, reached by a welded metal ladder.

For *Sea Diver's* maiden work mission, the crew planned to search in the Florida keys for cannon with friends Eddie and Marion Gale, and on Thursday, May 8, 1952, Marion recorded in her journal:

~ We left Angel Fish Creek this morning and headed for "Half Moon Patch" near Key Largo dry rocks. We searched the spot thoroughly, Ed in the crow's nest and the Gales on the bow. I ran *Sea Diver*. We had calm water but found no trace of cannon. Ed finally decided he was on the wrong spot. We headed out to sea, past the red nun marker. About 100 yards off, we suddenly struck bottom so hard *Sea Diver's* bow was raised right out of the water. Pieces of wood started floating to the surface. Ed, who was forward, saw a large iron tripod marker about three feet under water as we backed off. We dropped anchor and set the pump going. Ed went overboard to inspect the damage, which he thought was more or less superficial. The heavy wooden keel planking had been stripped from the bow, and gouged the whole length of the boat but there were no holes in the bottom. Huge bolts stuck out from the dead wood on the bow's curve. Ed took down a crowbar and pried off the hanging pieces of wood, then after lunch we headed for Tavernier anchorage. ~

Not until May 12 did *Sea Diver* arrive back at Miami Shipbuilding, where she went on the ways. The next morning her crew was surprised to learn that damage to the hull was more extensive than expected, "with the large protective curve of dead wood on the bow knocked off, bolts sticking forth, and the length of the keel chewed and shredded." Ed had seen other needs on the shakedown cruise, and the vessel underwent additional transformation. Rolling chocks were installed on the sides of the hull. Extra water tanks were added, as was a stainless-steel freezer. In the pilot house he had installed a loran (a long-range radio air-navigation instrument developed during the war), which, though standard equipment on ships today, was used chiefly in airplanes at the time. (NOTE: photo on pg. 173, #8). Marion wrote that ventilators, fans and an air-conditioning system were added, providing most of the comforts of home. With Ed's fertile mind focused intently on diving needs, *Sea Diver* was fast becoming one of the world's best outfitted diving research vessels of the day. Marion wrote in *Sea Diver*:

> ~ Dive equipment now included a twelve-cubic-foot air compressor, its 120-pound capacity enabling us to use air-driven tools either on board or underwater, as well as providing ample air for three divers at one time. Ed had put considerable thought into choosing and arranging his diving equipment so that it could be put into operation quickly, with a minimum crew. The air hoses had been wound on reels so that, after attaching the diving mask, the diver could go overboard and without assistance from the deck pull out any length of hose he might require up to two hundred feet. He could reach a still greater distance by connecting the hose from the permanent reel on deck to a second reel on one of the small boats, which could be anchored two hundred feet from *Sea Diver*. This reel, in turn, would allow two divers to operate from it with air supplied from the first hose. ~

The new 65-foot ship, much more convenient for living and working at sea, rapidly became an even greater extension of Link family life than the delicate Sparkman-and Stevens-designed *Blue Heron* ever could have been. There was plenty of room for the growing boys, who were now enrolled (for one semester only) in a private school in Fort Lauderdale, "so that the family would not be so widely separated," according to Marion, and the boys could easily join their parents on weekends and holidays for the coming adventures. *Sea Diver* was a sturdy workboat with comfortable living quarters that could accommodate a larger crew, the equipment requirements for handling old cannon and other artifacts, and all of their necessary diving gear. Ed and Marion had by then established a routine of wintering at home and spending most of their sea time when the boys were out of school and could be with them.

With the new *Sea Diver*, diving became a serious business, which meant that Marion's responsibilities increased substantially. Ed was already an off-and-on popular media figure, and since the news media was interested in sunken treasure as well as sustained diving, his recent activities were a natural draw for the press. It fell to Marion to become organizer and chief spokesperson. In addition, the increased capacities of the new vessel meant that her duties as wife, mother, researcher, writer and historian, would now include learning the ropes as ship's purser and cook (with help from Vital for larger crowds), a task made difficult by the unpredictable numbers of hopeful divers, reporters, photojournalists, old and new friends and other guests who soon took to streaming across *Sea Diver's* decks.

The Links' seagoing expeditions dramatically increased in number. They flew their five-place Grumman Widgeon south from Binghamton to have it on hand as an additional search tool. (NOTE: photo on pg. 173, #9). Shortly after returning to sea, one day while *Sea Diver* waited at dock, Ed flew the seaplane over their dive site in an attempt to make out reef outlines. As he did so, he made the amazing discovery that a petty theft was about to take place below. He saw two men in a fishing boat preparing to make off with a brand new, three-hundred-foot nylon line, which had been left tied to an anchor caught on the bottom coral the night before. The line was attached to a buoy marker on the surface for easy location and retrieval the next day. In her book, Marion described Ed's response to the scene below. Coolly assessing the situation, evidently much to the surprise of the thieves, he suddenly "wheeled the Widgeon into a steep dive, leveled off on a quick approach to the calm waters off the reef ...taxied to their boat ...[and] shouted indignantly, 'Hey, that's my line you're taking. What's the big idea?'"

*Sea Diver* became truly a second home. The boys were along at every opportunity. It was a time for oceanic adventurers to be at the cutting edge. Though wholesale entry into the oceans was yet to come, it was already possible to dive freely at several hundred feet with no ill effects for those who knew what they were doing. Diving was particularly intriguing to those bitten by the sunken treasure bug, as were the Links and others like them. The phenomenon taking place in the southeastern Atlantic's temperate waters was not unlike the California Gold Rush, but limited to boaters with time, determination, the necessary resources and the inclination to go deep into the sea. Eventually most of the salvagers then scudding about the lower Florida keys and the Bahamas, including the famous Mel Fisher, came to know each other.

By June of 1952 Ed had designed and was using a small glass-bottomed boat for scouring the bottom for clues. This proved on its first foray to be responsible for the discovery of a bronze ship's bell, found on their second visit to the Looe key wreck, which was inscribed with: "Soli Deo Gloria AO 1751."

As a reminder of his other life back in Binghamton, Ed was notified that on July 8, 1952, he had received yet another patent for the Link Training Device. Later that same year, he received an award from the National Society of the Sons of the American Revolution.

But Ed was off on a whole new set of adventures, and Marion was keeping track of them regularly through her journals, recording anything of note. Meanwhile, for loosening what he hoped would be valuable finds from coral encrustations, by 1952 he had created the underwater jet air hammer; had bought and rebuilt a land-mine detector, modifying and using the magnetometer for underwater metal detection; and had begun to develop an underwater vacuum type device that would become known as an "airlift." Worried that his jetting hoses might drive relics deeper into the sand, Marion wrote of a conversation with Ed, when he had defined what he needed as "...an air lift":

~ Then they could suck the sand up to the surface through a big pipe and redeposit it at a safe distance from the scene of operations. With [it] they could successfully remove the sand from around the wreck and at the same time uncover whatever objects were buried there. If they put a screen across the mouth of the pipe, it would prevent it from clogging and also keep any object but the smallest from being carried away. These small pieces could be salvaged as they emerged from the far end.

"But wouldn't it take a very special piece of equipment to operate such a contrivance," I asked?

"Yes," Ed said, "it would take a powerful compressor to do the job." There was room for one in the lazaret of Sea Diver, and he intended to have one installed before we returned the following year. ~

After the airlift was in operation, Jacques Yves Cousteau, who was by then getting his name around the diving circles, put it to good use. Cousteau in fact gave this enormously practical device, along with several of Ed's other oceanic inventions, public recognition many times through popular underwater television specials — though never mentioning Ed by name.

Aboard *Sea Diver*, the Links could now conduct serious work far beyond the Florida Straits, a diving area just about salvaged out anywhere near the interface, which "Pete" Peterson had early described to Marion as "the regular sailing path since the 16th-century between Florida and the Bahamas for most ships returning to Europe from the vicinity of the Caribbean." These waters hide a stretch of treacherous underwater reefs, which, combined with bad weather conditions, caused most of the shipwrecks that still attract many salvage divers. Marion wrote in *Sea Diver* that during the period when most of the wrecks occurred, the area was largely under the control of the Spanish, who "never seemed to learn that hurricanes occur only in the summer and fall months ...they sailed from Havana in summer months, calmly inviting disaster." Her notes on these wrecks also show that chief among their destinations was North America's first city, St. Augustine, founded in 1565 by Spanish explorer Pedro Menendez, who she said, "drove the French out of northern Florida in his own country's interests."

Underwater history became more and more intriguing to the Link family as they expanded their cruising territory. Between February and July 1953 this included a range from the Florida Straits to Cat Cay and elsewhere in the Bahamas, such as

Fresh Creek and Morgan's Bluff, the northernmost point of Andros Island; Nassau, Atlin Island, Warwick Key, Little Farmer Cay, Galliot Cut, Cave Island (where Ed explored the caves with his sons, Bill and Clayton, on leave from school), and Nichollstown, to name only a few. Marion observed in her book that shortly after their return to Florida early in 1953, they made their first dive on a wreck which ever after stood out in their minds as the most picturesque, "the richest and most interesting of all the old wrecks near the Florida keys which it has been our privilege to investigate." It was a galleon belonging to a silver fleet of 1733, that sailed under the command of Rear Admiral Don Rodrigo de Torres, which was overtaken by a hurricane soon after it left its rendezvous point in Havana Harbor.

Although cruising and diving on wrecks today is relatively commonplace, in the early fifties it was through the coverage of magazines like *Life* and *National Geographic* that the exploits of people like Ed and Marion Link were brought to the public. Friends, news writers and famous personages were now regularly joining them at various ports anywhere from Miami to the Bahamas, including such notables as Florida's Marjorie Stoneman Douglas, author, historian and leading conservationist; and anthropologist and philanthropist Henry Fields, accompanied by his lion-tamer wife who at the time was manager of the Miami Zoo.

The Mendel Petersons joined a *Sea Diver* expedition in July, 1953, to dive on a Spanish wreck off of Hens and Chickens Reef, as did two *Life* magazine photographers ferried to the site by Art McKee for an upcoming article on the wreck. Finds in the course of one day, fairly typical for the most part, included broken bits of pottery and wood, pieces of eight, a gold ring crudely molded and set with cut crystal, and a melted gold coin. The latter was presented to Marion, who loaned it to Peterson for an upcoming Smithsonian exhibition before eventually adding it to a charm bracelet made up of her deep sea artifacts.

The greater part of Marion's book *Sea Diver* carefully documents the numerous shipwrecks and their locations that the Links and their diving companions worked over, often with the intention of returning to further investigate promising lures on cruises that never panned out for one reason or another, usually because Ed was off on other pursuits. Even so, at a time when it seemed to be yet another manifestation of the "great American dream," to suddenly discover a fortune under the sea, at the height of treasure diving's popularity Ed would become somewhat disenchanted with the whole idea.

Later on, in the early sixties when *Sea Diver II* found herself docked near Mel Fisher's boat at Key West, Fisher invited Ed to join his diving interests, but he turned the invitation down, having decided at some point during his early diving years that a major discovery of treasure would ultimately involve more hassle than it would be worth. In his prophetic fashion, he even wrote a fictitious account of all of the problems that would ensue, including lawsuits brought by diving companions, in the event of a truly rich discovery. Fisher, who laid claim to just such a wreck, the *Atocha*, off the coast of Vero Beach, Florida, eventually stumbled into the very same legal mess that Ed had predicted. The litigation was covered in a 1987 comprehensive article in the *Miami Herald* by staff writer Sydney P. Freedberg.

While it is true that the excitement of treasure diving was not yet out of their systems in 1953, and though many minds categorized Link among the scores of other treasure hunters, he and Marion refused to be placed in such a limiting niche. Their aspirations were higher, she said. At one point, after "gathering a lot of heresay" on Bahamian treasure during a visit to friends at Green Turtle Key, she wrote in her notes: "Edwin and I had the impression that everybody in the Bahamas were treasure hunters, and that every beach and cave held some of that tantalizing pirate loot which inspired the tales." She then went on to describe their own position as they saw it:

~ We refused to be led astray, however, by all these tales. We told ourselves we were not treasure hunters but scientific seekers in the field of marine archeology. That our aim was to build up the knowledge and substance relating to early days in this beautiful part of the world which played such a big part in the development of our world today. We wanted to be marine archeologists. We would be more than thrilled if we should come upon some of the ancient treasure, but we would be just as happy with coral-covered objects of the past which would help complete the picture being put together by Dr. Peterson at the Smithsonian. In fact, if we found treasure, what would we do with it? Our relations with Uncle Sam were sufficiently complicated at the moment. ~

Obviously they had no need of treasure. The intricacies of accounting that she and Ed had met with after becoming exceptionally wealthy people were enough to deal with as it was. In any case, Ed was nearly ready to admit a complete change of course. Still diving for artifacts, he was thinking about Christopher Columbus. He was still going back to Binghamton to work for several months at a time, and had plenty of opportunity to think as he flew back and forth. He became more preoccupied with Columbus's history in 1953 after discovering an ancient cannon — a 16th-century lombard — at the bottom of the ocean. Finally he attempted to become fully retired, stepping down as president of Link Aviation and taking the mantle of board chairman. At the same time, while in Binghamton that year, he and Marion established the Link Foundation, which still provides scholarships and grants related to the mastery of the air and sea.

The ancient cannon, found during a diving episode near Burrows Cay in the Bahamas, is what finally inspired Ed and Marion both to commit themselves to the history of the New World. Several "cylindrical pieces" covered with coral were brought up and later identified by Peterson as being part of a lombard, "which," Marion wrote, "was in common use until the middle of the sixteenth century." She added in *Sea Diver*:

> ~ Just such a piece of armament had announced to Christopher Columbus aboard the *Santa Maria* that land had been sighted from the *Pinta*, as his small fleet approached the Bahama islands on that historic voyage westward in 1492. Pete [Peterson] says that these parts which we had found probably dated back to within sixty years of Columbus's discovery of America and, as far as he knew, represented the only lombard in existence today which had been found within the American continents. ...Unwittingly, we had found a sample of armament long since relegated to history. Thus were sown in us the first seeds which were to result in the climaxing voyage of our expeditions with *Sea Diver* — a voyage during which we would seek the place of Columbus's first landfall and his route through the Bahamas when he discovered the New World, and during which we would search for the unknown reef off the north coast of Haiti where the *Santa Maria* met her doom. The voyage would also include the faraway Silver shoals beyond Turks island, where one Captain Phips made fame and fortune with his discovery of a treasure-laden Spanish plate ship. ~

* * *

## Part II - Tracking Christopher Columbus and More Treasure

IN SPITE OF ALL HIS AVIATION ENGINEERING INVENTIONS and successes, Ed still saw himself as essentially a navigator. Perhaps it is significant that he had begun to think much about, and in some respects possibly even identify with, Christopher Columbus. After all, though Columbus was a man of mystery in many ways, and despite the "bad rap" some are bound to give the great navigator and explorer, it is universally accepted that he was a stubborn, strong-willed, brave and determined adventurer who got things done. Perhaps as Ed cruised the islands he had begun to think about the New World and Columbus in the same way that Einstein thought about the cosmos when he asked himself how, if he were God, he would have created it. Surely somewhere in the Bahamas it crossed Ed's mind to ask, if he were Columbus, how he would have made that fateful crossing from Spain which led to the first landfall and subsequent journey to Cuba. Perhaps a subconscious desire to experience what Columbus experienced had already begun to germinate in his facile mind.

But first he and Marion both read diligently, starting with an account by Captain Pieter Verhoog, *Guanihana Again*, which questioned the theory that Columbus had made his first landing on what was until 1926 Watling Island, since renamed San Salvador, or officially, "San Salvador or Watling Island" by an act of the British Parliament. Marion noted that Verhoog was an officer of the Holland-America line who had made many voyages through Bahamian waters, and who made "careful, well-documented arguments that Columbus had first set foot on the island of Caicos, farther to the south." She wrote in *Sea Diver* of their reasoning:

~ As his study was backed by years of research among the original manu-scripts dealing with all aspects of Columbus's voyages, it seemed to us that his selection of the Caicos archipelago and the consequent route which Columbus took through the Bahamas was worthy of consideration. ~

They then read naval historian Rear Admiral Samuel Eliot Morison's account of Columbus's voyages, *Admiral of the Ocean Sea*, and discovered that "the two scholars had traced radically different courses for the little fleet through the Bahamas to Cuba." With that, a new adventure was underway. The Links had no choice but to become scholarly on the subject themselves, digging into the known facts, following endless and often mysterious trails in literature, even to the extent of visiting archives in Madrid, Spain, trying to piece together the story of how and where it all really began. Their researches led them through libraries wherever they might be, and eventually brought them together with other prominent scholars in Cuba and Spain, led them on to an experimental cruise, and motivated them to write together a scholarly journal on Ed's own theories that was published by the Smithsonian Institution in 1958.

But docked aboard *Sea Diver* — which, coincidentally, was named *St. Christopher* when Ed found and bought her from the original owner — waiting out bad weather in Nassau, they continued to read, poring over "the writings of various histori-ans from Columbus's time, not neglecting to read and compare the various translations of Columbus's *Journal*," Marion wrote. And, discovering any number of plausible the-ories, like many other Columbus scholars, they grew more confused as they read.

Meanwhile, their good friend, famed navigator Philip Van Horn Weems, who had in 1940 co-authored and published a book on simplified navigation with Ed, showed up in Nassau for a visit and became himself intrigued with the issue, hav-ing been the one who put Ed onto Verhoog's theory in the first place. Long and heated discussions took place between them as, huddled over the table in *Sea Diver's* cozy galley, night after night they pored over their charts. At last the deci-sion was made to test their theories aboard *Sea Diver*, Captain Weems included, and retrace Columbus's possible routes; then, Marion wrote in her book, "It was while we were discussing this trip that Captain Weems fairly took our breath away with another idea. 'What chance do you think we would have of finding the remains of the *Santa Maria*?' he said."

Ed was immediately intrigued with the idea, but took it one step further; why not also pursue a once vague notion formed while poring over Captain William Phips's charts, to try to locate the remains of a Spanish galleon that had gone down more than three centuries before — with millions in gold, silver and precious jewels — on reefs at the remote Silver Shoals.

So there it was again; the prospect of finding a vast treasure had resurfaced, or was it the challenge alone that spurred Ed on? Even though the New England sea captain, Phips, had in 1687 found and salvaged much of the gold and silver on the wreck of the *Nuestra Senora de la Concepcion*, flagship of a fleet of 30 ships which sailed from Havana for Spain on September 13, 1659, his logs observed that he had been unable to penetrate a portion of the hull that had become heavily encrusted with coral. The last traces of treasure fever for some time to come had evidently lingered in Ed's mind ever since he first heard of this buried hull, which would now become the subject of a new search.

So it was that an extraordinary venture was to begin. It would include explorations of the dangerous reefs, even though Marion pointed out that she had no inclination to go to the Silver Shoals, writing, "After all, one could pick no more risky spot in the whole hemisphere, for the wreck lay in a forty-mile-square area of reefs far from any land." Still, if they were to take *Sea Diver* to Turks Island, where Verhoog believed that Columbus had spotted a light before reaching his first landfall, "it seemed reasonable to include a trip to Silver Shoals, only a hundred miles beyond." She continued in *Sea Diver*:

> ~ By the summer of 1954 our plans were pretty well set. We would begin our expedition by searching for the *Santa Maria* at Cap Hatien. From there we would go to the Silver Shoals, some 150 miles northeast. With this part of our trip completed by early summer, we would head for Turks Island and the Caicos to investigate the possible Columbus routes. We expected to spend several months in these three enterprises, varying the time spent on each according to our findings.
>
> Ed and I found ourselves swamped with correspondence in regard to the three projects — with Mendel Peterson at the Smithsonian, with Captain Weems, the Criles, and dozens of other candidates who hoped to join us at various times. There was an exchange of letters with officials in the Bahamas, Haiti, the Dominican Republic, and arrangements to be made for caches of fuel oil for *Sea Diver* and special aviation gasoline for the Widgeon, which Ed intended to have available for our searches.
>
> We corresponded with Captain Verhoog and Dr. Morison in order to clarify questions which arose as to points in their theories of Columbus's

route. We were swamped with requests for information about our plans from magazines and newspapers. And in our spare time we continued to hunt out every last bit of material we could find in regard to all three subjects. ~

Ed had the use of the newly installed radar and sonar, and a Bludworth depthometer, for navigation and his underwater searches. And he experimented with a special set of charts he had drawn up for the loran, "thus making it possible," according to Marion, "to use this instrument in a section of the ocean to which it had never before been adapted." In addition to their glass-bottomed boat, they had acquired a shallow-draft, 18-foot cruiser, also with a glass-bottom section, designed by Ed and equipped to go into waters not accessible to Sea Diver. Dubbed "*Reef Diver*," it was powered by a Kermath gasoline engine with a water jet extending only a few inches below the hull. *Reef Diver* could go forward, backward, and from side to side, all in very shallow water with treacherous reefs.

Ed made interesting use of the above mentioned loran and charts later on, in the Silver Shoals. Marion described in *Sea Diver* trying to follow an ancient chart prepared by Captain Phips, the first diver on the Silver Shoals, in an area of the sea where there were no markers but a rock. She tried to figure out how Ed proposed to locate the treasure:

> ~ It puzzled me how Ed expected to know when we had reached the latitudes Captain Phips indicated, for once we had left the rock there was nothing to indicate our position. I soon learned the answer, for Ed...[was on] his knees before the loran, his head covered with a dark cloth to shut out the daylight, observing its intricate lightninglike patterns. Within these trappings, he was able to pinpoint our exact latitude and longitude. ~

Meanwhile, in 1954 Ed had gained more unexpected publicity when he was honored with the United States Air Force's Exceptional Service Award. Throughout that year he and Marion and the children in their free time continued to cruise off and on in the Bahamas. Perhaps it was an omen that as their year began, while at anchor in Pleasant Harbor, Morgan's Bluff, on January 19, Marion recorded in her journal: "We saw an unexpected total eclipse last night. When we looked through the glasses, the moon looked just like a huge ping pong ball suspended in the sky." That year, like so many others in Ed's life, turned out to involve much coming and going and to be noteworthy as well. The retired *Blue Heron* was sold to the "Jim Riders," and Marion wrote in her journal on February 26, "...We went to Dinner Key with them immediately and signed over the papers ($16,000 cash)," at which time *Blue Heron*, to be used for racing, was officially renamed *Chance III*.

Earlier that year, on the 16th of March, 1954, another significant event had taken place; Link Aviation merged with General Precision Equipment Corporation (GPE), and it looked as though Ed was genuinely retired. Arthur Herzog later commented from an interview he had with Ed for a *True* magazine, 1964 article, that [GPE] was "...an outfit to which he sold his company in exchange for stock, as the only way to stop being a businessman once and for all." Meanwhile, the Links spent much of 1954 preparing for the upcoming Caribbean expedition.

That year they had managed to visit libraries and archives in Cuba in addition to their other studies, and were armed to the hilt with books and research notes as well as enthusiasm and inspiration when at last *Sea Diver* embarked from Miami in February, 1955, on her tri-legged journey. In addition to Captain Weems and the French Canadian crew member, Vital, Bill and Clayton Link (ages 17 and 14, and out of school for Easter Holidays) were aboard for the first leg of the cruise. At West End the Link party picked up "Captain" Ed Kemp, a well-known Bahamian seafarer who had sailed with them throughout their cruises the previous winter. Kemp had come to them on the recommendation of friends as having a sixth sense for knowing the bottom terrain by merely observing the water's surface. Now, with a full crew, *Sea Diver* sailed from West End for Haiti.

Marion wrote:

~ All night long *Sea Diver* ...rolled and tossed in a heavy cross sea as she forged through the rough waters between Great Inagua and the north coast of Haiti. From the moment we ...poked our nose out into the open waters beyond Northeast point, she ...wallowed on a wet and uncomfortable course. ~

During the passage, Vital, Bill and Clayton had all gone below at sunset with queasy stomachs, without dinner. Marion rose at dawn to take her morning watch as they approached the wide, deep trench of water separating Tortuga Island from the mountainous coast of Haiti. She leafed through Columbus's Journal, seeking the part that described these shores. Then she wrote:

~ ...My eye caught the name Isla de la Tortuga. I read, "That island seemed very high land, not filled with mountains, level like lovely fields...." I swept the ragged cliffs of Tortuga with my glasses. Where are the Elysian fields today? ~

*Sea Diver's* bow was soon cutting directly into the waves, making a more comfortable passage, and the boys got up from their bunks. She turned the wheel over to Weems and went to the galley to make breakfast. When next she looked they were halfway through the channel, and able to make out the historic French city of Port Paix nestled against the towering mountain. She thought about a passage in Columbus's Journal, which she quoted in her book:

~ "This land is very cool and the best that tongue can describe. It is very lofty and on the highest mountain, oxen could plough and all could be made like the plains and valleys. In all Castile there is no land which could be compared to this for beauty and fertility." ~

"The sun had now risen ahead of us in blinding splendor," she continued. Though Marion's expression here was undoubtedly poetic, she was a well trained journalist and a practical woman, not at all inclined to mystical ecstasies, so what she wrote next was all the more curious:

~ It was now past eight o'clock, and Tortuga was well behind us. As the sun gradually burned through the heavy haze, it high-lighted certain areas of the wooded mountainside, disclosing scattered huts and steep, narrow trails twisting up to the heights. The secondary ranges, pale violet shadows in the background, were revealed now and then as the swirling mists on the crests melted into the low-hung clouds, which broke up in fast-changing patterns in the winds from the ocean.

As I watched, I suddenly saw revealed in these twisting vapors of mist and cloud the shape of a cross — a large, heavy cross such as Columbus might have erected to claim these lands for his queen. It hung there in the sky for a long interval while I stared at it spellbound, scarcely daring to breathe. Then its base began to curl and fray at the edges, and it melted away into the rising mist. Soon the whole apparition had vanished. ~

She went off in search of Ed and Captain Weems, hoping she wasn't the only one to see the strange cross, but was disappointed to find both men in the wheelhouse, occupied with charts and navigation instruments. "They smiled a little condescendingly," she wrote, "when I told them of my vision."

They could make out Rat Island, called La Amiga by Columbus, marking the entrance to Puerto de la Mer de San Thomas, present day Acul Bay, which Marion described as one of the most beautiful and protected anchorages in the world. Columbus, she wrote, claimed, "'...now this surpassed all, and in it all the ships of the world could lie and be secure, with the oldest cable on board a ship it would be held fast.'"

"As *Sea Diver* skirted the rocky hillsides to Cap Haitien, we could pick out ahead of us Punta Santa, now Picolet point," she continued. When they came abreast of the point itself, a lighthouse appeared halfway up the slope, looking, to Marion, "eerily like a mechanical man standing guard over the entrance to the harbor." All their minds were on Columbus. Marion recorded in *Sea Diver*:

> ~ It was eleven o'clock on Christmas Eve, Columbus noted in his *Journal*, and he "was distant one league" from this point. The account continued, "Our Lord willed that at midnight as they had seen the Admiral lie down and rest, and as they saw it was a dead calm and that the sea was like a small bowl, all should lie down to sleep, and the rudder was left in the hand of that boy (a young ship's grummet), and the currents which were swift carried the ship upon one of these banks."
>
> Thus calmly did the Journal announce the disaster which resulted in the loss of the *Santa Maria*. ~

Marion had to ask herself:

> ~ Could this be the same Great Navigator who had led his ships across three thousand miles of unknown ocean to the shores of an unknown land, and then guided them with admirable judgment and ability through the intricate Bahamian passages to the reef-bound shores of Cuba? ~

"Was Columbus guilty of too much celebration?" She thought not. Discussing it with the others after speculating as to how he could have been so careless as to enter a reef-strewn harbor at midnight, she offered the following logical and perhaps valid theory:

> ~ I proffered the lame excuse that perhaps *Santa Maria* was following *Nina*, and that only the lead ship had carried any pilots. Because she was a smaller ship with less draft, *Nina* had either sailed over or skirted the reef without her crew being aware of it, while *Santa Maria*, only a few yards to port or starboard of her course, was unlucky enough to go aground. ~

Ed steered between Le Grand Mouton and shore. "Now that we are so close to our goal," Marion wrote in 1955, "I wondered again: Could we possibly find that historic wreck after 463 years?". From then on, it was the routine of search and discovery that Ed and Marion and the others had so well established, this time trying to delve into the mind of Columbus in search of his ill-fated flagship. Marion said it was:

~ ...probably the most famous and important shipwreck in history, for it resulted in the founding of the first European settlement in the New World, and thus established Spain's rights with the Holy See to this part of the earth for several centuries to come. ~

Attempting to remain on their cruise schedule, they were ready to work almost as soon as they arrived at Cap Haitien, but due to bureaucratic difficulties (it was the Saturday before Easter, Holy Week), the offices they needed for permission to explore for the wreck were closed. Marion noted that if it were not for finding and getting temporary permission from Colonel Maz Chassagne, chief of the Haitian Army in northern Haiti, and for Captain Weems, "with his unflagging enthusiasm," Ed would have given up in despair and left for Silver Shoals.

The situation was assessed in a telegram sent by Ed, with the help of Andre LeBon, assistant U.S. consul (who had an office at the Royal Netherlands Steamship Agency near the water front), to the American Embassy in Port-au-Prince. His message:

~ Capt Weems and myself searching Columbus Voyages. Also think we could find remains of Santa Maria. Last year our expedition was cleared for this search at Cap Haitien and Consul advised through Secretary Dulles but we were unable to come. Would you check with authorities to make sure there is no objection to make search now? Life Magazine sending representative to report and make picture record for the feature in Life. Immediate action necessary E. A. Link. ~

A return telegram informed him that no one was available to answer him and that he would have to wait until Monday to see where he officially stood. As it finally turned out, the little party got off to their first dive site on Easter Sunday with temporary permission, but was ordered to return to Cap Haitien that night to continue the process of obtaining permission on Monday. Ed, not always a patient man and intent on getting to work, found the situation extremely hard to bear. He was under stress because of the journalists, who were overdue and would have a limited amount of time to cover this aspect of the trip and be on their way, since they were bound to be working on a tight deadline; because the boys had to return to school the following weekend; and because *Sea Diver* was due to leave for Silver Shoals the week after that. Before they finally got off, Marion feared that Ed would "blow his top" at the obstacles in his path. Everything seemed to be stepped up and held back at the same time; there was much to do and a serious schedule to meet, and there they were stuck in bureaucratic paperwork.

Searching on Sunday with the little glass-bottomed boat, now dubbed "*Wee Diver*," they found signs of ballast from a shipwreck but high winds kept them from diving, or, for that matter, from even returning to Cap Haitien at the end of the day, which meant that explanations were due and even more red tape had to be endured the next morning. Thoroughly discouraged by the continuing holdup on Monday, Ed at one point grimly decided that if they couldn't get permission that evening and go back to work early in the morning, he was through. Then *Reef Diver*, on their return to the boat in the dark, hit the arm of an old anchor and Marion sustained painful injuries when she was pitched to the deck between the cabin and the engine box. Finally, just before midnight, Captain Weems returned to the ship with word that the necessary permit was being sent out at 4:30 the next morning.

The following day, while searching for the ballast seen on Sunday, two cannons were discovered from *Wee Diver*, but they were not thought to be old enough to be from the *Santa Maria*. Then the weather grew foul. They waited out another night. The next day when they were able to dive Ed checked out the cannons seen the day before. Everyone waited on board with bated breath as he surfaced, only to announce that they were "old French sakers." Meanwhile, life on board was becoming chaotic. Marion was in pain from her fall on *Reef Diver*; the *Life* magazine team — Peter Stackpole, world-renowned photographer, and Kay Hampton, reporter — arrived by launch; the seas came up again; the boys were seasick again; and the exploration had to be postponed for another day.

*Sea Diver* went to shore the next morning. Bill and Clayton had to fly back to Miami to return to Binghamton where they were now enrolled in school and staying at home when not sailing. Marion, it turned out after seeing them aboard their plane and visiting a doctor in Port-au-Prince, had badly damaged tendons but no broken ribs. Her side was bandaged and she was forced to rest and remain ashore for several days. The others went back to sea.

Feeling left out while at the same time developing a degree of sympathy for Ed's earlier feelings of frustration, impatient herself to get on with the mission, she sat in her room reading and wondering about the actual location of Columbus's first colony, Navidad, trying to piece it all together in her mind. She reasoned that since Columbus had recorded the discovery of one of the *Santa Maria's* anchors in the muddy bottom of the Grande Riviere, and if Navidad was in the vicinity of the Grande Riviere, it would be logical to look for the remains of the *Santa Maria* to the west of where they had been searching, on a line east of Punta Santo to the mouth of the river. Navidad, she noted, was thought by French historian Moreau de St.-Mery, who had lived in Hispaniola for a time at the end of the 18th century, to be established inland on the banks of the Fosse River, "which in Columbus's time probably emptied into the sea near Limonade Bord de Mer." And so on her own she organized a motor trip to Limonade Bord de Mer, which was, she wrote in her book, "the site of Navidad, according to Dr. Morison."

With a certain M. Beck, owner of the hostel in which she stayed, in his station wagon and in the company of his wife and children, Marion was able to get within walking distance of her destination, and, in spite of her painful injury, to walk the rest of the journey by footpath. After an arduous and winding hike, taking in every detail of her surroundings and thinking constantly about the conflicting theories as to where Navidad and the nearby Indian Village were actually located in Columbus's time, she finally drew her own conclusion that they had probably once existed somewhere along the shores of the Grande Riviere. She hoped to visit the area later with Ed and *Reef Diver* from the direction of the sea, but was not fated to do so.

Meanwhile, she was at last able to return to *Sea Diver*, where her own ideas paled in the excitement she found aboard ship. Ed had just hauled an interesting anchor aboard — but not of the Columbus era — when he suffered a minor disaster. Rushing to help newly arrived guests board the ship, he thoughtlessly crossed the deck in his bare feet and kicked the corner of the freezer box. "Feeling a quick stab of pain, he examined his right foot to find the fourth toe bent straight back on itself," Marion wrote, and "wrenched it back into place." He learned the next day on a visit to a doctor that the toe was broken and would take at least a month to heal. It was another setback; doctor's orders were for Ed to let the others do the diving. Then that night Marion had her second paranormal experience, as recorded in *Sea Diver*:

~ "I saw that Spanish cross in my dreams again last night," I said, as we ate our breakfast aboard *Sea Diver* the next morning, preparatory to starting the day's search. "It looked exactly like the one I saw in the clouds over the mountains the day we arrived." ~

In spite of the fact that Ed had once acted on his own intuition years ago, when he built an aerial electric sky sign that he first saw in a dream (Chapter III), he didn't react to Marion's comment. Preoccupied, he stared at her absent-mindedly and said, "Did you?". She went on:

~ I could tell his mind was not on this evidence of the supernatural's interest in our expedition. He was wondering why the Nordberg diesel was spitting oil and had suddenly become so cussedly hard to start, for he immediately said: "Vital, when you get the time, take the head off that diesel. I'd like to see what's wrong with it." ~

Whether or not the "waking vision" Marion had experienced as they approached Haiti, followed by the dream she had the night before, was a premonition of things to come is a matter of speculation. But it was on that day, after two weeks of searching the area, following a great number of leads that revealed an even greater number of old anchors — none of the vintage of Columbus — that Marion happened to discover a now famous anchor, thought to very likely be from the *Santa Maria*. This turned out to be their greatest find, as the remains of the vessel itself were never discovered. Marion was diving with Captain Weems when she saw the intriguing object, while checking out a lead offered by Charlie Martin, pilot of the harbor launch, on another, "different looking" anchor that both she and Weems had rejected as Columbus's. She reported seeing her ancient anchor at about a hundred feet from *Reef Diver*. It was:

~ ...much smaller than the one Charlie had brought us to see. It was heavily encrusted with coral, its simple lines unbroken by flukes. (NOTE: photo on pg. 174, #10). The ring part of the shank was missing. This was much more the type for which we had been searching. ...Ed climbed clumsily over the side of *Reef Diver*....He looked it over carefully, making crude estimates of its length with outstretched arms. Then, instead of swimming over to the larger anchor which had puzzled Captain Weems and me, he swam toward the boarding ladder on *Reef Diver*.

I followed him to the surface, arriving just in time to hear him say, "I think perhaps we've got it." ...There was an excited interchange of data. It was the right shape and size; it was heavily encrusted with coral; its ring and flukes were missing. ~

In spite of his injury, Ed and a team of divers took *Reef Diver* back to the site to retrieve the anchor. The others waited aboard *Sea Diver*, until:

~ ...At last we heard the boat's high-pitched hum. We hurried to the rail. We could sense excitement in the men's voices and their smiles as they approached *Sea Diver*. The anchor was lashed to the iron superstructure of the little cruiser, the broken end dragging in the water.

"This looks like the real McCoy," Ed said. ~

Though it may never be certain, the anchor matched all requirements for being one from Columbus's fleet, and after taking into consideration that it was encrusted in coral and its pointed flukes were missing, it matched exactly another anchor thought to be from the same fleet, which was located at the National Museum at Port-au-Prince, and which was regarded as one of Haiti's most prized possessions. However, the museum anchor had been found in the muddy bottom of the Grande Riviere, in the 18th-century, not found loose on the coral bottom where Marion spotted hers. Mendel Peterson came with Ed to Cap Haitian five weeks later on a trip from the Silver Shoals and vicinity, and studied the anchor thoroughly, about which Marion wrote:

~ It unquestionably dated back to the time of Columbus and could very well have come from the admiral's flagship, he said. He noted that the crescent shape of the arms placed it before the seventeenth century, when V-shaped anchors were first made. ~

Peterson compared their find to the anchor at Port au Prince, and she reported his reaction:

~ "I believe these anchors definitely came from a shipwreck," Pete declared, "for it is most unlikely that a ship would otherwise lose its two main anchors in the same harbor. As the *Santa Maria* was probably the only ship of that period to go down in Cap Haitien harbor, it seems very logical that both anchors come from her." ~

Peterson later took samples of the metal from both relics to be tested by the U.S. Bureau of Standards, whose reports confirmed that the two anchors were fashioned from iron of the same type and period.

But there was yet a mystery to the discovery. Marion's anchor was found in a location where it evidently could not have lain for the past 463 years, on a reef rising from a hard coral bottom. If it had been there for any length of time, its coral encrustation would have been solidly cemented to the coral reef. Instead it was lying completely free from the hard bottom. To be as loose as it was, it would have had to have lain on a sand bottom as it became encrusted with sand coral throughout the years. The only explanation was that the ancient anchor had to have been moved. Marion developed the theory that the anchor was taken up from a soft resting place by local fishermen and used for a fishing trap weight, as was their custom with the many old anchors and other heavy debris found sunk in the harbor bottom. Though Ed's party could never be certain how the anchor got where Marion spotted it, they were convinced that it was not where the *Santa Maria* had gone down.

Further studies of the area led Ed to believe, just as Marion had surmised, that if Navidad was located on solid ground up the Grande Riviere as they had read, it must necessarily have been some distance inland. He speculated that Columbus might have taken an open and accessible passage between the inner line of reefs and shore to the Grande Riviere. Marion wrote:

~ In this case, he might have gone aground on a shoal lying less than a mile from the sandy shore just east of Cape Sable and directly in the path of such a course. There is a wide expanse of deep water both on the outer side of the shoal and between it and the shore.

A study of an air photograph of this area indicated that the shoal consisted more of sand than coral. We felt sure that our anchor had lain for centuries on a sandy bottom while its thick coat of sand coral was formed. ~

The journey to Silver Shoals would resume nearly on schedule. Meanwhile, Ed intended to continue searching for the *Santa Maria* on a return trip, for, as Marion wrote, "our finding of the anchor had convinced us that someday the remains of the *Santa Maria* would also be found." Perhaps so, but not by this team of investigators; as it turned out, weather conditions on *Sea Diver's* later return to Cap Haitien prohibited any further investigation at sea, although Ed did scout around the Grande Riviere with *Reef Diver*, where Marion had hoped to return, and developed the convincing theories later reported in her book. Meanwhile, it had been their lot to find the Columbus vintage anchor, which they eventually presented to the Haitain government, only to learn later that it was sadly neglected over the years and is even now corroding beyond redemption.

* * *

WITH NEW PEOPLE TO ACCOMMODATE and new schedules to meet, it was time to move on. Marion wrote:

> ~ At last Ed and I were on our way to the Silver Shoals, mecca of every treasure hunter for the past three hundred years. The greatest treasure hunt of our lives had begun.
>
> Silver Shoals! The very name was enough to send thrills of excitement up and down the spines of everyone aboard *Sea Diver*. ~

Marion recorded her thoughts while underway. Barney and Jane Crile had joined their party at Cap-Haitien shortly before they left for Silver Shoals on April 25, as had one Glenn Krause, a civilian employee of the hydrographic department of the United States in Germany. She wrote that Krause was "a map maker, a photographer, and a seaman — a long, thin, very bald man in his forties, with the nonchalant air of an adventurer. ...Glenn had come as an emissary for Alexander Korganoff, that White Russian historian and researcher from Paris who had visited the Silver Shoals as part of an expedition a few years earlier," and whose original expedition had ended in mutiny by the crew. Karganoff had then returned on his own, in a sail boat, and later claimed to have found the site of the galleon wreck. He originally planned to join *Sea Diver* that April, after spending nearly a year in correspondence with Ed regarding the mission, but untoward circumstances led to his substitution by Krause.

The 40-mile area now to be searched was in the open sea, 80 miles from Puerto Plata in the Dominican Republic and 100 miles from Turks Island, "the first land to be encountered" to the northwest. "Elsewhere," Marion reported, "there is only ocean and more ocean, much of it nearly two miles in depth." As they approached the reef-strewn waters — where foaming white breakers could be seen tossing spray high into the air above pale brown coral heads lying just beneath the surface — they fully realized what a remote, wild and dangerous place it was to be. They instantly recognized why the Silver Shoals had been carefully avoided by all but a very few of the most determined salvagers, ever since the 17th century Spanish galleon, "heavily laden with the wealth of the New World and badly crippled by a hurricane, had foundered as it sought to reach the Spanish Harbor in Puerto Rico for repairs."

Now the Link party was to be among those rare salvagers, and they were fully prepared to find any wealth that might still be buried at sea. "On board Sea Diver we probably had the most complete diving and salvage equipment available in the world today for exploring waters such as those to be found on the Silver Shoals," wrote Marion. In spite of making an unorthodox approach from Cap-Haitien rather than from Puerto Plata as others had done before them, Ed managed to find the exact position where Korganoff had indicated the wreck might lie. But to no avail; the most dazzling treasure they were to discover was the site itself, as seen from *Reef Diver* and described by Marion:

> ~ I was overwhelmed at what I saw through the glass bottom of the boat — great towering coral cliffs, honeycombed with caves, rising from a white-sand floor, topped by pinnacles bizarrely fashioned like something from the Arabian nights. There were vast outcroppings of every kind of coral — tangled jungles of branch coral like berry bushes in a pasture, solid beds of lettuce coral, waving Gorgonia..., and topping all, the lovely yellow-brown stag coral, forming shady parasols for the teeming colorful small fish beneath it. Not only were the reefs a tumbled mass of coral, but the whole ocean floor was scattered with these formations, some close to the bottom but many towering thirty and forty feet. ~

Signs of wrecks were plentiful enough to convince the seekers to press on in spite of all hazards, but nothing truly substantial was ever found. The Criles brought up two round ballast stones, indicating the presence of a wrecked ship, but the winds increased that day and prevented further search. Much of Ed's precious time was spent searching for a safe anchorage among the very same reefs that had cost the lives of those aboard the Spanish galleon. "We must be very sure," wrote Marion, "that in spite of wind or storm our anchor did not fail, or we could find ourselves dashed against these same reefs which had claimed the *Nuestra Senora* so many centuries before."

Marion was again the one to spot an anchor of some significance, at which point, she wrote, "Ed put on his Scott mask and tank and went overboard to investigate....It was a very old one, probably seventeenth century. It might have come from the *Nuestra Senora*, or perhaps from one of Phips's salvage ships." Further searching revealed ballast. Then "a peculiar-shaped object, flat and oblong, with two curves along one edge like bites" was retrieved. On bringing up a section of this item, which broke away in the attempt, they saw that it "was about eight inches long and five wide. It was blackened metal, heavily corroded." Then, after locating signs of metal detected by the magnetometer and blasting with dynamite through coral solid as concrete they found "a badly deteriorated section of a gun barrel, and some pieces of metal which looked as if they might be the oxidized remains of silver coins." To their dismay, the surface of the water was also scattered with dead fish, killed by the blast. They vowed not to blast again. The metal later tested out to be iron, and the coins silver. All of this was tantalizing, but none of it led to the great treasure they were seeking.

Just before returning to shore, Krause discovered another anchor, which led the party to the remains of an ancient shipwreck, but after the initial excitement wore off and serious investigation got underway, Ed realized that though the ship was of the same century as the *Nuestra Senora*, it was noticeably smaller. Their disappointment deepened as further examination yielded little, certainly nothing in the way of historic artifacts or treasure.

With that the first leg of the Silver Shoals mission came to an end, but after delivering several of his party members to Turks Island, Ed was to return with a somewhat different crew. One last look around and they sailed away, feeling lucky to have timed their expedition as they had; huge swells were coming in over the shoals, warning of an impending storm. Making their way to Puerto Plata, the party proudly noted what a congenial crew they had been, for fear, greed and superstition in the past had led to mutiny aboard other treasure ships; in fact, theirs was one of the few strictly salvage missions ever to be conducted on the Silver Shoals that had not ended in mutiny.

At Puerta Plata, Weems left for Annapolis, planning to rejoin *Sea Diver* in time to track the Columbus route. Marion flew home where she helped Bill, who had his own plans for the summer, to get established and prepared Clayton to return with her to *Sea Diver*. Meanwhile the Criles left for their home in Ohio. This left Ed, Vital, Kemp and Krause. Then Mendel Peterson and Ed's sister Marilyn flew to Turks Island in the Widgeon, along with a pilot friend, Leonard Thompson, who later ferried Ed's seaplane back to Nassua. *Sea Diver* was ready to return to the shoals, cruising first in the vicinity of the Caicos archipelago then between Cap-Haitien and Silver Shoals.

Ed and Marion had begun a habit of writing and mimeographing accounts of their journey and sending them back home to friends and family. With Marion away in Binghamton, it fell upon Ed to keep a running account of events. He wrote from the start that the next leg was without a full complement of crew because Bahamian

Leonard Thompson and his brother Roscoe, who were scheduled to join them, had canceled out at the last minute to go with another party in search of the same wreck elsewhere. Ed noted:

> ~ They have the theory that the Phips wreck was actually salvaged from the Mouchoir Shoals rather than the Silver Shoals, though after our visit to the Silver Shoals, we are sure they are wrong, for the Silver Shoals meet with Phips's description absolutely. ~

Before departing again for Silver Shoals from Turks Island, with his sister Marilyn as pilot, he carefully viewed the site from overhead in the Widgeon. He was amazed to learn that his intuition had been on target when he anchored *Sea Diver* there the first time, for clearly he had unwittingly placed his anchor exactly in a well protected spot. On board his vessel once again, he sat in the wheelhouse and wrote:

> ~ We certainly had a piece of luck in picking the best spot on the whole bank for an anchorage on our first expedition, as this is almost directly in the center of the whole shoals, and completely surrounded, with a large round lagoon in the middle. We could easily see our buoys left previously, exactly in the middle of the lagoon. After surveying the whole Bank from the air we realized that we could not have picked any spot that would have been as secure as this one if we had searched for months. It is the only protected, open water space in the whole of the shoals and is easily identifiable by the peninsula with the shoals and the dry rock on its southern portion. ~

However safe the anchorage was, the journey back to it was a different matter. This time Ed had to rely on technology and his five senses, without the extraordinary intuition, or beginners luck, that had guided him there the first time. Picking his way with caution, sensing hazards all around, he was uneasy and said so when it was over: "It was an interesting but not too comforting thought that the Silver Fleet for which we were looking might have been wrecked in exactly the same courses we were steering." Relying on the fathometer, he continued on, seeming in his mind to go far too long without seeing any sign of the reefs. Then suddenly they were there, and *Sea Diver* was in a predicament: "We ran into a mess of them, finding ourselves completely in a mass of shoals." At this point, as Ed said, there was nothing to do but gingerly seek a path through the reefs:

> ~ It required picking our way very carefully to get through them safely. Unfortunately the wind was very high, 20 to 25 miles an hour, with a big

sea running. After a complete night of this we were somewhat tired out. I had been on duty since three o'clock in the morning, as I knew we were nearing the shoals and wanted to be sure that every precaution was taken with all alertness possible to prevent a shipwreck. ~

After sailing for hours he learned that he was not where he had estimated, "being considerably eastward instead." Still he pressed on. Later he described in detail his efforts at trying to relocate his anchorage and marker buoys:

> ~ ...instead of having fairly clear sailing, I sailed right back into the mass of shoals again, which required double watch and extra alertness for the next two hours, picking our way through. By this time we were all so tired and somewhat unnerved by the alertness necessary to avoid hitting the shoals that it seemed to me we would never reach our goal. I feared that we might have overrun it, and be on the eastern part of the shoals, and I dreaded the return back through them to find our anchorage. It was also reaching late morning and my eyes were burning for lack of sleep.
>
> Peterson was completely useless and knocked out, being seasick all night and practically green in color. Vital was also fighting seasickness, leaving Kemp and myself and Glenn to run the boat practically all night. Glenn spent four hours in the crow's nest while we were picking our way through the shoals and Kemp the same length of time in the bow, while I was on the wheel being relieved occasionally by Marilyn. This being her first sail, and since she also was experiencing some difficulty from seasickness, I tried to be easy on her. ~

Ed wrote that it was nearly noon before he spied the large dry rock for which they had searched so eagerly, since it marked the only area of safety they hoped to find. "It was a most welcome sight," he noted, "almost like reaching home." Rather than to secure a new anchor with its heavy chain, he said they were so tired out that they tied temporarily to the old anchorage and "immediately turned in for a little rest, which was very much needed." Still fatigued and perhaps still unnerved, Ed on waking became most aggravated with crewman Kemp, during a frustrating attempt to secure a permanent anchorage. He described the incident:

> ~ Along about four o'clock in the afternoon, after having some rest, I decided to put down our big anchor and heavy chain to replace the temporary light chain buoys which we had previously used. This was accomplished after some difficulty. ...Kemp let the anchor get away from him

with the whole business falling on the bottom, chain and all, tangling up with the old buoys and making a general mess out of everything. I had considerable diving to do to straighten out the mess, and working at 50 feet was considerably fatiguing. Peterson was in no condition to dive ...which left me with all the work to do. ~

It was almost dark before the 51-year-old sea captain had the new anchor and chain securely set. He unraveled the tangle underwater the following morning, learning as he did so that divine providence had certainly been with him once again. What he saw in the crystal clear water, in the light of day, was that had he continued to rely on the old chains, he very likely would have had a disaster on his hands. A link had almost cracked off one of the older chains and the other was strained almost to the breaking point. He wrote that he had previously done the right thing in using double anchors:

~ I ...felt that I exercised good judgment in at least placing two of these down, for with one of them nearly ready to break, had we depended on [the other] and had the break occurred, we could have joined the numerous shipwrecks on these Silver Shoals, considered to be the most dangerous waters in the world. ~

Ed's dogged perseverance was put strongly to the test on this portion of the expedition when he began extensive work with his delicate magnetometer, a land instrument for detecting buried metal which he had converted for use underwater. As he said, he "spent considerable time on it," since, from the previous leg in the Silver Shoals, he had learned that in looking for ancient wrecks, "visible evidence was practically nonexistent." He was convinced that he had to depend on the magnetometer if he was to have any success, and wrote about the frustrations of trying to use it far from shore without even a permanently dry rock as a base:

~ Unfortunately the magnetometer has been a great disappointment; it is impossible to keep it in adjustment. In the first place, to adjust it is a most difficult task as it requires the detector portion to be secured on solid land, completely away from metallic influence. Though probably these shoals can provide solid land, they are not dry and the winds and waves breaking over them continuously present a considerable problem. However, after much searching we located a coral head which nearly reached the surface, on the inside of the shoals, protected somewhat from the surf breaking on them at low tide. By doing some chiseling with the crowbar and a considerable amount of work, we were able to erect the tripod to support the detector so that it was out of water and dry at low tide. But at high tide the waves would break over the shoals and make it impossible for us to do any work, even on this inside coral head. It is also such a very small head that it is just about possible for two men to stand on it with no extra room. Also, we have found that the tide at the shoals is about three feet, for the tripod is four feet tall and, being ...a foot in water at low tide, it is nearly covered at high tide.

...It was a considerable job to get the detector on the tripod, and also to prevent it being washed away we had to ballast it down with all the old iron and chain we could find, until the detector was situated. This provided weight enough to hold the tripod in the water. It was then necessary to remove the iron and chain ballast before adjustment could be attempted. All in all, with rough weather, breaking surf, and waves, this presented a large problem, but with all hands working we managed to overcome our difficulties and get the detector finally into adjustment. However, in removing the detector after adjusting with the above described adverse conditions, we gave it a bump, and in trying it out, we found that it still seemed to be out of adjustment. By this time, the tide was up and there was nothing else to do but wait for low tide the next day and try again. ~

After going through the same procedure the following day and wandering around among coral heads in a heavy sea with the detector, at first to no avail, he reported that at last it suddenly "gave several big indications." He said the dive team was "highly elated" to think they had maybe found the main part of a wreck, but that then, "it sort of went wild, and we found that the detector had given up again." Finally even Ed had to pack it in, and said when the day was done: "I have decided that this detector in its present stage is so sensitive and so difficult to adjust and handle that there is no use trying it further until more is learned about it, to stabilize the unit to be more reliable."

Of course he wanted the magnetometer to work, not only for what he might have found but to prove that man can do work in the sea beyond the capabilities of his own senses with carefully engineered and operated instruments. "Where there's a will, there's a way" was to him a maxim to live by. It was an important part of the venture to go against the odds and make things happen with his own stubborn will. In fact, it is far more likely that he was in these dangerous waters, facing this practically insurmountable challenge because it was a challenge, not because he ever truly expected to find treasure there. After all, the stable, stoic and dependable Ed Link was not a gambler in the true sense of the word. He knew that no matter what, he would gain something from the exercise. He knew that if he took chances in places like this his only certain reward would be the hunt, but nevertheless he continued on there for days. Without the detector he went back to scuba diving in the same area of the shoals where the two anchors had previously been discovered, and on resurfacing wrote:

~ I first swam the inside of the reef from the small anchor down on the bottom and the old ballast stone to the west, under water at about 30 feet, with the small outboard *"Wee Diver"* following me along so that when I ran out of air I could surface without the necessity of returning to the starting point. ~

That day he spent several hours diving at varying depths, ranging from 30 to 50 feet, and all that he found, after checking out what could have been the shape of a bowsprit but turned out to be only a coral formation, was a greater appreciation of the fantastic reefs themselves. And this was no small reward. When he first witnessed the scene in all of its wildly extravagant beauty, he returned for his camera, to take, as he said, "considerable pictures, both on the surface and in the water, hoping to have from this trip at least some good pictures to take home." Ed was also unusually expressive when writing of what met his eyes there:

~ The bottom coral is indescribable in this area. I have never seen anything like it. It is the most rugged and weird of any place I have ever seen. Though I have not found any wreckage of a ship, the swim around these shoals was like a trip to the moon, and I certainly would not have missed it. It was the most awe inspiring and beautiful, with coral caves, coral bridges that one could swim under, coral heads which rose from the bottom like church spires, almost to the surface, large lumps of brain coral, sea fans, fish of all colors and descriptions. ...I was picked up by the small boat and returned to *Sea Diver* pretty well worn out from my long underwater swimming, but nevertheless, I would not want to miss this unusual experience. ~

The second search ended like the first, to no avail, though Ed wrote, "It would seem that our trip to the Silver Shoals could go on for months." Finally it was his contention that no further finds would be made there without more advanced electronic technology. Furthermore, salvaging could only be done by blasting through the reefs with dynamite, which would cause more trouble than it was worth, not the least of which would be the destruction of the reefs. He also had no heart for needlessly killing any more fish. He further concluded, based on the evidence, that thorough salvaging had already taken place. In addition, the deterioration rate of the shipwreck already located by his team indicated that such a search would probably be fruitless in any case.

Meanwhile, valuable experience gained there would one day be applied to the design of a highly practical articulated crane mounted to the stern of a ship for lifting objects out of the sea. But for the time being, he had "reworked the hoisting equipment" on *Sea Diver* and made plans for modifications to the ship itself while working in the Silver Shoals. He planned to add stabilizing plates to the sides of the ship as well. As he said:

~ ...I expect to be able to hoist up *Reef Diver* without experiencing the difficulties we had the last time, and nearly wrecked it because of getting stuck with it partially aboard and partially in the water. The rolling plates on the side will also assist, reducing a lot of the roll of *Sea Diver* and minimizing the danger of getting the small boat swinging on the end of the hoist which, when it occurs, is nearly impossible to stop. ~

After a second intense try at locating the remains of the *Nuestra Senora,* Ed left Silver Shoals empty handed. He wrote that they weighed anchor on Wednesday, May 25, at 3:20 in the afternoon, after rigging another line to his anchor to tug it off the coral bottom where it was caught. Once underway, a more serious problem presented itself, and Ed again was provided with protection from his unknown source of consistent "good luck." As he made his way through the shoals he suddenly discovered that *Sea Diver* was off course. "A very definite radar signal," he wrote, had indicated numerous islands where he "expected to see one big one: Turks." He went on:

~ It was most confusing and most difficult to understand, but finally I realized we were on the southernmost part of Turks Island, and the islands we were seeing were some small ones on the south end of Turks. At the time it was a mystery to me how in the world we could be so far off our course, and be south, but I later found, in trying to discover what happened - with such a large navigational error - that something had happened to our compass that had changed its local deviation from 265 west, which it had been continuously, to 280 west; a change of 15 degrees and enough of a change to throw our course off this amount.

What was most disconcerting — and certainly we had a great deal of luck — was that in replotting this course I found that we came very dangerously close during the night to the Mouchoir Shoals and might even have sailed through some of the northern heads without knowing it, though in all probability we were still very slightly north of the northern shoals. It sort of gives one the creeps to realize how dangerously close we came to the shoals in the night, and with a heavy sea running which we had all night. If we had hit one of these shoals, it would have been the end of *Sea Diver* and we would have been shipwrecked. ~

\* \* \*

MARION HAD BEEN AWAY FOR SEVEN WEEKS. Now Ed could at last pick up his first mate, with their son Clayton, at Turks Island. The Columbus expedition could resume. Meanwhile, Ed had flown over the area in question in his 20-year-old Grumman Widgeon, and returned to sit in the wheelhouse of *Sea Diver*, mulling over what he had seen and taking up his narrative — which had become more like a record of his thoughts — where he had left off:

~ Returning to my flight over N. Caicos and the Silver Shoals, I have not mentioned that upon my return to the Caicos Islands from the shoals I again flew over the northeastern part of Caicos Islands and again rechecked on the conditions as described in Columbus's Journal. The sand beach which could have been referred to by Columbus, where he made his first landfall and which we had checked from our sailings from Turks Island to Caicos, stands out quite plainly with a bordering reef. This reef extends and gets thicker as it gets to the northeastern part of the island. There is a peninsula on the northeastern part which Columbus could have referred to as the place where the Indian houses were located and which was a good site for a fort; it could be separated from the island by digging through and making it isolated as he refers. Also to the north-ward the reef gets very intense with considerable space inside forming a protected lagoon or harbor. Four or five miles to the northwestward there is a very definite opening into the reef and there is also an island in between the two Caicos islands which he could have referred to as a har-bor, as it appears like a harbor from the outside and I believe it would appear to have deep water. However, from the air it can be seen that this is too shallow, though the outside lagoon formed by the reef does form a very well protected harbor, and with water "still as a well" as Columbus described. Again I might say that so far, from all my searching, Caicos Islands from both the land and the air meets perfectly with the landfall of Columbus as described in his Journal. The big problem in proving this lies with possible discrepancies between Caicos and Cuba that can exist and of which we are familiar.

Again comparing it with the present known San Salvador, or Watling Island, certainly Caicos meets the description of Columbus's San Salvador much better than the Watling theory or any others that I have read, including Turks Island, which I have searched now both from the land and from the air, and found that it does not meet with Columbus's description of San Salvador. It is my opinion that the Turks Island theory is entirely out as well as the others. This leaves only the Watling and Caicos theories as making any sense whatsoever, with both of them having certain discrepancies. ~

The Links later wrote in a Smithsonian paper, "A New Theory on Columbus's Voyage Through the Bahamas," that they had "long ago eliminated all other theories, including those of Navarrete, Markham, Washington Irving, F. V. Fox, and Capt. A. B. Becher of the Royal Navy, because of palpable fallacies in their deductions."

Although they had read a great deal before forming any theories, for their primary source of information they adhered to the transcription from Columbus's *Journal* appearing in Bartolome de las Casas. "Bartolome," Mendel Peterson wrote in his foreword to the Link and Link paper, "is supposed to have made his transcription from the Journal that Columbus had sent to the Court at Barcelona after his return to Spain." But the drawback to their source was as Peterson stated:

> ~ It is highly unlikely that Columbus would send the original of the Journal prepared on shipboard [to Spain] but would most probably send a "smooth" copy. Thus the Journal as it appears in the surviving Las Casas manuscript must be at least third-hand. ~

Peterson continued to point out other areas of difficulty for those who would ferret out Columbus's first moves in this land:

> ~ Two other factors add to the confusion. The appearance of the Bahamas has changed considerably since the first landfall. The large trees that grew on the islands in the time of Columbus have disappeared almost without exception, and many of the islands now present a much lower silhouette from a distance. The loss of the trees has led to extreme erosion of the soil, and islands once fertile are now comparatively barren and rocky. ...Also, it should be remembered that Columbus approached these islands as a man full of wonder... ~

The book *Sea Diver* and the Smithsonian paper by Ed and Marion both present highly convincing arguments for the theories resulting from their studies combined with their subsequent journey through the islands. To start, they were convinced that researchers other than Verhoog had paid too little attention to the light Columbus reported seeing, confirmed by crew members, to the east of the *Santa Maria* and four hours out from land. Verhoog concluded that this light was actually a fire built by Indians on Turks Island, and *Sea Diver's* cruise, taking into consideration all that Ed had learned from Spanish historians, proved this to be a viable theory.

As Ed told Arthur Herzog, for his 1964 *True* article, "I found out...that no one even knew what a league was in Columbus's day — whether it was one mile or three. The only way to prove anything was to sail the islands at the same speed we calculated that Columbus did, checking the time elapsed, as Columbus recorded it, against our own, and against the landmarks Columbus saw."

Ed also became convinced — giving solid arguments together with Marion in the Smithsonian paper — that the Caicos Islands best fit the description of San Salvador as recorded by Christopher Columbus. But from there on, he discounted Verhoog's theories regarding the journey to Cuba. In particular, the authors noted a passage in Columbus's Journal referring to his approach to a second island which he seems to have bypassed. They wrote:

~ ...We read and reread various translations of the *Journal* for Sunday, October 14, and Monday, October 15, which indicated that Columbus had sailed for a second island after visiting San Salvador, but [he wrote] "as from this island I saw another, larger, to the west, I clewed up sails to navigate all that day until the night, and still was not able to reach the westerly point; this island I named Santa Maria de Concepcion." ~

The Links theorized that by using Caicos as the first island it would have been possible for Columbus to sail past the north shore of Mayaguana and on toward Samana, which, they argued, could have been his Santa Maria de Concepcion. They continued:

~ From there he could have gone on to Long Island, which could have been Fernandina. From here on, the course seemed naturally to follow that laid out by Morison to Crooked Island and thence to the Ragged Islands. ~

Capt. Weems and Mendle Peterson accompanied the Links on this notable expedition, the first ever to visit the Bahamas in search of the Columbus track with the intention of investigating "not one but three possible solutions." After flying over the islands several times to lay out their possible courses, they took *Sea Diver* to Turks Island, Caicos, Watling, Great Inagua, Crooked and Long Islands, and "sailed the courses between these islands and any others where Columbus might have gone." They wrote that while most Columbus scholars had only studied books and charts, while Morison had sailed only the single course he had previously determined, and Verhoog had viewed only the main channels of the islands from the deck of a fast ocean liner, they were able to appraise each possible course "first-hand on the scene." This was in addition to taking into consideration contributions made to their work by a scholar on Columbus's Journal itself and a Spanish language expert, as reported in their Smithsonian paper:

~ Because we found many differences in various translations from the Spanish into English, we early realized the necessity of enlisting the aid of a competent Spanish language scholar to interpret the original text for us. This we found in Dr. Armando Alvarez Pedroso of Havana, Cuba, author of "Cristobal Colon, Biografia del Descubridor," a man well versed in old Spanish and necessarily a thorough student of Columbus.

To test our theory of the existence of an unnamed island that Columbus passed by after leaving San Salvador, we asked Dr. Pedroso upon our first meeting to read the original text for October 14 and 15 and to make a simple chart of his interpretation of it. He verified our conclusions completely. Later, in order to confirm his own interpretation, Dr. Pedroso queried Dr. Ramon Menendez Pidal, president of the Royal Academy of Spanish language in Madrid, who replied that he could find no fault with it. Since then we have asked many others to interpret this section of the Journal, with the same result. Almost invariably they conclude that Columbus passed an island that he did not name before anchoring for the night off the shore of one he called Santa Maria de Concepcion.~

Ed Link's approach to the problem was different, heeding details apparently not taken seriously by others probably because they seemed to make little sense in light of preconceived notions. His tendency was to gnaw away at these very items, treating them as highly significant clues in a jigsaw puzzle that had necessarily to be adjusted overall until each clue fit as a viable piece into the larger picture. He could not dismiss Columbus's report of seeing a light before sighting land. Neither could he dismiss Columbus's reference to an unnamed island. In fact, not a single discrepancy between the *Journal* and other theories of the Columbus voyage was merely written off by the party aboard *Sea Diver*; instead, each point was investigated and examined. Details in the *Journal* that appeared to make no sense were looked at from new angles and made to make sense wherever possible, even if that meant eliminating theories of their own or contradicting the so-called experts. Their conclusion:

~ Without taking undue liberties with the text of the *Journal* we were able to conclude that it was entirely feasible for Columbus to have landed at Caicos and to have sailed from Mayaguana to Samana to Long Island to Crooked. It was impossible to follow either Dr. Morison's or Captain Verhoog's proposed courses without finding startling and many times unexplainable discrepancies. ~

The location of the first landfall, which Peterson called "one of those turning points that shape the course of history," is a difficult problem to solve. Perhaps no one will ever prove Link to be either right or wrong. As Peterson indicates in his foreword, Columbus hardly spent enough time where he first touched land to leave much of a permanent record:

~ Columbus remained at Guanahani only a very short time and then in a flush of excitement pushed on to other islands. He never returned to the point of his first landfall, his energies being devoted to new and more alluring lands to the south. ~

Although absolute proof of where the first landfall occurred was not possible, Ed and Marion, through open-minded reasoning and trial and error, became convinced that it could well have been Caicos, and they were equally certain that it was not Watling. Prior to giving their arguments they wrote in their paper:

~ To substantiate our conclusions we shall attempt to set down the questions we faced, to compare the sites we visited and their relative agreement with the descriptions in Columbus's Journal, and to point out the errors in each theory. ~

And so they did. Not least among their arguments was what they considered the impossibility of incorporating a large number of discrepancies regarding the Watling theory of the first landfall into any kind of a larger picture drawn of Guanahani by Columbus. Before their own journey ended, Ed became absolutely convinced that Watling Island could not have been the one Columbus renamed San Salavador. Marion too feels certain to this day that though the theories they developed on Columbus's journey through the islands to Cuba are still open to question, Watling Island was not the site of the first landfall. In summary, they reported that their theories were based on the following line of reasoning:

~ 1. There is little possibility that Columbus could have seen a light four hours before sighting San Salvador if he were approaching Watling Island, for there are no islands east of Watling in any direction, and no fishermen would venture 30 miles out to sea in an open canoe at night with strong winds and heavy seas. Columbus certainly could not have been mistaken when he claimed to see a light, for several others on board also saw it; and he would never have claimed the 10,000 maravedis from his sovereigns without the light as proof that land also was necessarily there.

2. The eastern coast of Watling is virtually unapproachable, with heavy seas breaking over thickly scattered coral heads along the rocky shore. There is no mention in the Journal of Columbus's having gone to the western side of the island to land.

3. Watling Island does not fit the description of San Salvador as well as Caicos. True, it does have a large lake in the middle, but it is not "very large and very flat" as compared with Caicos. It is 13 miles long, about a third the length of Caicos, while Las Casas describes San Salvador as 20 leagues long; and while Watling might be described as bean-shaped, it certainly is not triangular, as Las Casas implies.

4. Columbus describes "a great ridge of rocks that encircled the whole of that island." The only line of barrier reefs on Watling are on the north side where they form a large harbor. Elsewhere there are only scattered coral heads.

5. If Columbus landed on the west shore of Watling and went in the ships' boats in a north-northeast direction to explore, this would have brought him to the reef harbor on the north side, which he described as "no more disturbed than the water in a well." We found it so rough even in a moderate prevailing wind that we were forced to put two of our party ashore before we dared return across it. Also the commanding officer at a nearby US Naval base told us that his men were forbidden the greater part of the time to go out on it in small boats because of its rough condition. On the contrary, we had found the reef harbor on the northeast side of Caicos to be sheltered from the prevailing wind.

6. We visited a rocky island point on the east side of the harbor fordable from the mainland at low tide which might have been Columbus's "piece of land which is formed like an island although it is not one," but unlike Caicos this point had no body of water near it on the shore, and because of the heavy salt spray from the ocean it is doubtful if "the loveliest grove of trees that I have ever seen" would have flourished near it. There are none today.

7. There is no justification for the statement "I saw so many islands that I could not decide to which I would go first." Watling is too small to give the impression of many islands within itself, and no

other islands are visible in any direction. Even with the added height of the virgin forests of that day, it is doubtful if Columbus could have sighted Rum Cay, the nearest island, whereas the Caicos archipelago is made up of many islands.

8. Rum Cay is too small to answer Columbus's description of the second island: "The coast which lies toward the island of San Salvador runs north-south and has 5 leagues, and that the other, which I followed, runs east-west and has more than 10 leagues." Rum Cay is six to 12 miles. Rum Cay is southwest of Watling and does not "lie toward" it, as does Mayaguana to Caicos.

9. Although it does not appear on the charts, we found Columbus's "maravilloso puerto," according to Morison, a few miles north of Burnt Ground on the northern part of Long Island, a shallow indentation separated from the sea by two narrow mouths and a rocky islet between them. It had no depth whatsoever, and neither entrance was deep enough to permit access by the ships' boats. It was far too small to hold a hundred ships. We hold with Lieutenant Murdock (who otherwise selected the same route as Morison) that Clarencetown harbor farther down the eastern shore answered the description more aptly.

10. The coast does not run east and west at the northern tip of Long Island, but after rounding the point it immediately falls off to the southwest. Thus it would be impossible for Columbus to have "discovered all the part of the island as far as the coast which runs east-westerly."

11. Furthermore, with rain and failing winds, it is doubtful if Columbus could have covered the distance from the northwesternmost point of Long Island to the southern end from dusk of one night to dawn the next day, a distance of approximately 70 miles. ~

From this point on the Links said they took no exception to the accepted theory that Columbus went on to Crooked Island and from there to the Ragged Islands, the Columbus banks, and Cuba.

Herzog commented in his *True* story: "The Link theory, published by the Smithsonian Institution, caused anguished shouts from Watling, with its monument [at a site commemorated by the Bahamaian government as the first landfall], but Link sticks by his observations and many specialists are with him."

No theories were put forth immediately at journey's end, not until Ed and his companions could reason and hash out their conclusions. Marion said in *Sea Diver*:

~ Our tour of inspection was at an end. Our check of the islands and routes which we set out to examine was complete. It remained now to digest the information we had gathered and to try to reach a conclusion. There was no obvious answer.... ~

Homeward bound across the water aboard *Sea Diver* they analyzed the results of their expedition. Several days of arguments ensued. Capt. Weems started out convinced that Verhoog had formed the correct theory all the way through to Cuba. According to the statement in Marion's book, she and Ed "at first leaned toward Morison's theory, and later awakened to the possibilities of the Caicos landfall." Like a true scientist, Peterson had remained neutral, "although," Marion wrote, "when Ed had come forth with the idea of the unknown island, thus making it possible to trace Columbus's course by way of Samana, this suggestion had immediately excited his interest."

As *Sea Diver* crossed Exuma Sound in the Bahamas, with Columbus's *Journal* as their guide they again went over the entire problem. They reread each passage aloud, comparing various translations and interpretations as they went. Then, Marion wrote, Weems's championship of the Verhoog theory had softened, "worn down by point after point of unexplainable differences between it and the original text." They found that Morison's arguments "made a better showing," with fewer obvious discrepancies, but they found it impossible to reconcile the circumstances surrounding the first landfall with Watling island and its environs, still feeling that on this issue, Verhoog had made a good case for Caicos. Marion continued:

~ As our discussion proceeded, both Pete [Peterson] and Captain Weems showed an increasing interest in Ed's theory of the additional island on Columbus's route, which in turn supported the theory that his first land-fall had been at Caicos.

All that day we argued, and again that evening, after we had anchored for the night just beyond Ship Channel in the Exumas...we once again gathered in our cabin to continue our debate. Each controversial point was discussed, summarized and recorded, along with the passage involved, on the dictaphone. ...Our final conference took place the next morning at *Sea Diver's* dock in Nassau. ~

Additional research was conducted, including the visit to the archives in Spain, before the Smithsonian paper was published, but, their theories did not change as Marion concluded in *Sea Diver*:

~ ...when all the factors had been carefully weighed, we found that everyone was inclined to agree that of the three theories involved, Ed's revolu-
tionary idea of the unnamed island contained fewer discrepancies, and
fitted more completely the descriptions given by Columbus from beginning to end, than either of the other two.

Unless additional original material or charts should be turned up in
the future, we concluded there could never be positive knowledge of
Columbus's exact route; but we had proved — to our own satisfaction, at
least — that he landed first at Caicos and from there followed a course
from Mayaguana to Samana to Long island, and from there to Crooked
island, the Ragged islands, the Columbus banks and Cuba. ~

Another chapter in the adventures of Ed Link had come to a close. Marion later
wrote that at this time what he called his Man-In-Sea project first began to take shape in
his mind. In her later publication, *Windows in the Sea*, (Smithsonian Press) she wrote:

~ Today, exhibits in the Hall of Undersea Exploration of the National
Museum of History and Technology at the Smithsonian contain many
fascinating objects from these explorations — sections of the oldest cannon ever found in the New World, a bronze ship's bell dated 1733, a
Queen Ann pewter teapot, elephant tusks and copper basins undoubtedly
from a lost slave ship, and even an anchor believed to have come from
Columbus's wrecked flagship *Santa Maria*. ~

Ed's fame had grown from the Columbus and Silver Shoals expeditions, and as
a result, he was approached for possible new adventures. Immediately he began to
lay plans for the first of two investigations of the sunken city of Port Royal of
Kingston, Jamaica. Following that expedition, he and Marion flew to Israel at the
invitation of the America-Israel Society to view possible dive sites at Ceasarea,
Acre, and the Sea of Galilee. There was barely enough time for Marion to write
about their recent activities for her book before she began new journals on the Port
Royal work. "No sooner had we returned home than new possibilities seemed to
unfold all at once, right on top of each other," she says today. "Next we would visit
Banner Reef [offshore from Kingston, Jamaica] and conduct initial studies on the
sunken city of Port Royal, then we were suddenly off to the Middle East to prepare
for that whole thing there. It was just unbelievable!"

But after the first visit to Israel, before the next two missions could get underway, Ed began designing a more appropriate vessel for extensive work at Port Royal
and for sailing to Israel. *Sea Diver II*, to be designed by Ed as an underwater archeological yacht, was waiting in the wings.

# CHAPTER VII

# HISTORIC UNDERWATER SURVEYS AT PORT ROYAL

**1956–1960**

*Heaven and earth and all between - Is like*
*a bellows; Empty but not used up. The more it moves,*
*The more comes out of it.*

— *Lao Tzu*
*Tao Teh Ching*

What Ed had started so many years ago, inventing by redirecting the principal of the bellows in the organ to make a moveable, realistic flight simulator, was like a never-ending yeast to his bread of life. He would use his successes to constantly expand his interests until the day he died. He could apply the proceeds to going from project to project and adventure to adventure, and he could apply the principals of compressed air to underwater work, including making pneumatic tools in support of his ripening new interests. Now he was taking all his past gains and going on, from the Columbus and Silver Shoals explorations to the barely realized field of underwater archeology.

With the boys in school (18-year old Bill now at Cornell and Clayton, 15, attending school in New York until joining his parents in the summertime), Ed and Marion traveled almost constantly from mid-January to the second week of October, 1956. The year of travel began in Manhatten where Ed attended to business and Marion saw an agent regarding her book, then they continued to make numerous trips between New York and Binghamton. Next they rejoined *Sea Diver* in Miami and sailed for Jamaica, making a number of stops along the way, including Key West in Florida and Havana, Cuba where they met with Armando Pedarosa and went over his translations of the Columbus Journal for their Smithsonian paper on Columbus's first landfall. The last stop before reaching their destination, Port Royal off Kingston, Jamaica, which had been swallowed by the sea in a 1692 earthquake, was nearby at Banner Reef.

At Banner Reef, 60 miles off the coast of Jamaica, they explored the wreckage of a Spanish galleon. From there they conducted their first of two surveys on the sunken city of Port Royal, then went to Israel and stopped in Spain on the way to further research the Columbus material. Back home they were met by photographers and reporters from the Associated Press, which set off a string of calls from all manner of news reporters seeking interviews for feature stories that appeared around the country for months afterwards.

And at home they enjoyed reunions with family and friends. At last there was a period of peace. Ed left for several days in New York and Marion was content to spend time at home alone with her sorely missed son, Clayton. Meanwhile, she was writing *Sea Diver* and working with Joan Davis, a New York agent who had lined up Rinehart, Inc. as a publisher. At the same time she wrote a story on the Banner Reef dives and conducted research for a book she had begun to write on the history of Port Royal in context with the two diving expeditions there; a book never completed due to Ed's other endless activities, including a visit to Israel after the first Port Royal mission and an expedition to Israel after the second surveys in Port Royal.

With the exception of comments and summaries by the narrating author, this chapter is largely dedicated to Marion's as yet unpublished material on Banner Reef and more particularly on Port Royal, writings which all came about through her devoted partnership with Edwin Link.

* * *

### Port Royal, Cruise I - Leg I

So IT WAS THAT IN MAY, 1956, the Binghamton couple found themselves once again in the company of Art McKee in Florida. McKee had persuaded them to follow his lead to a cache of sunken treasure he said he was sure to find at a shipwreck he had visited the previous January off the coast of Kingston, Jamaica. Even though consenting to follow Art's lead, Ed was much more interested in his own plans to dive on the nearby sunken city of Port Royal. McKee, however, was more than eager to pursue his dream of finding that one great and elusive treasure which he was convinced would one day be his. Between the lines in Marion's account is the suggestion that he even put a little pressure on Ed to get on with the Banner Reef dives.

During these latest of Ed's activities, providence somehow gave Marion the necessary time for preparing the following article on their work at Banner Reef:

### BANNER REEF: *by Marion C. Link*
1956

~ Ed did not get excited over Art's story. He felt sure that it must be a worthwhile wreck to have aroused Art to such enthusiasm, for in the past he had found the wreckage of several interesting old ships within a few miles of Plantation Key in Florida where he maintained his Museum of Sunken Treasure, and otherwise would never have spent the time and money to reach Banner Reef initially in January. But Ed had become very blase about wrecks that had already been discovered and salvaged. True, in the old days, without proper diving equipment, it was impossible to reach many sections of a sunken ship, but as it mouldered away there were always fresh adventurers seeking what might be exposed anew. There was only the long chance that coral or shifting sands might now and then conceal some overlooked treasure.

However, we had been considering making a trip to Jamaica with *Sea Diver* for some time. We were interested in exploring the possibilities of the sunken city of Port Royal off Kingston Harbor. And, in line with our investigations of Columbus's early voyages, we were curious as to whether we would be able to trace any signs of the two sailing vessels which the Admiral had left mouldering in a bay on the north shore of Jamaica at the end of his fourth voyage. This combination of diving possibilities led Ed to finally decide to make the trip, and Art was signed up to go along as part of our volunteer crew. He could hardly wait for us to muster the rest of our crew and stock *Sea Diver* with the necessary equipment and provisions.

When we arrived in Kingston Harbor on May 22nd we had spent a solid week cruising from Miami to Nassau and across to Exuma Sound, south past Long Island and Crooked Island to Great Inagua, from there past the mountains marking the eastern end of Cuba and thus around the southern end of Jamaica. In the course of the voyage I had re-injured several ribs that were hurt in a fall on my trip to Haiti the previous year, and by the time we reached Kingston I was again in need of a doctor's care.

Consequently, instead of starting immediately for Banner Reef, it was decided to spend a few days at Kingston until I would be able to risk going to sea for two weeks with the attendant dangers of rough seas and possible strain. During that time Ed proceeded across the harbor to Port Royal to make some preliminary and exploratory dives on the sunken city. That was when Art's eagerness began to boil over.

In addition to Art McKee our crew consisted of Fred Logan, another skilled diver from Florida; Barney and Jane Crile who had been our diving companions on several previous adventures; John Cebula, a valuable man Friday all during the expedition, who had come with us from our hometown; and my husband Ed and myself. Later we were joined by Coles Phinizy, writer, and Peter Stackpole, photographer, for two nationally-known magazines, and Mendel Peterson, curator of Naval

History at the Smithsonian, who once more came to augment our diving
crew and to lend his valuable experience in identifying the discoveries
we hoped to make. He too was a skilled diver and with the others was
most helpful in assisting our efforts.

We left our anchorage at Port Royal on the evening of the third day of
diving on the old city, much to Art McKee's relief. He had been a good
sport about the whole thing and joined in enthusiastically with the other
divers in their first attempts to penetrate the murky waters covering the
sunken city. But his face lit up that morning when Ed suggested setting
out for the Pedro Banks before sunset; he was so certain of finding there
his pot of gold at the end of the rainbow.

Finally we were actually heading for the banks, but Art still could
not control his impatience. For months he had dreamed and talked and
planned for the day when he could return there, to the wreck on
Banner Reef. He had seen just enough of its anchor and cannon and
buried timbers, to say nothing of the 18th-century cup hilt sword, the
nearly perfect pewter plates and the dozens of tiny bronze crosses
which he had found when he had visited it in January, to feel certain
that at last he had come upon the treasure-laden galleon that would
make his fortune.

During the months he spent in Grand Cayman he had bombarded Ed
with letters and cables urging him to bring *Sea Diver* there and join him.
Not that he wanted to share his find with a second person; it was only
that there was no equipment in the vicinity of Grand Cayman or Jamaica
capable of salvaging the wreck. *Sea Diver* was the only boat to his
knowledge that could get in to these reefs and once there provide the necessary airlift [an ingenious suction type device designed by Ed for lifting
small artifacts up from the bottom] and diving equipment.

When he returned to Miami he immediately contacted Ed, regaling
him with talks of sure success. He told of finding and exploring the
wreckage of *Genoese*, a Spanish galleon heavily laden with treasure,
which in 1730 foundered on Banner Reef, a part of the Pedro Banks off
the Jamaican shore. He was even more certain of finding treasure there
because of talks he had previously had with two old seamen who had
taken part in exploring the wreck during an earlier salvage attempt.

One of these, Capt. Willy Bodden, a grand old Cayman Islander now
in his eighties and almost blind, had described the spot to him so vividly
that in January he had been able to locate it, in spite of the battered hulk
he had chartered out of Jamaica and its unprepossessing native crew.
However, lack of equipment, uncooperative weather, and the threatening

certainty that, should he find anything valuable, he might never return to shore alive, had finally caused him to postpone his search.

Wild reefs located many miles from shore in rough and open seas are no longer a novelty to us, having recently spent weeks offshore at Silver Shoals in Bahamian waters. This time we were approaching Banner Reef in the center of the Pedro Banks 60 miles south of the Jamaican coast and almost in the center of the Caribbean.

Here we had been told lay the wreckage of the *Genoese*, a Spanish galleon heavily laden with treasure, which in 1730 was proceeding from Cartagena in South America to Cuba when it foundered on the shoals of Pedro Banks. The crew had escaped to Jamaica in small boats. Subsequently, a partially successful attempt at salvage had been made. Again in the early part of this century, turtle fishermen from Grand Cayman Island 300 miles away had found gold on these same reefs, which, they believed, came from this very galleon.

We spent nearly two weeks on the site, anchored in the fairly quiet water on the west side of the reef. Trade winds blew at a constant 20 knots for the most part, occasionally reaching a velocity of 30 to 60 knots. Consequently, not once did we have a calm sea to explore the reefs, with huge white breakers constantly marking their otherwise hidden location.

The wreck itself lay in a declivity between two reefs in about 20 feet of water, beautiful coral cliffs forming steep walls on either side. We had traveled all night from Kingston to reach that spot early in the morning on our first day out. Later that same morning, after an initial foray to investigate the area, the men again scanned the reef then returned to the ship with the intention of placing permanent anchors and buoys in strategic locations, so that on a calm day we would be able to take *Sea Diver* into the wreck site. This was most important to our plans, for only thus could we make use of the airlift equipment on board ship. Just as Art had insisted earlier, we saw that without the airlift, there was little chance of getting to pay dirt on this wreck since the bottom was composed of heavy pieces of broken coral that would render Ed's jetting hose ineffective.

We nearly lost our small boat that first afternoon, to say nothing of divers Art and Fred. The two men had returned to the wreck site with buoys and an anchor, which after much difficulty in the rough waters they succeeded in placing well inside the blind channel where the wreck lay. They had climbed aboard the small boat and Art had started the outboard when a large roller caught them athwarts, drowned the motor, and half-filled the boat with water. Both men immediately jumped out to prevent it from foundering. They were still a quarter of mile from *Sea Diver*, which couldn't come close enough into the reef to rescue them, and, to add to our frustration, *Reef Diver* had not yet been launched. Somehow Art had finally managed to get the outboard started, then while Fred bailed madly with an old coffee can, Art risked swimming alongside the whirling propeller to guide the boat toward *Sea Diver* and into calmer water.

We cheered them on from the decks of *Sea Diver*, unable to be of any assistance until they were within our reach. They had almost arrived alongside when their motor suddenly gave out. Art then seized the tow line from our ship and pulled with all his might while Fred continued to hang onto the side and bail. Just as they came across the stern, Fred grabbed a line hanging from the ship's davits. He had barely secured it to a ring in the bow when the whole kit-and-kaboodle submerged below the surface, dunking the boat and spilling its cargo into the sea.

A mad scramble to unfasten the outboard and hand it aboard ensued, then Ed immediately took it apart and got it into fresh water. At last the lines were secured and Fred dove to the bottom to retrieve the lost gear. Needless to say, the two men were tired out, but otherwise were none the worse for their experience. However, it took Ed the rest of the day and part of the next morning to completely and carefully restore the outboard so that no trace of saltwater would be left to cause damage. Since we had only one other outboard with us, it was vital that both be kept in working condition at all times.

A perpetual problem encountered at sea was to adequately maintain the outboards in saltwater, salt spray and even salt air. No matter how carefully the engines were looked after, they would at times falter, spit, and refuse to function until they were taken apart and their fuel lines flushed of the gummy substance that seems to form from a combination of oil and salt, eventually blocking even the filters. In addition, Ed had found it necessary to flush out the tanks with clear water every time this clogging occurred, a situation that would have been even worse were it not for the old felt hats he used to filter the condensed moisture that formed in the fuel containers on deck before the fuel entered the outboard tanks.

We found our spot behind the reefs somewhat protected, but not enough for the barrier to break the seas completely. The prospect of *Sea Diver* pitching and rolling for the next ten days soon had the men out setting the rolling plates — heavy iron sheets, approximately three by 10 feet, that are suspended directly out from either side of the vessel so that their flat surfaces can create a dampening effect as the boat rolls, steadying it at anchor.

An important part of the mission included a precise system of setting the anchors over the wreck on the second day. The heaviest anchor was placed inside the blind channel reefs, holding *Sea Diver's* bow in position should she try to poke her head between the reefs. Two others were set and buoyed just inside the reefs, in deeper water to the left and right of the channel, to keep the stern from swinging into the coral rocks just below the surface on either side.

No one realized more than Ed what a hazardous operation it was, for if we should accidentally stove a hole in the side of the ship while executing this maneuver, or even afterwards if a line should break, we were in danger of losing not only our ship but also our lives. Just as when we worked in the open sea at Silver Shoals, we once again found ourselves far from any steamer lanes, far from land, and in waters so dangerous that even fishing boats avoided the area. Knowing the dangers, Ed had resolved not to make the attempt until he was certain that wind, seas, and mechanical contrivances all combined to work together to his satisfaction.

That afternoon before placing the anchors, awaiting that perfect moment when the early strong winds would let up, we decided to launch *Reef Diver* and take her to the inner buoy. Using Desco masks and air hoses to explore the wreck, we thought we might even have time to use her jetting equipment.

Once again I thought of what an ideal boat *Reef Diver* was for our work. John had remained aboard *Sea Diver* while the remaining six of us were in *Reef Diver*, loaded with heavy air tanks and other diving equipment. In spite of her load, she bobbed up and down over the waves as we approached the reefs, her jet propulsion carrying us steadily and smoothly toward the anchorage. When we had picked up the buoy and were attached to the anchor, she rolled and tossed in the turbulent waters from the breakers on either side, but continued to serve us calmly as one by one the swimmers and divers disappeared overboard until only I was left in the cockpit.

Ed soon returned to attach the jetting hose, switch the belt and make necessary adjustments to the engine. Then he was back underwater with Art, who was directing the stream of water from the other end of the hose toward the base of a cannon lying on the broken coral bottom. He returned an hour later without having uncovered anything of interest, but at least we were started on our search.

We set out the next morning again with *Reef Diver*, as the wind was blowing even harder than on the previous day, making it impossible to use *Sea Diver*. Barney and Jane were in tow behind us in *Wee Diver*, which was loaded with photographic equipment they meant to use for documenting our activities in the water and aboard *Reef Diver.*

Art went over the side as we approached the buoy, planning to pick up the anchor on the bottom and carry it closer to the breakers so that he could reach a more distant section of the wreck. Suddenly we were in for some frightening moments; the anchor dragged, and Art with his air hose became entangled underwater with the anchor line and the jetting hose. At this point the two boats started to drift toward the breakers on the other side of the pass. Several of us managed to free the jetting hose and the anchor line and haul Art into the boat, then Ed quickly gave power to the engine and we retreated into calmer water. Meanwhile, Barney and Jane paddled madly with their oars in the small boat to keep it from swamping with all their camera gear. Next Fred went over in his free diving equipment to unscramble things below and reset the anchor, then he signaled us to make another try. This time we succeeded, and soon Art with the jetting hose was hard at work on the wreck. The rest of the party spent the time exploring, picture taking and poking around with crowbars.

We dared not go far from Reef Diver, for in addition to the breakers on either side, the incoming tide set up a tremendous pull through the passage, which took a strong swimmer to combat. However, the current was not as strong below, and I found when I went down with the Desco that I could easily reach the spots I wanted to explore. Not so on the surface, where I allowed myself to swim only directly into the tide so that if I became tired it could carry me toward rather than away from the boat.

High winds and cloudy skies marked our fourth day on the reef. Perhaps we could have coped with these, but all day long sudden squalls swept across the ocean, first from one direction and then the other, and we were afraid to take a chance on being caught in a storm out on the reef. Consequently we spent the day aboard *Sea Diver*, impatient to be at our task. It was then that Barney observed:

"This is a funny crew. Everyone has a different interest. Ed is perfectly happy as long as he has something to repair; the more it taxes his ingenuity the better. Jane and I want nothing but a chance to take pictures. Fred is contented only if he is skin diving. And Art is nearly crazy because everything seems to prevent his finding the treasure."

As Ed was the only one able to satisfy his desires, for the diesel generator had needed overhauling for some time, he probably was the only contented one in the crowd.

But life brightened a little the following day. It was possible to work on the wreck, and at the end of the day the divers had quite an array of finds. There were more than a hundred various sized crucifixes and religious medallions made of copper; dozens of fine ivory combs; nine large brass buttons, some still attached to a frayed piece of fabric. There was a brass snuff box, a broken square green bottle, and some broken bits of pottery. Art had even uncovered some broken wooden barrels containing cocoa beans. However, all this did not seem the sort of cargo to be expected on a galleon laden with treasures returning to Spain. Rather, we thought it appeared more like the merchandise of a small trading ship on its way about the islands.

As we became more accustomed to working in the swift tide, in the proximity of the roaring breakers, we found ourselves daring tasks which would have seemed impossible when we first arrived. So the next morning, although the wind was blowing harder than ever, and we could see that the waves were breaking straight across the reef even where we had been anchoring *Reef Diver*, the men decided to move our anchor buoy back a short distance and attempt to work regardless. The wind was by then kicking up so badly that in our usually calm anchorage we were surrounded by white caps and choppy seas, and it was difficult to bring *Reef Diver* alongside to make the trip to the reef.

Once out in the open, it was frightening to be on the reef with breakers roaring in on every side and tidal currents so strong that it was a constant battle not to be swept away. *Reef Diver* bounced madly about, tugging at her anchor line and threatening to break loose each time a particularly large wave rolled beneath her. Once having become wet, we were cold in the strong winds, yet when the sun came out, it was strong enough to scorch our skin. There was no comfortable place to sit or stand while the boat gyrated about, and the roar of the engine, combined with the noise of the breakers, filled our ears with a terrible din. It was probably more tiring to brace oneself aboard *Reef Diver* and put up with the noise than to battle the currents beneath the surface.

Three more days of searching uncovered a battered brass teapot with raised figures of nymphs at the base of the spout and handle, and from the amount of black corrosion covering it, we thought that it had evidently been silver plated in its day. A scattering of crosses and medallions and some broken clay pipes completed the count.

Only one morning did the wind die down to a low 10 knots, which made it possible for us to take the two smaller boats across the waters covering the reefs where the breakers had previously kept us away. It was then that we saw the anchor of a ship and other scattered cannon on the surface of the reef to the right. Securing *Reef Diver* to one of the cannons, Ed went overboard with the metal detector. In spite of the tremendous tides, which prevented me from letting go of the anchor line while I watched, he managed to search the area surrounding the anchor.

That afternoon the men returned to the site and broke up the bottom coral, hoping that here might lie some of the galleon's treasure, but much to their dismay, all they uncovered was cannon balls. This seemed to indicate that there was no use in further search, not unless it were possible to bring *Sea Diver* in on the spot and by means of the airlift, penetrate deep into the coral and sand surrounding the timbers of the wreck. We reluctantly concluded that the natives in Jamaica had been right when they told us that the trade winds start blowing hard in May and increase throughout the summer. As we dared not trust *Sea Diver* in these waters during hurricane season, which is soon followed by winter storms and blows, there seemed small chance of our ever accomplishing this mission.

Even Art conceded the futility of further search under the existing conditions.

"Perhaps," he said, "I can get back here again sometime, when it is possible to get to the wreck with an airlift. I'm sure if you could ever get down to the base of that wreck, you'd find something worthwhile."

A few days later in Kingston he visited one of the old men who had helped to take gold from Banner Reef, then returned to us half elated, half disgusted.

"We were on the wrong wreck," he said. "The old man said they got the gold from another wreck on that same reef." With that, he started making plans to return to Pedro Banks the following year for another try. ~

* * *

IT WAS PERHAPS APPROPRIATE that Ed and Marion celebrated their 25th wedding anniversary, on June 6, aboard *Sea Diver*, at sea in the midst of dangerous reefs and roaring breakers. Even so, all things seemed to conspire that day to make it a special occasion. Marion recorded in her journal that a booby which had previously adopted the crew tagged around with them all day long. They had found their breakfast table set early that morning with old silver from the wreck: a porringer, a fork and a tea pot. Later in the day their friend Barney presented them with a tape recording of a lyric poem he composed about the booby and their wedding anniversary. That night they headed for Northeast Cay and were surprised to hear the welcoming shouts of a large group of men on an island they thought uninhabited except by the thousands of nesting terns they had come to see. The day ended with a visit to the terns and a quiet evening amongst new and old friends at Northeast Cay.

\* \* \*

## Port Royal, Cruise I - Leg II

BY JUNE 8, THE LINKS WERE IN KINGSTON readying ship and crew for the next leg of the mission, to dive on the sunken city of Port Royal. As the work proceeded, Marion managed to participate in and observe Ed's undersea work and also get to archives in Jamaica to learn more about the history of Port Royal, all of which resulted in the following, previously unpublished account:

### PORT ROYAL: *by Marion C. Link*
1956

~ When *Sea Diver* dropped anchor in Kingston Harbor just northeast of the sandy spit which is the present-day Port Royal, our crew of divers had very little idea of what adventures lay ahead of them.

Nearly three hundred years before, Port Royal, then one of the wealthiest and most famous cities of the New World, had stood where today our fathometer showed up to sixty feet of water.

We had come to this place across the harbor from Kingston, Jamaica with our completely equipped exploring and diving ship *Sea Diver* to investigate these waters both from the surface and on the bottom. We hoped to locate some of the vast accumulation of valuables which had disappeared beneath the sea when an earthquake in 1692 sent it to its doom.

We were most curious as to what we would find beneath these waters where two-thirds of the 17th-century city had disappeared. Very little was known as to its depth, the state of preservation of the ruined buildings, and the actual area of the destroyed city. Exaggerated tales from unscrupulous pens had indicated that it lay at a depth of thirty fathoms, at which depth could be seen the "ghost city"—-" a place of spectacular beauty rising in majesty from the sandy sea bed," even "a great cathedral holding its roof aloft by massive columns."

Other brief accounts from the files of the Institute of Jamaica, an outstanding and excellent national library and museum in Kingston, had indicated that only a few attempts had been made to dive on this area over the centuries, and that little was known as to what might be found. The most recent attempt had been the previous year when divers associated with an underwater motion picture were filming in that vicinity and made a brief survey. They reported a depth of 35 to 60 feet with water so murky that the visibility was only five to six feet. They also reported seeing many sharks in the area.

Early records of the earthquake told a different story.

It was a still morning in June in 1692, and Port Royal basked in the somnolence of a hot summer day. Trade went on desultorily in the warehouses lining the waterfront. In the deep water just offshore a score of ships with furled sails floated easily at their moorings. Pedestrians ambled along the narrow, dusty streets hugging the shade cast by the encroaching brick walls of the stores and grog shops, while slatternly women leaned from the windows of second and third stories shouting at their heedless offspring in the street below.

It was the quietest time of day in Port Royal, for the drunks and roisterers who had kept the town in a roar with their carryings on all through the night had at last taken to their beds. The noisy taverns were almost deserted; their proprietors busy at restoring order to the shambles left behind.

A meeting of the Council had just broken up at King's house, headquarters for the government overlooking the harbor on the northeast side of town. John White, president of the Council and Acting Governor, had sat down in his library for a glass of wormwood wine with Dr. Heath, rector of the nearby Port Royal church.

Suddenly, only a few moments before noon, there was a violent earthquake shock. It was followed almost immediately by a second and a third. The last one was so tremendous that houses toppled in ruins; the streets along the waterfront were precipitated into the sea; and for several blocks behind, houses continued to crumple as the land beneath them slowly sank beneath the water.

The church steeple fell with a great crash. The bell jangled madly; then suddenly went silent as water rose around the ruins.

Great crevices rent the earth, devouring broken buildings and panic-stricken people. A tidal wave formed and swelled and rolled in from the sea, battering at the walls of Fort Charles, inundating the only section of town that had survived the earthquake. The two smaller fortifications on the inside of town, Fort James and Fort Carlisle, had disappeared, victims of the first shocks. The earth continued to tremble and shake as the very mountains towering over the main island formed new patterns. The paths of rivers shifted, and fresh gullies sundered the hillsides, while landslides completely filled many of the valleys below.

More than 2,000 lives were lost in Port Royal alone in the course of that day; and when the narrow spit of land finally ceased its terrifying convulsions, it was found that almost two-thirds of the doomed town had disappeared beneath the sea. Only 200 houses were left, and these were so battered, as well as flooded from the invading tidal wave, that they were scarcely habitable. Fort Charles still stood, the guns on its highest ramparts pointing out to sea, but the batteries along the seawalls adjacent to the fort were destroyed, their guns toppled into the encroaching ocean.

Since that day Port Royal has been visited again and again with disaster. Only twelve years after the earthquake, the newly rebuilt town was completely wiped out by fire. And in 1744 a devastating hurricane swept across the peninsula, demolishing every structure raised following the fire. The surviving inhabitants who still attempted stubbornly to cling to the barren land were then assailed by terrible epidemics of disease.

Port Royal would probably have died then and there, had it not been that it was chosen soon after as headquarters for the British West Indies fleet. A large and complete Naval Station was established there to protect British holdings in the New World against her enemies, and a town consequently grew up around it.

In 1815, just at the end of the Napoleonic wars, fire once again swept the little town but spared the Naval station. From then on both Port Royal and the Naval station led a fairly quiet existence until the Dockyards were closed in 1905 at the order of the Crown. The town that had once contained the wealth of the West Indies was now a poor cluster of houses of fishermen and boatmen, with a total population of about twelve hundred.

It would seem that fate would have tired of stacking the cards against this little town, but in 1907 it was again shaken by an earthquake, which this time finished off the remnants of the old walls and structures. It remained for a hurricane in 1951 to deal the coup de grace. Out of 260 houses then existing, only ten were left standing. Fortunately the loss of life was small as the people were able to take refuge in a few well-constructed buildings such as the schoolhouse.

Now, five years later, we gazed curiously toward shore at what was left of Port Royal. Our eyes were confronted by an elaborately built stone and brick wall surmounted with iron pilings. Behind it stood a big three-story building with large sections of its red tile roof missing. Around it was clustered a collection of crude huts roofed with an assortment of heavy paper, tarpaulins, or wooden planks held down by a scattering of stones.

The high wall continued around this area, and on its north side a narrow street came down to the edge of the water where a low stone landing was flanked by a group of native dugout canoes drawn up on the shore.

We learned later that this was the Customs house, and that the large building within the wall, each floor surrounded by wide galleries, was the old Naval hospital which had withstood fire, earthquake and hurricane since the early part of the previous century.

Present-day Port Royal, it was evident, was still a shambles from the last hurricane. The poor fishing folk who were the main inhabitants had established themselves in the deserted Naval hospital, crowding it to the limit. Those who could not find space inside had constructed the hovels within the grounds. Here they had continued to exist while the stunned government of Jamaica fumbled with attempts to finance and rehabilitate the town.

Now, five years later, complete demolition of the hurricane-damaged walls and houses had been accomplished, and several rows of unimaginative but well-built apartments had been erected. In other areas of the destitute peninsula we could see the framework of additional buildings under construction. The low, cement-block structures presented an incongruous appearance contrasted with the few dilapidated houses still standing as relics of the previous century, the solid brick walls of Fort Charles in the distance, and the substantial old parish church of St. Peter with its cement-faced walls of brick built soon after the 1692 earthquake.

Close to our anchorage was a cone-shaped metal marker buoy labeled on the harbour chart as "Church buoy." The name naturally associated itself in our minds with the story of the church that disappeared beneath the waters during the earthquake, and also with persistent tales of a church bell that, it was said, had been heard ringing beneath the water many times during the intervening centuries. Again it recalled the account we had read of the vast cathedral thirty fathoms below, which the imaginative American film diver had conjured up, its walls still intact and its vaulted arches rearing high beneath the sea.

We soon decided that none of these stories could be true, for a survey of the surrounding water with our portable fathometer showed an irregular bottom with variations of only a few feet and an overall depth ranging from twenty feet inside the marker to sixty feet in the open harbor beyond. The greatest depth on the harbor chart showed only eleven fathoms.

Later research in the archives at the Jamaica Institute also told me that the only church in the pre-earthquake city had stood on filled land connecting the original island of Port Royal to the series of sandy cays known as the Pallisadoes. When the church collapsed with the earthquake shocks, the land beneath it had also sunk, causing Port Royal to become once more a separate island. The ruins of the church lay in the water bottom. It was not many years, however, before silt and gravel washed in by the seas again filled this area. With further help from the British Navy, which set about constructing a Naval yard in this area during the following century, the old church was soon buried under land rather than water. "Church buoy" therefore could not refer to the sunken church and was clearly a misnomer for the marker that appeared on all charts to the middle of the 19th century as "White buoy."

Shaded patches on the map showed the approximate areas of the destroyed city that was still under water. This included a large triangular section stemming from the Church buoy near which we were anchored along the north shore toward a coaling station that we could see about a mile away, and to the southeast past the farther end of the Naval hospital. There was also a small section just west of Fort Charles. According to this chart, a great deal of land that had disappeared in the earthquake had been replaced by the action of the sea, even in many places, including outside Fort Charles and the fortified wall known as Morgan's line, building out the coastline a good half mile beyond its original position.

Thus we found that while a large part of Port Royal disappeared beneath the water in 1692, today more than two-thirds of that same area is again filled land long since included as an integral part of the town.

The long sandy hook known as the Pallisadoes, which reaches out into Kingston Harbor, its tip crowned by the imposing brick ramparts of Fort Charles, was originally a series of sand cays that were gradually joined by means of upright logs, like palisades, driven into the intervening openings, causing the ocean sands to settle against them to form land.

When the British under Admiral William Penn and General Robert Venables took Jamaica from the Spanish in 1655, there was no settlement on this sandy spit. It was then known as Cayo de Carena, for it had been chosen by the Spaniards to beach and careen their ships because of the deep water of the harbor extending right up to its inner shores.

The English immediately fortified this strategic spot at the entrance to the harbor with a series of forts. The largest of these, Fort Charles, faced the sea. Fort James protected the passage into the inner harbor; and Fort Carlisle on the northern shore of the peninsula completed the security pattern. With the manning of the forts, a town soon formed outside the walls.

In the 36 years that transpired between the founding of the town and the earthquake, Port Royal had become one of the most important harbor cities in the New World from point of volume of trade and the wealth of its citizens. It was also known as the most wicked city soon after it became the headquarters of the buccaneers who had been driven by the French from their island refuge, Tortugas, off the north coast of Haiti.

Here at Port Royal the pirates learned they could come with their booty and find a welcome. Great quantities of the riches of the New World piled up on the beaches and docks of Port Royal, and were bartered with the greedy merchants who made fortunes in the transfer of the loot to Europe. With their ill-gotten gains, the buccaneers turned the fast-growing city into a center of drunkeness and license.

Port Royal reached the apex of its fame in those years when Henry Morgan, most spectacular buccaneer of all times, fortified with letters of marque from the Jamaican governor, Sir Thomas Modyford, laid waste the Spanish cities throughout the Caribbean, sacking and destroying as he went, and returning to the Jamaican port with the stolen wealth of these communities.

The narrow sand spit was gradually extended by fills, and two and three-story brick buildings crowded the narrow streets. Taverns and houses of ill repute stood shoulder to shoulder with warehouses and shops and the homes of shopkeepers. Farther to the east, near the King's house and the fine church, still uncompleted, stood the houses of the more substantial citizens.

In 1664, in order to separate the government from this brawling town, it was decided to remove the government offices and the residence of the Governor to Spanish Town across the harbor, but Port Royal continued to grow, and in 1668 numbered a population of eight thousand including slaves.

Britain's king, pleased with the wealth which Henry Morgan had wrested from the Spaniards, as well as the destruction he had wrought among them, closed his eyes to the questionable methods by which it had been accomplished and rewarded the buccaneer by making him a knight. At Modyford's death in 1679, Morgan succeeded him as Lt. Governor until his own death three years later. He also held the offices of Chief Judge of the Admiralty Court and Custos of Port Royal. Although his official residence was in Spanish Town, Morgan spent most of his days during his term of office at Port Royal in the company of the seafaring adventurers with whom he had associated all his life. And when he died he was interred in the burying grounds just east of the city on the adjoining cay.

Nowhere else in the New World did license and debauchery, crime and dishonest trade reach such an extent as in the Jamaican city. The stench of its wickedness carried to every port, and there were few citizens on either side of the Atlantic that were not aware of its ill fame.

Consequently, no one was amazed, four years after Morgan's death, when news of its destruction by earthquake reached their ears. It was God's punishment, they said. And ministers of the church preached solemnly to their people of the lesson to be learned.

Archival material obtained at the London Library included a poignant description of the tragedy, which appeared in London the following year, called "The Truest and Largest Account of the Late Earthquake in Jamaica, June the 7th, 1692." It was written "by a Reverend Divine there to his Friend in London, With some Improvement thereof by another Hand."

It read in part:

"Our magazeen and only Store houses of Port Royal is three parts swallowed in the Sea, ships and shallops now riding at anchor where great numbers of fine Fabricks have been not Long since; the Relation of which single Places Sufferings to give you in particular, would not only weary your eyes, but make your heart ake to read it; many very eminent merchants, before worth thousands are now scarce worth more than the blew linen on their backs; several are dead, either overwhelmed with their houses or drowned in the Sea which flowed in suddenly upon them; while they fled from the Sea, the Earth devoured them in her gaping jaws, or they were knocked on the head with the houses falling on them, and while they fled from the gaping chasms of the earth, or the tottering buildings, the sea met them and swept them away.

"A whole street (which we call the wharf, where most of the noted merchants lived, and where much of the Planters Goods was landed for convenience of sail and shipping (more especially sugar and cotton) sunk at once from one end to the other, with a general crack at the very beginning of the earthquake, together with two forts, guns, etc, built thereupon; and which is more dreadful, all those poor wretches perished that were either upon, or nigh it without any warning; and presently after this, while the people were in the greatest horror and consternation imaginable, neither having time to fly, or thoughts where to fly, for safety, two or three more streets in their whole length tottered and fell, and were immediately sunk, land and all together deep into the sea, as far as the Jews Street; all the upper part of the town, together with the church, and all above it towards the Palisadoes itself where their burying place was, is now no longer earth but sea (and ghastly to behold) the very dead corps that were submerged (I may say) instead of inhumed, even at their funerals floated from thence to all parts of the harbour.

"Such houses as do yet remain; are from the Jews street, and backward, to that we call the great Sea side, but many of them so rent and
torn, others so deeply sunk in the water, whereof some as high even as
the balconies, that they are unserviceable; the wall at Pallisadoes is utterly ruined, with the part thereto belonging; and the Morgan's Line (which
stands the best of all) the principal fort, (and as they say) Walker's Fort,
do yet stand, yet they are sorely shaken and rent, and so sunk, they are
not tenable; the whole place that is yet above water, sinking daily by
those earthquakes we have ever since had, sometimes four, five or six
times, more or less in twenty-four hours—-

"The reputed number of the dead"———-"is commonly reckoned at
1,500 persons besides blacks, who 'tis probable may be six or seven hundred more, a multitude of whole corps floated a great many days from
one side of the harbour to the other, which caused such an intolerable
stench that the dead were like to destroy the living—-

"Port Royal in its flourishing condition was a famous empory and
mart town for these Indies whither were brought partly by a private and
partly by a publick and allowed traffique (the Achiento being settled
here) a very large share for so small a place, of the riches of Peru and
Mexico which not only enriched our merchants and factors here, but
whereof yearly were transported for England in coin and bullion vast
sums, so that tis not to be computed what is lost, but many people think
at least to the value of 400,000 pounds at Port Royal only—-"

We read this account with great eagerness, for with the help of the
chart from the Institute we were then able to visualize with greater clarity
the sections of the city upon which we wished to dive. According to our
calculations the area still underwater and available to our equipment
included Fort James and the line of docks and warehouses extending
from it to Fort Carlisle to the northeast, as well as the waterfront known
as Fisher's Row extending southeast to a swampy area known as
Chocolata Hole which is today the parade ground connected with the
Army quarters at Fort Charles. It also included the streets immediately
adjacent to and behind these waterfront areas.

Thus it would seem from the Reverend Divine's description, our best
chances lay in uncovering the two forts that must remain as substantial
ruins, and the very rich warehouses which lined the waterfront in
between. Whatever more may have been destroyed or lost beneath the

sea in that far off day had either been recovered since or was now buried beneath the land that had since filled in these areas and upon which subsequent settlements had been built.

We have become used to the hazards of anchoring our boats close to jagged coral reefs and foaming breakers, but Port Royal presented us with a new set of problems, not nearly as spectacular as some we had seen but every bit as dangerous to the person of the divers.

That first day, anchored near the so-called Church buoy several hundred yards off the west end of present-day Port Royal, we found the water so murky it was impossible to see the bottom twenty-three feet below. Our first dive divulged the fact that visibility under water was only a few feet. And when the airlift had been put to work, thus clouding the water even more, the divers found they could see only within a radius of a couple of feet in front of them.

Sea urchins seemingly as large as dinner plates littered the bottom and had to be removed before starting any operation. Even then it was commonplace for the diver manning the airlift to step back and brush against a stray urchin that had been sucked back again in the brief interval. Every member of the crew at one time or another nursed a patch or two of black needle tips broken off in his tender flesh.

That sharks and barracudas haunted these waters we were certain, for the fishermen on the shore moved out and anchored frequently in this area just to hunt them. We ourselves had already caught glimpses of sharks as they circled the ship just below the surface. It did not add to the diver's comfort to know that they were there, constantly around and invisible in the murky gloom.

Once the diving operations had started, and the airlift engaged in uncovering first the heavy brick walls of the old fort then the rotten timbers and tumbled masonry of a nearby building, the divers had frequent narrow escapes as the airlift sucked away the silt and gravel from beneath the walls. Working in a small radius of clear water surrounded by an aura of muddy water created by the airlift, it was impossible to gauge the exact instant when a seemingly firm wall, becoming undermined, would unexpectedly precipitate itself into the hole created by the diver.

Sudden squalls sweeping in from the sea or down from the mountains towering behind Kingston to the north created frequent emergencies, causing the crew on *Sea Diver's* decks to scurry around resetting anchors and letting out air hoses stretched to their limits as the weight of the boat shifted violently from one anchor to another. Sometimes the anchors dragged, and it became necessary to signal divers aboard; to set the airlift free, marked with a floating buoy; and, when the storm was over, spend precious hours reestablishing *Sea Diver* in her former position. This was invariably accomplished with a great confusion of tangled anchor lines, air hoses, marker buoys, and airlift pipes and tubes.

One of the most insidious hazards, not always invisible, was waste from the row of latrines lining the nearby shore, constantly used by the scores of hurricane victims who now lived in the hovels behind the sea wall. Even though our faces were protected by masks, there was constant speculation as to the chances of infection through the ears, and I noticed that every diver as he came back on board *Sea Diver* made an immediate pilgrimage to the freshwater hose middecks where he rinsed himself off most thoroughly.

*Sea Diver* was supposedly designed and developed to provide its owners and their friends with the ultimate in diving pleasures. Heretofore we had delighted in crystal clear waters, beautiful coral, brilliantly colored fish and white sand bottoms. Not so at Port Royal. It took guts and persistence to descend day after day into these unpleasant waters. The ordinary diver receiving a good stipend for such work would no doubt have grumbled or even rebelled against such an assignment. But these men who dove for the pure love of it, plus that tantalizing, beckoning prospect of what the unknown might produce, met their stint each day with unfailing zeal and anticipation. As they penetrated deeper into the muck and clay and gravel, their expectations soared, for they knew that they were approaching the earthquake strata, and the possibility of uncovering articles of historic interest and value increased accordingly.

We soon discovered that the sinful city of Port Royal must have maintained its reputation for imbibing well past the time of the earthquake, for we found layer upon layer of bottles. That first day of diving, the bottom surface yielded only modern rum and beer bottles, but just beneath the surface appeared a wonderful collection of 19th century bottles of many shapes—-liquor bottles, torpedo-shaped soda bottles, soft blue and green and brown medicine bottles, discards from the Naval hospital on shore which in that day had battled epidemics of yellow fever, malaria, and other tropic diseases within the King's Navy.

Another foot of excavating revealed 18th-century rum bottles, their hand-blown shapes more round, the glass a darker blue, which flaked to the touch. The crowning delight was the uncovering of those bottles of pre-earthquake origin, onion-shaped, their dark iridescence marked with coral encrustations of the centuries. Here indeed was a treasure house for the bottle collector. As our excavating proceeded, we loaded the deck of *Sea Diver* with a tremendous assortment, many of them in perfect condition. It was astonishing that no matter where we dug, there were bottles. There must be literally tens of thousands of bottles in this area.

Our first day was spent in making a cursory survey by skin diving and with the air hoses. Each time a diver surfaced, he handed up some object plucked from the bottom. We were amazed to see coral-covered chamber pots, not one but several, appear; these no doubt also deposited there from the old Naval hospital. There were many bricks and more bottles. However, we were fairly certain that objects so close to the surface muck could not be from the earthquake period, as Bernard Lewis had told us that the objects recovered by divers with Aqualungs from the motion picture team two years before were not of the earthquake period.

Our swimmers then set out to look for any signs of irregularity in the bottom, for it was disappointingly regular in its appearance, sloping gradually out to sea. In the murky waters with scarcely any visibility, they were able to locate only a few coral formations jutting slightly above the surrounding muck. These they marked with buoys for further investigation with the airlift.

Ed also discovered a triangular-shaped formation of brick and coral that he thought might be an abutment of the old fort. He and Art soon had the airlift sucking away at the silted bottom at one side of the buried structure, hoping to determine its height (or depth) and its shape. By the end of the day they had succeeded in removing the accumulation of silt and debris of centuries to a depth of six feet. At the base they found flagstone paving, a scattering of broken bits of pottery——and bottles. The bricks and flagstones brought to the surface matched exactly the type we later found in Fort Charles, the only surviving fort from the time of the earthquake. This, coupled with the fact that the wall was eight feet thick, made it pretty certain that we were on the ruins of Fort James, which had guarded the western point of Port Royal.

During the next few days the divers took turns working at the airlift in shifts of from one to two hours, depending upon the extent of their enthusiasm for the project. The others, in their Scotts, searched for other signs of the fort, placing small buoys with yellow flags wherever they found suspicious rises on the bottom. Fred came back one afternoon to report a projection topped with corrugated metal that looked like lead.

The following day the airlift was shifted to this new site, and the men worked away at it. Fred emerged with a crumpled sheet of copper bristling with nails. At first we thought it must be roofing from some part of the fort, but then Mendel Peterson looked at the nails and knew different. They were machine-made; much too late a date for this fort of pre-earthquake times. Further study revealed that the copper had been evidently stripped from the bottom of a ship during the past century as it scraped over the top of this section of the old fort.

The same day's work, however, produced a second section of much heavier copper sheeting, this one with obviously handmade nails, and a sheet of lead pressed into deep corrugations as if from a mighty force. It was irregularly sprinkled with holes the size a bullet would make. From the size and shape of the structure underneath, it could very well have been a sentry box at the apex of the little fort. Square, red, sunbaked tiles about a foot across, and more stone paving blocks about 24 by 18 inches were also brought up.

To get to the bottom of these walls, the divers went through several layers of detritus that had settled following the earthquake. On the top they encountered a muddy silt, then broken finger coral, clam shells and other marine debris. This rested on a grayish clay deposit studded with broken coral, and was followed by a coarse gravel made up of round black pebbles and sand. All through these later layers they encountered bricks and more bricks. Each one had to be picked up and sucked clean of silt before being deposited to one side, or it muddied up the water so badly that the diver was soon unable to even see what he was doing. At the first location they came upon a mass of black coals, possibly used to heat cannon balls before firing them into the decks of invading sailing ships.

Several times while these explorations were going on, I made attempts to inspect their efforts, but it was impossible to see anything from the surface. A skin dive afforded only a quick glimpse of a flat, cement-like structure and a muddy stream rising toward the surface from the airlift. So I followed Ed down one day in a Desco. The visibility was so poor I had to swim within two feet of his red air hose to keep it in sight. I watched him for a while as he swam back and forth with the metal detector. I had been warned not to touch the bottom as it would rile the water and make it impossible for him to work. Beneath me I could just make out the triangular shape of the first abutment they had worked upon.

I carried a yellow-painted brick with me which Ed would use to mark any spot on the bottom giving an indication of the presence of metal. He hoped to locate one of the cannons that had fortified the old fort. Back and forth he swam, just off the bottom, the clear plastic disc of the detector projected before him. I followed with the yellow brick. At last he got an indication. I could tell, for he returned to the same spot several times, watching the dial as he passed over it. He looked around for me. I handed him the yellow brick and he carefully placed it just inside the brick wall.

He continued his search, and I swam in wider circles, examining the bottom for the first time on my own. It was possible to see only a few feet in front of me. I lost track of Ed almost immediately as I struck out for the buoy marking the sentry house. Several times I swam to the surface to locate buoys marking other work areas on the bottom and then returned to look them over.

When I returned to *Sea Diver* I had a somewhat clearer idea of what had been going on below, but I still could not visualize the layout of old Fort James. It was several days later, after several more flags fluttered on the surface marking the location of additional masonry beneath, that it was possible to see in my mind's eye the neat brick walls of the old fort with its formidable cannon pointing out across the harbor to take up the defense of Port Royal where Fort Charles on the outer shore necessarily ended.

In the meantime, Ed kept *Reef Diver* busy combing the surface near our anchorage and the shore waters off the north side of the town. He carried with him a portable fathometer that indicated on a running graph the variations in depth to an accuracy of six inches. From time to time he dropped yellow flag buoys in several places that showed the presence of irregularities on the bottom. At some spot just opposite the Morgan's Harbor Yacht Club, Fred skin-dived to discover in 30 feet of water, about 150 feet from shore, an abutment similar to those we had uncovered at Fort James. From our chart we were sure that we had located the third fort, Carlisle.

Ed continued his tracing of the bottom contours by fathometer whenever he had any spare time, gradually filling in on his chart the outline of the sunken city. It curved close to the north shore, extended out into a wide point to the west, capped by Fort James, and then swung in to shore south of the old Naval hospital toward the Army parade grounds that in the past had been a swamp known as Chocolata Hole. Nowhere did he find a depth greater than 40 feet, becoming less deep on the shoreward slope, while beyond this line it dropped off abruptly into harbor depths of approximately 60 feet.

After several days of hard work on the site of Fort James, our crew became impatient to work on a site within the city itself. There is no doubt they were lured on by thoughts of the chests of silver and gold which we felt certain were buried deep beneath the rubble of crumbled brick shops and homes.

There were no banks in those early days where money could be safely deposited. Instead each householder of any wealth owned at least one iron-bound chest with intricate locks in which to cache his valuables—- "the bars and cakes of gold, wedges and pigs of silver, pistoles, pieces of eight and several other coyns of both Mettles, with store of wrought plate, jewels, rich pearl necklaces" described by Francis Hanson in his "Laws of Jamaica" in 1682.

Hanson also had commented on the great quantities of gold and silver, "some of which our goldsmiths there work up, who being yet but few, grow very wealthy, for almost every house had a rich cupboard of Plate, which they carelessly expose, scarce shutting their doors in the night—." He claimed that there was "more plenty of running cash (proportionately to the number of inhabitants) than in London."

Wouldn't it be wonderful if in penetrating this brick shambles beneath us, they should stumble upon the workshop of one these goldsmiths, or at least upon one of the houses with its cupboards filled with plate! Bricks and bottles were all very well, but they had had enough for the time being. Now they intended to find whether there was any truth to these stories of fabulous wealth buried beneath the earthquake's debris.

So they chose a spot about 150 feet shoreward from the site of Fort James. According to their calculations this should place them on the far side of the street that followed the shoreline of the old city in the vicinity of whatever buildings had once existed there. Here they picked a coral formation that might indicate something solid underneath and started to excavate with the airlift.

I drove into Kingston with Sir Anthony [Jenkinson, British owner and operator of the local Morgan's Harbor Yacht Club] that day to do some digging of my own; but I was digging in the archives of the Jamaica Institute for whatever information I might glean on the early history of Port Royal.

When I returned in the late afternoon I found much excitement on board *Sea Diver*. The divers had unearthed the worm-eaten timbers of a building, wood flooring, and a section of brick wall. On board they exhibited a pair of leather shoe taps, a copper medal or token of some kind, the flint from a musket, some broken bits of blue-decorated porcelain—-and bottles. Underneath the flooring they had found a coil of rope, but were unable to bring it to the surface as it was already falling apart. There were also some broken pieces of clay pipe and some bones, obviously the bones of animals for they were too large to be human.

Was this a shop or a house? Was the wood planking ceiling or floor? Were they working at ground level, or should they excavate much deeper? It was difficult labor, for the loose bricks made it necessary to proceed very slowly, removing each brick as the airlift uncovered it and placing it aside. The brick wall had loomed higher as the pipe of the airlift bit deeper, and soon a hold had begun to take form beneath the heavy timbers. It was then that they were forced to abandon the project for lack of daylight.

They were eager to start work the next morning, and everyone was on hand promptly for breakfast. The task was divided among Fred and Art and Pete and Ed. Working from one-and-a-half to two hours each, from six to eight hours of digging could be accomplished each day. Art started this morning in high spirits, with every expectation of uncovering a vast collection of artifacts from the tumbled building. The airlift spouted muddy water high into the air, and a circle of mud spread out and drifted seaward with the slow tide.

It was a particularly murky morning underwater because of silt from the mountain streams washed down from heavy rainstorms in the mountains back of Kingston during the week, and it was not long before Art was in trouble. He shouted up from the foot of the boarding ladder requesting help in freeing the digging tool, which he said had burrowed its way so deep under the timbers he could not extricate it. Fred quickly donned his Scott gear and went down to assist him, but the combined efforts of both men failed to get it free.

Finally, after shutting off the compressor, it was necessary to hitch the airlift to the lifting gear on *Reef Diver* to pull it clear. Art went back to work. Twice more during his stint *Reef Diver* was called upon to free the airlift. The climax came when Art with some sixth sense sprang clear in the water as a slide of bricks and earth came tumbling down into the hole he had so carefully dug.

Meanwhile above water, dark clouds had been piling up in the sky to seaward. As Art came on board to report this predicament, heavy gusts of wind assailed *Sea Diver* from the direction of the storm. Soon the whole crew was employed in adjusting anchor lines and attempting to keep the trawler from shifting its position in relation to the location of the airlift.

Much the same story recurred at intervals during the day, ending up with a mad scramble in the afternoon as another violent storm swept down from the mountains. This time it was necessary to loose the airlift equipment, marking it with a buoy, and to take in the stern anchors. We then found *Sea Diver* dragging its bow anchor down the harbor and creeping consistently closer to the shallow water near shore.

There was nothing to do but start the Caterpillar diesel and pull up the anchor. As it was near the end of the afternoon and there was no chance of further work that day, we went into the dock for the night, a very discouraged group of divers. Total accomplishment for the day, zero.

We were fortunate to have a fine dock available at the site of the old Naval Station where we were able to tie up at will and to secure fresh, pure water piped from Kingston on the mainland. It was more often our fate to be so far from harbor that we were forced to endure whatever conditions the elements chose to deal out.

The historic old Naval Yard, now leased by Sir Anthony Jenkinson for his yacht club, is today a large open area divided from the town by a high, 19th century cut-stone wall. The naval buildings have long since been torn down, but in the center of the area can still be seen colorful relics of its past—three huge anchors, each with one bent fluke and heavy wooden stock, which Sir Anthony had removed from the nearby harbor where they formerly served as mooring anchors for the ships of the Navy. Nearby, four-square around the old flagstaff, are four cement foundations bearing the names of now defunct Admiralty ships. The figureheads of the ships that formerly rested upon them have since been removed to Bermuda.

Just opposite the dock and adjoining the quaint, low-roofed brick house of early vintage that Sir Anthony uses as his office, a picturesque arch pierces the high stone and brick wall offering access to the town. We debated long as to whether this arched section of the wall was a part of the original pre-earthquake town, for the bricks exactly matched those we had found in the old fort. It was finally established that it was part of the original Naval Yard built in the 18th century and left standing when the later wall was built, which now encloses the Yard.

Tracing back the history of the Dockyard, I found that most of this area was originally filled land upon which had stood the pre-earthquake church, the original King's house where the Governor of Jamaica lived, and the town residences of many famous people. These were destroyed when the filled land sank back into the sea at the time of the earthquake. Gradually this area had been reclaimed by gravel and silt washed in by the sea, a process assisted during the next century by the British Navy when it decided it needed more space. As a result, today this entire section is once more covered with soil. Who can guess what still lies beneath it?

I believe every foot of the soil of Port Royal is historically rich in its composition, for wherever we walked upon the paths or across the open lots, we found evidences of its previous eventful existence—broken bits of glass and pottery and handmade nails. While on the other side of the wall in the village where workmen were engaged in digging cesspools for the new houses, broken china, bottles, clay pipes, and many signs of its early years were constantly uncovered.

At Morgan's Harbor Yacht Club, constructed at the far end of the Dockyard, many items of salvage were found and made use of by Sir Anthony, including the heavy sheets of black slate that now form the tops of handsome wrought iron dining tables.

The club was a lifesaver for *Sea Diver's* crew, including her cook. We were served wonderful dinners each evening, freeing me from the responsibility of preparing the main meal daily in our small galley for at least seven hungry men, though we still had breakfast and lunch aboard ship.

Sir Anthony showed a keen interest in our activities, and his invaluable help with transportation, office space and equipment, and securing supplies for *Sea Diver* was keenly appreciated.

In fact, it seemed that all of Jamaica, including the governor, Sir Hugh Foot, was most cooperative. Officials from the Government Survey office took time to work with Ed in establishing base lines and locations, while other officials at the Customs house made contributions of equal value. We were also much indebted to our fine American Consul-General, David Maynard, and to C. Bernard Lewis, head of the Jamaica Institute, both of whom had much to offer. Lewis, in fact, was a steady visitor, driving the eighteen miles to the end of the peninsula from his office in Kingston at the end of each workday to inspect our progress and to provide assistance wherever he could.

Through Bernard Lewis we met W. Adolph Roberts, historian, author and editor of the *Kingston Gleaner*; S. A. G. Taylor, hydraulic engineer as well as local historian and writer; H. P. Jacobs, critic and historian, and archeologist and historian C. S. Cotter from Jamaica's north shore; all of whom, visiting *Sea Diver* at various times, contributed greatly in knowledge and information to our search.

It was Taylor who described to me what happened geologically, when the 1692 earthquake caused Port Royal to sink into the sea. According to his version, in late geological ages, the changing of the course of the Hope River in the Jamaican mountains, opposite a series of underwater reefs where the Pallisadoes now stand, caused vast quantities of gravel and soil to be washed down from the mountains in the general direction of the reefs. This detritus finally settled down on the north side of the cays, in a heavy layer over the top of peat moss beds. Then when the earthquake started a minor underwater landslide on the steeply sloping seabed facing the harbor, the weight of the gravel combined with the weight of buildings erected on shore caused the peat to squeeze outward from the bottom of the slope, thus causing part of the town to simply slip into the sea.

Apparently after the earthquake, detritus still continued to be deposited along the shore until in time much of the land on the north side, which had been partially submerged, was gradually replaced. On the seaward side also a similar, wide beach began to build outward from Fort Charles.

He further suggested why we found only the top bricks in the walls of the fort to be covered with coral, while the base of the walls remained clean. His theory was that immediately after the earthquake, due to tremendous changes in the river beds as they coursed through the mountains, extremely heavy deposits of detritus had surrounded the bases of the sunken buildings, too soon for coral to have an opportunity to form.

Bernard Lewis one day drove me to a spot on the south shore near the airport to show me a section of the beach that he claimed had built out as much as two hundred feet in the past few months. If this could happen in so short a time, it was easy to see how the land beyond Fort Charles had formed and disappeared at least several times throughout the centuries. Had there been buildings on these areas, they too would have suffered the fate of the old town.

The following morning after spending the night at Sir Anthony's dock, we reset *Sea Diver's* anchors in the center of the yellow flag buoys. Again there were scattered storms during the day which kept the crew busy adjusting *Sea Diver* to her moorings. Instead of working the spot where they had been digging, the divers made three test holes in various nearby places, hoping thereby to uncover some more workable site. At the end of the day they had accomplished nothing.

Another day of drilling test holes without discovering anything worthwhile sent them back to the original site where the cave-ins had occurred. Painstakingly, they cleaned it out again, and then began excavating from the low brick wall toward shore. Fred, who was the last to work that afternoon, reported hopefully that we might be getting into pay dirt once more. He brought aboard some broken pottery identified by Pete as being from a choice 17th-century piece. Unfortunately, in the gloomy depths a very valuable bowl had been broken into several sections by the airlift, some of which must have been carried to the surface and lost with the other debris.

On top of the deck cabin of *Sea Diver* we were carrying a large wire cage intended for use on the surface end of the airlift pipe to catch and sift the debris, in case we started uncovering small objects that might be of value. We had found no necessity for using it up to that moment, but had nevertheless looked forward in our more hopeful moments to the day when the pipe of the airlift would start spilling forth shining gold coins from deep beneath the water.

We did not have long to wait, for two days later as Ed and Bernard Lewis stood on the deck looking over some of the relics that had been brought up, Lewis suddenly shouted, "Look there," pointing at the stream of muddy water that came shooting out of the airlift. In the midst of it there was the momentary gleam of small, glittering objects cascading through the air and descending to the bottom.

Ed donned a mask and went quickly over the side, streaking downward toward the spot where the debris was falling. He returned at once with a handful of shiny coins. On closer examination after removing his mask, he found them to be only Jamaican copper pennies fresh from the mint, dated no later than the past few years.

Then Art poked his head out of the water at the foot of the ladder with a broad grin playing across his face. Pete and Bernard Lewis were in on his joke on the Skipper, and they all seemed more than pleased that it had worked even better than anticipated.

Peter Stackpole had been aboard a solid week, photographing the explorations on deck and on the surface of the water, hoping that the water would clear enough to allow him to shoot the action taking place underwater. Completely discouraged, he had finally made the decision to leave with only his surface material when he woke one morning near the end of his stay and found the water clearer than we had ever seen it. We all watched the water carefully, fingers crossed, hoping that the clarity would last until the sun was at a high enough angle to provide suitable visibility for underwater shots. At last, wind, weather, sun and tide all worked together in our favor.

Nine o'clock found most of us in the water where for the first time we could actually see, to a distance of fifteen to twenty feet, the walls and structures that the divers had been patiently uncovering as well as the gaping holes they had dug. For the first time we could swim from one yellow flag buoy to the next and get a fairly clear picture of the ruins of the old fort that lay beneath us.

This, coupled with a careful check made by Ed the day before using the marks given him by the Government surveyors, proved the little fortress to be pentagonal in shape and about a hundred feet across. There were embrasures for two cannon in each of the five sides including those which faced the town. Some of the walls were eight feet thick. A battery wall had extended from the fort southeast along the shore to further cover the waters between Fort Charles and Fort James against attackers. It was this wall, punctuated with embrasures, that had previously confused us as to the shape and location of the fort.

It had evidently confused Philip Morris, the maker of the chart we were using, also, for in 1827 when it was made, it was probably possible to still see some of these walls from the surface, yet he had not indicated the battery wall on his chart. Rather, he had placed Fort James away, on the site of the battery wall.

Later, attempting to reconcile the old chart of pre-earthquake Port Royal to the survey by Morris, someone must have changed the lines of the streets to conform to the position he had chosen for the fort.

Ed, however, did not leave anything to chance. He took careful bearings from each of the yellow flag buoys marking sections of the fort below, making his triangulations from the flagpole in the center of Fort Charles, Church buoy, the end of the old wall that enclosed the Naval hospital, and the customs house tower. The results confirmed his calculations as to the size and shape of the fort and its exact location.

It remained now to establish an accurate picture of the arrangement of the streets and buildings that had sunk adjacent to the fort. An intense search was then underway for an early chart of Port Royal, through Peterson at the Smithsonian and Lewis at the Jamaica Institute, for no one seemed to know where Morris had obtained the one he used in making his 19th-century projection of the underwater city. As far as we could ascertain, there were no others in existence.

The last day of our stay was upon us. Although much had been accomplished in charting the areas of the old city and in uncovering many of the interesting ruins, the whole party felt disheartened, I think, that nothing spectacular had been found. That morning it was decided to move the airlift from its labors on the ruins of the old structure opposite the fort, and to put it to work where Ed had placed a yellow brick sometime before at a signal from the metal detector. Perhaps they would find a cannon, for it seemed the right location, just inside one of the embrasures of the fort.

Fred was working on the spot when the airlift finally bit deep enough to uncover the castable and then the rounded surface of a cannon barrel. He worked madly at it then, refusing to give up his place to Ed who soon after swam down to relieve him. It was his first experience at finding a cannon, and he wanted to savor the complete thrill of uncovering it himself.

When it was finally free and a chain placed around it, it was hauled close to the surface to be towed to shore by *Sea Diver*. Getting it onto the dock turned out to be quite an operation, even with the assistance of Sir Anthony's heavy duty crane. We thought it was no wonder when the weight markings on the breech had been uncovered and we learned that it weighed 5,228 pounds. This was the largest cannon Ed had ever raised. Beneath the encrustation on the barrel, we found the symbol of the Crown and Rose which has marked English armament for centuries. ~

\* \* \*

SO ENDS MARION'S TALE of their first underwater investigations on the sunken city of Port Royal. Ed's airlift, jet hammer, other pneumatic tools, and other of his own rigged devices and inventions had now been applied to serious underwater archeology in the retrieval of items long hidden on the ocean floor, and he had also orchestrated an important initial survey of that sunken city. From the conditions described by Marion, it becomes evident that on this mission he once again exercised — as did his devoted crew — extreme diligence and a perpetual ability to focus on the purpose at all costs.

Their work at Port Royal was highly significant in terms of breaking ground in the field of underwater archeology and in the practical application of new tools. The team was the first to achieve a thorough study of the sunken city. The importance of Ed's work in correcting past errors and providing the beginnings of an adequate chart for all future research on Port Royal cannot be over-emphasized. Further, he had begun retrieval of items of historic value that would take their place in the growing body of artifacts now treasured at the Jamaica Institute. In 1959 he would return and complete the charting process with both his friend Capt. Philip Van Horn Weems and a United States Navy underwater team.

No sooner were Ed and Marion back at home from their first Port Royal mission than they were bound by plane for Israel, in the early fall of 1956, in response to an invitation from the America-Israel society to view possible archeologically important dive sites at Caesarea, Acre, and the Sea of Galilee (covered in the following chapter on Israel). Ed was immediately intrigued by the prospects of conducting a full-fledged mission in Israel, but realized that he would need a bigger boat to cross the Atlantic and a better equipped one to accomplish extensive undersea archeological work there as well as on his planned return to Port Royal.

But before *Sea Diver II* was to become a reality, in February, 1957, Ed and Marion ran into trouble one last time at sea aboard *Sea Diver I*. Cruising along the Atlantic coast from Fort Lauderdale to the Ocean Reef Club in the Florida Keys the weather turned foul and they were forced to anchor in a stormy sea to get their pumps working, but then had to contend with an anchor that refused to come up again. Meanwhile, huge waves tore the anchor chain into the bow rail and broke the metal platform; then Ed, trying to free the anchor, got his hose caught in the propeller and lost his diving equipment. Only at the end of a three-hour struggle did he at last cut the chain and let the anchor go.

Although a new ship was now on the agenda, it remained for providence to create the perfect opportunity, which had come about just before they left Fort Lauderdale for the Keys when an offer was made on *Sea Diver I* of $40,000 cash. Marion documented the event in her journal: "We are strongly considering it for Ed has to confine his activities for at least a year to working for GPE [General Precision Equipment Corporation] in New York, and he would like to build a new steel ship capable of taking us to Europe."

Shortly afterward, on February 28, she noted a new milestone in the same journal: "Karl Kail arrived with the underwater television he and Ed and Gunne Lowkranz are developing." This was the start of what would turn out to be history's first patented prototype of what is now known as an unmanned submersible, or a remotely operated vehicle (ROV).

The sale of *Sea Diver* "was consummated" on Sunday, the 3rd of March, 1957. After visiting a number of shipyards, on Saturday, July 6, Marion wrote that they went to Quincy, Massachusetts to talk with a "Mr. Whiting," owner of the Quincy Shipyard, regarding the building of an all new *Sea Diver*. Ed found what he was looking for at the yard, and they began immediately to order materials and work up plans from those he had already drawn himself.

So it was that Ed designed a 93-foot steel, double-hulled working yacht. She was built at the Quincy Shipyard, largely under his own supervision with the help of John Cebula, despite the fact that neither of the of men had any previous experience at boat building. The new *Sea Diver* turned out to be a practical, sturdy and reliable work boat. With modifications, she remains in operation today, some thirty years later, in the service of marine science and ocean engineering at Harbor Branch Oceanographic Institution. From the day she was launched to the present, *Sea Diver II* has been written up any number of times in leading magazines and newspapers all over the country, and was pictured and featured, along with Ed and his work, in a 1986 Encyclopedia Britannica yearbook article on the history of underwater archeology.

Ed's stubborn ingenuity went into the ship's design. She was considered by most standards to be the best such small ship in the world at the time, and the only one built from the keel up specifically for underwater archeology. She was the best only because her designer followed his intuition, knew what he wanted, had new ideas and wouldn't take no for an answer when other people said they couldn't be done. As one of his friends was quoted as saying, "When Link gets interested in a problem he becomes almost obsessive about it."

Ed had much on his mind over the next few years. Wanting to be at sea, he had in spite of himself been pulled back to the aviation industry. After several years of at least semi-retirement, since the merger of Link Aviation with GPE in 1954, he now found himself appointed as General Precision's president, established with an office in New York City, and living part time in a Manhattan hotel apartment with Marion for yet another home away from home. Throughout 1957, 1958, and until his final retirement in May of 1959, he was back at the industrial grindstone, burdened with the responsibilities of the presidency of an organization that employed more than 15,000 people and grossed over $185,000,000 annually.

The new *Sea Diver* was launched on April 5, 1959, "amongst great fanfare and with a goodly crowd present," wrote Marion, "with batteries of cameras at every angle." Yet another new world was opening as Marion proudly stood by the bow, paused briefly with a bottle of champagne, then struck the christening blow. "The bottle, bedecked in red, white, and blue ribbons, broke the first time; but I did swing it like a baseball bat," she said, then later added in her journal:

~ And what a thrill to see that beautiful ship glide down the ways and into the water. We had a bouquet of red roses. Everyone swarmed aboard afterward. After going to dinner with relatives, Bobby and Joe Murray and family, we came back to a deserted ship in the afternoon and Ed and I had a chance at last to admire and calmly plan before he had to go back to New York in the evening. ~

All of Marion's journals refer to numbers of visits to both *Sea Diver I* and *Sea Diver II* by notables and dignitaries of all ilk. The launching of *Sea Diver II* attracted such eminent visitors. Marion herself had just left a Tea in her honor at a bookstore, where she signed autographs amid much fanfare and publicity for her book *Sea Diver*, which was released by Rinehart coincidentally with the launching of the new vessel. Among a host of distinguished guests at Quincy were the Luis Mardens and Gilbert Grosvenors (National Geographic), and the Mendel Petersons (Smithsonian).

During the shakedown period and after most of the finish work was done at the shipyard, others came to report on the new vessel, including writers and photographers from *The Boston Globe*, which did a magazine cover story; and representatives from *Newsweek, The New Yorker, This Week,* and *Life*. When they were not interviewing Ed and shooting endless pictures of the new ship, they were covering the story of Marion and her book about her adventures with Ed aboard the first *Sea Diver*.

On May 10, when the finish work on *Sea Diver* was complete, a commissioning party was held with nearly fifty people present. On the following day Marion flew to Key Biscayne where she was joined by Bill and Clayton to await the arrival of Ed and their all-new *Sea Diver*, which had left New England on her maiden voyage on May 13, 1959. The ship's crew included Capt. Weems, John Cebula, Gunne

Lowkrantz; and friends George Egglesten, Dean Smith, and Curt Scott. Meanwhile, while awaiting Ed's arrival, Marion and the boys began preparations for the coming second mission to Port Royal.

In her second book, *Windows in the Sea*, Marion would elaborate on the historic beginnings of the new *Sea Diver* , describing her in detail:

~ When Ed's dream ship finally sailed from Boston Harbor in April of 1959 on her maiden voyage to Miami, she was beautiful to behold. Her gleaming white steel hull with flared and rounding bow was surmounted by an octagonal pilothouse joined to galley and lounge. Above, towered a 50-foot-tall mast crested with crow's nest and radar antennae. Behind the deckhouse stretched an unbroken work deck of sufficient size for almost every need.

As her captain glided her past the outer beacon of the harbor, his face glowed with pride. Surely, fully equipped as she was for her coming tasks in underwater archeology, she was the most modern and efficient research salvage ship for her size in the world.

Two GM6-110 diesel engines of 240 horsepower insured a cruising speed of about 10 knots. The vessel was further provided with two GM4-71 engines to drive both a 30 and a 50 3-phase AC kilowatt generator to supply unlimited electric power. One of these engines also drove the large pump providing energy for the bow thrusters. By using these hydro-jets, *Sea Diver* could be turned in her own length.

When coupled in another way, the same engine powered a 250-cubic-feet-per-minute air compressor to operate a 10-inch airlift. Two other compressors in the engine room provided compressed air for the ship's utilities as well as furnishing air for the divers.

On deck were heavy booms and winches as well as a 6-ton lift. No longer would Ed have trouble raising heavy cannon from the sea bottom. And when that day came that his SDC [Submersible Decompression Chamber] was completed, this same lifting gear would also handle it.

Resting in davits on the stern was *Reef Diver*, the 18-foot auxiliary cruiser that had been such a valuable partner to the old *Sea Diver*. Powered by a diesel engine to remove any fire hazard, she was steered by water jets instead of a propeller so that there was no danger of divers being injured by whirling blades.

At the center of the large aft deck was a wide entrance hatch to the diving compartment below. In this ample hold were two high-pressure, 2,500-pound air compressors, one of 3 1/2 horsepower, the other 7 1/2 horsepower, for filling the divers' scuba bottles as well as two low-pressure compressors for hookah gear.

The diving compartment was crowded with tanks and bottles, reels of air hoses, rubber suits, fins and face masks, weight belts, and the assorted equipment necessary to maintain a well-supplied team of divers. But most astonishing of all, the stern bulkhead contained a steel flap about 4 by 6 feet which opened outward providing access to the water only a few inches below the lower edge. *Sea Diver* also contained a viewing chamber with two heavy glass portholes reached by ladder through a special hatch on the foredeck. From here, it would be possible to survey the bottom — a feature of great importance when seeking lost objects or wreckage. The viewing chamber would also be a never-ending source of entertainment for those on board to observe plant and fish life.

*Sea Diver's* pilothouse was equipped as thoroughly as the largest ocean liner with an astounding array of navigational aids. Knowing that compasses, depth finders, radar, and communication systems were absolute essentials at all times, Ed had supplied the vessel with two of each.

There was a Plath compass on top of the deckhouse, in addition to the standard one on the automatic pilot. There was a permanent depth finder near the wheel, and a second one which was portable and could be transferred for use on *Reef Diver* when needed. There were two types of radars, one on either side of the helmsman.

Additional navigation equipment included a sea scanner or sonar that could be used to search the waters ahead of the ship from 90 to 180 degrees vertically; and a Loran for radio fixes, as well as several types of sextants and chronometers for celestial navigation.

Besides regular ship-to-shore radio communications of 135 watts, there was a large commercial-type 250-watt transoceanic receiver and transmitter and a number of other receivers so that several frequencies could be monitored at one time.

The all-electric galley was furnished with two large refrigerators and freezers, a four-burner stove and grill and separate oven, and a dishwasher, all in stainless steel. Beneath the wheelhouse were also two large freezers capable of holding 700 pounds of meat or other perishable supplies.

The roomy and comfortable wood-paneled lounge was notable for the attractive fireplace fashioned from coral-encrusted bricks previously airlifted from the sea floor at Port Royal. It was decorated with many trophies from previous expeditions.

[The lounge also held a built-in, wooden bookcase with glass-paneled doors. Beside the end of the bookcase closest to the galley door, Ed had permanently installed a lovely, ebony-colored mermaid, too small to be a figurehead but large for the lounge, which came from his cherished collection of mermaids. Wood paneling and gleaming brass contributed to the warm and salty atmosphere that permeated the vessel.]

Forward of the engine room, directly below the lounge, were crew quarters composed of a four-bunk cabin in the forecastle, two double staterooms, and two heads (toilets). Aft of the engine room, also reached by a stairway from the lounge, were two large and comfortable cabins for owner and guests, each with its own luxurious head.

Off the hallway separating these cabins was a well-equipped dark-room for photographic developing; and at the far end of the hall was a large storeroom, later slated to become a laboratory. From the storeroom a door led into a small office, and aft a steel door opened into the diving compartment which was also accessible from the aft deck.

Six waterproof bulkheads with heavy steel doors could seal the ship into seven separate sections in case of flooding in any area. The entire lower deck was air conditioned except the engine room which was cooled by large blowers.

The space between the double walls of the hull formed tanks to contain the generous supply of water and fuel oil. In addition the engine room was provided with a system for making fresh water from sea water. There, too, was a complete workshop with lathe and drill press and other metal and woodworking tools, as well as a combination washer-dryer for the ship's laundry.

After leaving the Boston area, *Sea Diver* paused briefly at City Island in New York City before continuing on to Miami where final additions were made to her equipment. ~

*Sea Diver* arrived at Miami on May 18, 1959 and was off again on May 24 for the next phase of the Port Royal work. They saw the southern shore of Jamaica on their starboard side at 6:00 a.m. on Friday, May 29. Once during the crossing rough weather drove ship and crew in to Porto Practique on the north shore of Cuba to anchor for the night. Marion commented on the incident: "I must say, we were dubious as to our reception under Castro, but only met with the usual desire for money - $48.00 to anchor overnight, reduced by $16.00 when we promised to leave at sunrise.

* * *

## Port Royal, Cruise II

A NEW ERA WITH A MUCH BETTER EQUIPPED VESSEL was initiated on *Sea Diver's* arrival in Kingston in 1959. Preparations for a more thorough survey of Port Royal were underway immediately. By now press conferences were to be expected in spite of a certain shyness on Ed's part as well as Marion's. And though they had little time to socialize, they found themselves increasingly being treated as celebrities by both the press and local officials. On June 4 Marion wrote:

~ ...[we] were invited to the King's House today for lunch with the Governor and Lady Kenneth Blackburn. The King's House was once a Bishop's palace, set in an extensive and beautiful park....The dining room is a separate building... The service was sumptuous. I sat at the left of the Governor, and Miss Laster, a singer, was on his other side. ~

Still Marion and Ed preferred the company of *Sea Diver* to socializing, and she soon noted: "We are preparing more dinners aboard as going ashore at night is becoming tiresome." On June 6 they spent their 28th wedding anniversary hard at work setting anchors on their dive site, while, Marion observed, one Vernon Steven, a civil engineer, worked at contouring and graphing the bottom. But anniversaries were not to be overlooked; that night Ed took the entire crew ashore for dinner and champagne to celebrate.

Anxious to get down to work seriously, they were hard pressed by the media to give interviews and were constantly inundated with guests, including celebrities. On June 7 Marion wrote:

~ We spent most of the day on location today. There was quite a crowd aboard; Errol Flynn and his "secretary-girlfriend" (he is trying to pro- mote Ed on doing a movie) ...six club divers...etc. There is much confu- sion but out of it they managed to place buoys at the fort site, the places where we dived three years ago, and at the probable location of the King's warehouse. ~

Marion had learned more about Flynn when next she wrote:

~ Errol [drinking heavily] and his sixteen-year old child bride really kept everyone entertained, though I would certainly hate to have him taking part in any way in this expedition. ~

On June 8, Ed flew back to New York on business and returned on the 12th with Clayton, who was out of school and overjoyed to join the crew for the duration of the mission. Other crew members kept changing as diving acquaintances came and went, including Capt. Weems and Barney and Jane Crile. On June 19 they were joined by a Navy Underwater Demolition Team (UDT) of six, who promptly set up headquarters in the area and went directly to work with Ed mapping the bottom terrain. Marion wrote as their work got underway: "The UDT team has laid out areas in the vicinity of Fort Carlisle and after marking the walls have begun systematically combing the bottom and marking all irregularities."

She observed on another occasion that in spite of Ed's coming down with the flu, he proceeded with "a good day's work," in which the divers brought up a typical day's find:

~ A fine brass tool, broken dishes and plates, pewter spoons and a beaten-up pewter dish, ...broken pipes, all kinds of bones, including a jaw bone with teeth. I was sure some of them were human, but an expert in our party says "no." Our bottle collection is becoming spectacular; beautiful black and greenish tinted rum and wine bottles... ~

On another day she wrote:

~ ...The bricks, spanish tiles for roofing, burnt chimney bricks, wattled plaster walls ...tell of a house with a fireplace, the bottles, broken dishes, animal bones, cooking pot and brass ladle of a meal in preparation over the coals. A grindstone was found... We are also working the Navy team on the area where the paving blocks are. ~

*National Geographic* photographer Luis Marden arrived on July 6, just in time to shoot photos over the next few days as the team brought up sad evidence of a violently disrupted home life: an iron cooking pot with a brick holding the brass cover aslant; a pewter plate, platter and porringer; an iron fireplace grill; a big copper kettle, a bottle and a huge pewter platter which broke into pieces as it came up due to the water pressure. On July 9, the Navy team, working within one of the forts, brought up one end of a bar shot and a four-pound cannon ball. That same night in town they met hoosier comedian Herb Shriner, who wanted to include *Sea Diver* operations in a TV program he was doing on Jamaica. Then another person tried to set them up for a Jack Paar show. The next day an archeologist took the Links to Discovery Bay where Columbus had visited, and on to St. Ann's Bay where Columbus was marooned for nearly a year.

On July 14, Marion noted:

~ It was a rather quiet day today with nothing spectacular - a small bottle and what we think is a glass pestle. They located a brick wall covered with white mortar on a horizontal level, possibly a ceiling. ...Clayton worked for three hours, all by himself, on the airlift this morning. ~

The media continued to show interest in their mission. Comedian and TV host Herb Schriner set up an appointment for a five-minute interview for his documentary. Bernard Lewis arranged for a press conference in which a number of their artifacts were exhibited. With some consternation Marion wrote: "...we rushed around to get together a press release that would cover the subject without giving away our fire," and agreed to an interview over Jamaica Broadcasting. Then she noted a happy coincidence: "Just at the height of things, our divers brought forth from the depths an interesting collection of pots from the bottom."

On July 23 a more thrilling find occurred. She wrote with excitement:

~ The find of the expedition today - a gold watch with its works intact - thick case, face with Roman numerals, silver or platinum heading decoration, name, Paul Blondel on the back of the works.

Ed spent hours carefully cleaning and taking it apart. It has marvelously tiny wheels and cogs. The hands had disappeared into the coral covering its face. Ed said, "Wouldn't it be wonderful if X-ray revealed the position of the hands at 11:40, the time of the earthquake." ~

What followed was typical of all dive teams after such a find. She continued:

~ After that, the boys really worked like mad all day. ...the barge was so loaded it was almost sinking. Ski, who found the watch on the barge (it had come up in the airlift), worked four hours under water that afternoon, and no one wanted to quit even for hunger and darkness. ...Word reached New York about finding the watch and Lucille Lewis was queried by her news agency. The magic of gold! ~

Ed celebrated his 55th birthday at sea on July 26. He was elated when the sea gave up another special find that day, which just happened to be brought to the surface the moment a *National Geographic* team arrived. Marion said it was a banded 15th-century swivel gun, corroded but whole, "in pretty good shape considering its age." Two weeks later she wrote:

~ Prime Minister Manley and his wife and party paid *Sea Diver* a visit and appeared pleased. Ed had the vessel at Morgan's Harbor dock, and we laid out all the artifacts on the dock alongside — hundreds of them. They were photographed at every angle, with and without people, by Luis Marden and Jean and by amateurs. All this was followed by a visit from Bernard Lewis and Sir John Carberry, who, with Ed, comprise the committee for dividing the spoils. ~

When the expedition was over it was listed in Historic Underwater Events: "Ed and Marion Link in *Sea Diver*, with Capt. Weems and crew, and the Navy Underwater Demolition Team (UDT) made historic dives and prepared a map of the submerged portion of the city of Port Royal from pre-1692 maps." They are also credited with demonstrating that the city did not just sink, but actually slid down the bottom of the slope of the ocean, though Marion credited the theory to hydraulic engineer, S.A.G Taylor. Most significantly, Ed had recognized the site for its true value, assessing it as "one of the most important historic finds for 17-century artifacts." Port Royal today is considered to be the most important marine archeological site in the Western Hemisphere. Much of old Port Royal's history, lost when the city was deposited on the ocean floor by the forces of nature, was now restored. In the future, scholars and marine archeologists would follow Ed's lead, their job made easier by his inventions of underwater tools and his initial survey of the old and wicked sunken city.

*Sea Diver* was later immortalized by a stamp issue of the Jamaican government for Link's exploration of the former capital, Port Royal. The stamp shows a portrait of *Sea Diver* against a blue sea and coastal background, with artifacts in the foreground, and is printed with: "Port Royal Exploration of Sunken City."

A side trip was on the agenda before heading home. On August 7 *Sea Diver* left Kingston for Cozumel Island, Yucatan. Ed and Marion were delighted with the change. "Cozumel: a delightful little town ...warm, friendly Mayan people," she wrote, then contrasted it to old Port Royal, "the city of shameful history and murky waters. ...We fell in love with the charming place and its people, the magnificent, clear water and beautiful sea floor."

They made contact with a professional team of divers working a shipwreck off the coast, referred to in Marion's journals as the "CEDAM [Mexico's official marine archeological society] expedition," and lent them a hand after clearing up an initial misunderstanding regarding their motives. "Ed assured their leader that we had no intentions of grabbing artifacts..." Marion wrote on August 14, adding, "We turned over our air hammer to them to chisel guns from the coral, and then raised the guns for them with our winch."

She wrote of seeing artifacts in what she described as "a whole room full of CEDAM's findings," which included "quantities of crucifixes, religious medals, needles, pewter plates, belt buckles (silver over brass), glassware, cuff links set with cheap stones, beads, etc." On August 11 she mentioned that CEDAM'S helicopter "cracked up," evidently at sea, and they helped to right it with *Sea Diver's* boom. Ed's specialized equipment also helped to hoist up a long swivel gun with a breech block as well as two breech block sections of lombards, which he estimated were early 16th-century, dating back to the time of Cortez.

By August 17, 1959 the weary travelers were back in Miami. On the 21st Marion made her final summer mission entry in the journal: "Ed and I knocked ourselves out doing last minute things today, then took a four o'clock plane for New York." They were home again, not to rest, but to prepare for *Sea Diver's* long crossing to Israel.

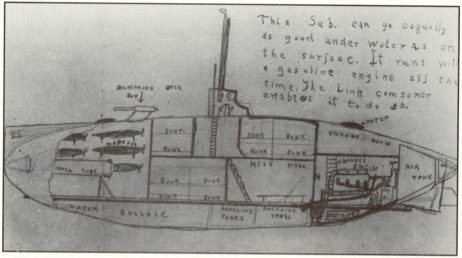

#1. Submarine drawing by Edwin A. Link as a child.
*Photo courtesy of Roberson Museum and Science Center.*

#2. Edwin A. Link at age 14.
*Photo courtesy of Marion Link.*

#3. Edwin A. Link (far right) lent a helping hand to Charles A. Lindbergh (second from left) in 1928 when Lindbergh and Major Tom Lamphier, both flying Curtis P-1 pursuit planes, were forced down in Choconut, PA, by bad weather and engine trouble. Link and pilot Richard Bennett (third from left) flew to Choconut with spare parts for the downed planes. Lindbergh and Lamphier stayed overnight with Father Walsh (left).

*Photo courtesy of Roberson Museum and Science Center.*

#4. Link Employees, 1935.

*Photo courtesy of Roberson Museum and Science Center.*

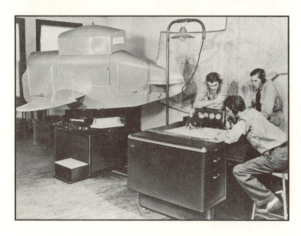

#5. Early Link Trainer with Instructor.

*Photo courtesy of Roberson Museum and Science Center.*

*Above:* #6. Ed and Marion Link with early model Cessna.

*Photo courtesy of Roberson Museum and Science Center.*

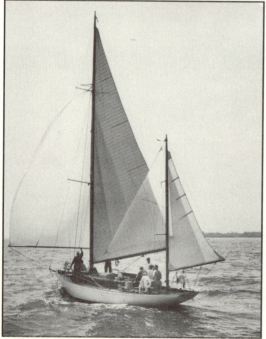

*Left:* #7. *Blue Heron* cruises before the wind on Bahamian waters.
*Photo courtesy of Marion Link.*

#8. *Sea Diver I* at anchor off Andros Island with native sloop in the background.
*Photo by Ed Link, courtesy of Marion Link.*

#9. Ed Link's Widgeon sus-
pended over aft deck of *Sea
Diver II.*

*Photo by Ed Link, courtesy of
Marion Link.*

#10. From *Reef Diver* Marion Link raises ancient anchor she discovered on the ocean floor near Cap-Haitien, north coast of Haiti, thought to be from Columbus's flagship, *Santa Maria*, which sank in the vincinity in 1492.

*Photo courtesy of Marion Link.*

#11. The Link family on the terrace of their Binghamton, N.Y. home with a cannon, dated 1617, raised by Ed Link from a Spanish galleon near the Florida Keys. L to R, Clayton, William, Marion and Ed Link. *Photo courtesy of Marion Link.*

*Above Left:* #12. Marion and Ed Link in Villefranche, France, aboard *Sea Diver II* before their fireplace made of bricks from the sunken city of Port Royal. Ed inspects Dr. Harold Edgerton's mud pinger. Over the mantel is a painting of the Caesarea Harbor in Israel where the Links conducted archeological research. Amphora and other artifacts are seen stored inside the fireplace and on the hearth.

*Photo by Dr. Harold Edgerton, courtesy of Marion Link.*

*Above:* #13. Ed Link's sister Marilyn Link in her New York City, Mohawk Airlines office in 1965 where she served as a public relations special assistant.

*Photo courtesy of* Flying *magazine.*

*Left:* #14. Ed Link at his drafting table in 1970 with model, made by Link in 1969, of his original *Johnson-Sea-Link* (then called *Sea-Link*) four-man lockout submersible.

*Photo courtesy of Harbor Branch Oceanographic Institution.*

#15. Marion and Ed Link in London, England at the 50th Anniversary Celebration of the Link Trainer.

*Photo courtesy of Marilyn Link.*

#16. Ed Link (left) and Seward Johnson with hardhats in the construction area at Harbor Branch Oceanographic Institution (then Harbor Branch Foundation) before *Johnson-Sea-Link II.*

*Photo courtesy of Harbor Branch Oceanographic Institution.*

#17. Land photo of four-man lockout submersible, *Johnson-Sea-Link I.*
*Photo courtesy of Harbor Branch Oceanographic Institution.*

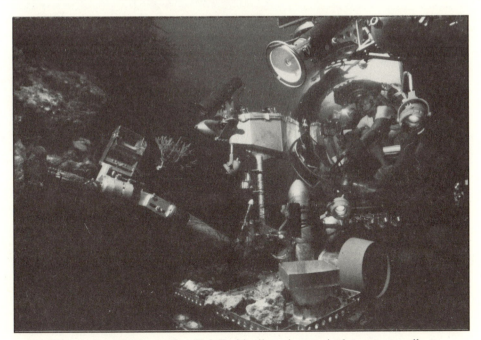

#18. Frontal view of *Johnson-Sea-Link II* with pilot using manipulator arm to collect
marine specimens from several hundred feet beneath the surface.
*Photo courtesy of Harbor Branch Oceanographic Institution.*

#19. *Sea Diver II*, prior to further extension in 1993, with Ed Link's articulated crane at home port at Harbor Branch Oceanographic Institution.   *Photo courtesy of Harbor Branch Oceanographic Institution.*

#20. Harbor Branch board chairman and sculptor, J. Seward Johnson, Jr., with Ed Link (right) before two of the four "Safety in the Seas" works created by Johnson. Link gazes at his son, Clayton, who was lost in an accident at sea along with fellow diver Albert Stover. Out of camera range were busts of Stover and J. Seward Johnson, Sr., which completes the grouping.

*Photo courtesy of Harbor Branch Oceanographic Institution.*

CHAPTER VIII

# EXPLORING BIBLICAL WATERS

**1956&1960**

*Once the Zionist state was founded, it expressed itself*
*not merely in history, but above all in archeology. Statesmen, and generals,*
*like Ben Gurion, Moshe Dayan and Yigael Yadin, and thousands of ordinary people,*
*became passionate archeologists, both amateur and professional. The study*
*of deep antiquity rose to the height of an Israeli obsession.*

—*Paul Johnson*
— *A History of the Jews*

**B**ack in 1950 Ed had on two occasions tangled dangerously with the forces of nature and survived by keeping his wits about him, once in a close encounter with a wounded polar bear and again in a knockdown at sea during a raging storm (Chapter V). But if these harrowing incidents were somehow part of a psychic rite of passage from sky to sea, there was to be a third. It was not enough that he constantly faced potential hazards due to the nature of his oceanic work, but he must also endure a seaplane accident while commuting between New York and Binghamton, serving as president of General Precision Equipment Corporation (GPE).

He was trying out a friend's newly acquired amphibian — one of the first planes with an engine in the back — when the accident occurred. He took off from La Guardia airport and flew the plane over Long Island Sound, intending to land on the water near the airport and then go back to La Guardia and go on home to Binghamton. However, as he made his landing approach the plane's owner, riding in the co-pilot's seat for the first time, reached over Ed to set the flaps for a water landing and grabbed the wrong lever, letting down the wheels instead of the flaps. Ed only realized what had happened when he hit the water, too late to pull away. The plane immediately "pitch-poled," tail over nose, and sank to the bottom of the Sound. In a flash, it seems, he knew what to do next.

Within the context of a later interview with Col. George A. Vaughan for a *True* magazine biographical sketch, writer Arthur Herzog had observed: "Link has an almost uncanny ability to think out a problem in advance." Vaughan in turn described Ed as being, among other things "'...a man of imagination and practically no nerves.'" Herzog went on to tell of the event and its aftermath:

179

~ Link demonstrated his nervelessness not long ago when a friend's sea-plane, with Link [as pilot], overturned on landing and began to sink in Long Island Sound. Link, taking a gulp of air, kicked out a door and dragged his [nearly] unconscious friend to the surface, taking with him a life jacket and fastening it on his friend. He then went below again with a rope and a buoy which he attached to the plane so that it could be found and brought up. ~

In a state of damp and muddy disarray Ed went directly from the plane crash to board another plane for home where he was met at the airport by his mildly surprised wife. By then accustomed to his casual treatment of the extraordinary, in retelling the tale to Ed's biographer, Marion's only remark about seeing him that day was: "I was impressed by his peculiar appearance."

Herzog again stressed Ed's unique traits with a quote by William W. Wood, former president of the Simulation and Control Group of General Precision: "Link has two characteristics that have helped him enormously. He can stay cool as hell in an emergency, of which there have been plenty. And he can concentrate on a project regardless of the opposition — look how long it took to get his trainer accepted."

\* \* \*

ED AND MARION'S FLIGHT TO ISRAEL in 1956 to assess diving in the Holy Land (following their initial work at Port Royal) had convinced Ed at the time to go back to Israel and conduct underwater investigations, but with his own boat, the new *Sea Diver* that had been constantly on his mind to build. Motivated by the tantalizing prospects of finding ancient, perhaps biblical artifacts, he was already working on ship sketches on the flight home. From the moment of his arrival in Binghamton, his spare time, while still serving as president of GPE, went into two occupations: building the new *Sea Diver*, and working on a dawning concept of a dive chamber that could help him solve the problems of remaining underwater for longer periods of time. Eventually what would become known as the submersible decompression chamber (SDC), found its way to the drawing board and not long after had its rudimentary beginnings.

It was during this interval that the City of Cortland dedicated a Bronze Plaque at the Airport to "Edwin A. Link," evidently in complete forgiveness of his sneaking away from the old city-owned airport so many years before over a disagreement regarding the rent. The year 1956 also marked the Smithsonian Institution's publication of the bound paper titled *A New Theory on Columbus's Voyage Through the Bahamas*, by Edwin A. Link and Marion C. Link with a foreword by Mendel Peterson. During that same period, at the office Ed concentrated on a new issue, as noted by Herzog: "Ed became occupied with the developmental problem of air traffic control while serving as president of GPE, and had strong ideas regarding improving the system." He wrote of his concerns in an article later published in the 1961 October issue of *Flying* magazine, titled "Toward Better Air Traffic Control."

By the time *Sea Diver II* was commissioned in 1959, her skipper was chomping at the bit to get back to sea. Having tried to retire already, he was more than eager to step down from his latest position as president of GPE. Then, as reported by Herzog:

~ Link became a $10,000-a-year consultant to the Link Division of General Precision Equipment Corporation [later an arm of the Singer Company], an outfit to which he sold his company in exchange for stock as the only way to stop being a businessman once and for all. ~

He remained a consultant to the Singer Company from 1959 until 1977, managing to serve reliably throughout the years while at the same time growing in fame for his underwater exploits. And somehow he also was able to remain a simple man of simple tastes. Herzog described Ed's office as being, "utterly unpretentious, the silent testimony, one supposes, of a man who means it when he says he doesn't like business: a small room, an old desk, a couch, a few model planes...," and he commented on the occupant: "Link, in a baggy sports jacket and old trousers, suggested lunch in the company dining room, a cafeteria at which everybody from the executive floor on down eats side by side..."

Ed discussed with Herzog his work at sea as well as his philosophy concerning money, at one point stating wryly: "I know there's money in the sea because I put it there," referring to the bulk of his income which he spent annually on his expeditions in addition to selling stocks to pay for larger items such as the $500,000 it cost to build *Sea Diver II*. Again making his often repeated remark that he had never been much interested in making money, though he knew it was necessary for survival, he went on to tell his interviewer:

~ I fixed my own salary as a consultant purposely low because I didn't want stockholders asking, 'Where's Link?' I've got between three and four million dollars left and I'm spending it as fast as I can. What I can't spend I'm giving away as quickly as taxes let me. I've more than enough to last me. I don't think people should leave substantial sums to their kids, and my two sons agree. ~

The year 1960 turned out to be yet another significant one in the life of Ed Link. "Exploring the Drowned City of Port Royal," written by Marion C. Link and based on the work Ed orchestrated the year before, was published in the 1960

February issue of *National Geographic* magazine. That year *Sea Diver* made its extended cruise to Israel. Yet another patent was issued in December, to co-inventors Edwin A. Link, Gunne Lowkranz and Karl Kail, awarded for the remotely operated underwater television propulsion apparatus which they had begun working on as early as 1956, and since named *Shark*. According to Chris Tietze, a patented inventor in his own right and a Harbor Branch Oceanographic Institution engineer who later worked with Ed on one of the earliest unmanned submersibles, *Shark* is thought to be the prototype of all unmanned submersibles. If not the world's first model, it was certainly the first U.S. patented model of what is now universally known as the ROV (remotely operated vehicle).

By now Ed was well equipped to carry out his underwater programs overseas. What he hadn't built into *Sea Diver* from the beginning he added after giving the vessel its initial underwater work trials at Port Royal. "My aim," he told Herzog after offering a lengthy explanation of his ideas for building the vessel, "was scientific sufficiency." *Sea Diver* as well as several of Ed's underwater tools and systems impressed his interviewer, who reported:

~ Virtually unsinkable because of its steel double hull, *Sea Diver* has a range of 7,000 miles. A freshwater plant tapping the sea, and cavernous food storage space...mean that Link can stay out of port as long as fuel lasts.

*Sea Diver's* broad afterdeck is capable of taking Link's seaplane, and the ship can turn in its own length — an invaluable ability in coral waters — because of high velocity water jets in the bow....

Link describes his ship as a workboat, and, though he is a member of the New York Yacht Club — which entitles him to use yacht club facilities anywhere — he has been sometimes waved away because attendants think his must be a proletarian vessel of some kind. On such occasions Link leads his tormentors [inside] and points out a full electric [galley] with [two refrigerators], dishwasher and [ice making] machine, a cherry-paneled salon that has a woodburning fireplace.... ...The bunks are another Link innovation. Against the protest of the fitters, he had them installed at right angles to the sides of the ship, instead of parallel as in other vessels, so that the sleeper wouldn't be tossed out of bed when the boat rolled. Link says that the arrangement works well....

In the stern, *Sea Diver* has a special water-tight compartment that opens just above water level so that divers can slip directly into the sea. They go down either with scuba equipment stored in the chamber or with special lines attached to tanks on board.

Once down, the diver has what is probably the most advanced underwater archeological equipment in the world to work with, most of it designed by Link. There is an underwater chariot for towing divers, and 10-inch diameter airlifts, underwater vacuum cleaners used for clearing sand from around buried undersea objects. There are pneumatic tools and complete dredging gear. There is a Link-invented underwater metal detector so sensitive that it can pick up buried tin cans, which is often a nuisance, and even a self-propelled underwater television camera that can be directed from shipboard by remote control.

With this equipment, Link was ready for bigger archeological game and he took his undersea probes to the Mediterranean, where he made history. ~

In 1960 the all new *Sea Diver* was prepared to follow up on the initial investigations in Israel that Ed and Marion had conducted in 1956, both of which are covered extensively in this chapter by including much of Marion's original text material. She had begun yet another book, this one covering current events in Israel in context with the sum total of their accomplishments there during both expeditions. However, as was the case with her planned book on the sunken city of Port Royal, she was unable to complete the work due to Ed's non-stop excursions, and as a result she had yet another impressive body of work that went unpublished.

The expedition was sponsored by the Princeton Theological Society and the America-Israel Society, while *Time* and *Life* magazines had first story rights in return for partial payment.

\* \* \*

## The Israel Expedition - Part I
### 1956

IT WAS DURING THE EARLIER, 1956 SURVEY MISSION, before *Sea Diver II* was built, that the Links flew to the Holy Land and observed first hand the historical predicament of modern day Israel. They soon recognized the critical role which that nation, being built by people drawn out from modern civilizations the world over, plays in the painful growth process taking place as the Middle East — where many people still live in the dark ages — struggles to enter the 21st-century. On their initial foray, the Links tapped Israel's historical undercurrents even as they broke ground for their later mission, to conduct the first substantial underwater archeological research in Israel.

The 1956 mission was carried out at a perilous time, with Israel still in the throes of her birth pangs; a tiny nation occupied with trying to create itself in a totally hostile environment. It was a nation of fewer than a million people surrounded on all sides by two hundred million bitter enemies whose avowed intentions were to push all of the Jews into the sea. This was a pressure unequaled in the history of mankind, requiring a kind of blind faith and reckless courage that perhaps could only have come about because of the unspeakable sufferings already endured in the Holocaust.

In her opening paragraphs of what she tentatively titled *Exploring Israel's Historic Waters* Marion wrote of their first visit after flying to that "cradle of ancient civilizations":

> ~ September of 1956 found us exploring the Mediterranean waters off the coast of Israel, that Palestinian country bearing the marks of cultures which came and went thousands of years before the American continents were even known. We were there at the invitation of the Israeli government, sponsored by the America-Israel Society.
>
> Interest in archeology might be said to be the outstanding enthusiasm of the Israeli people. Yet while learned and experienced archeologists from all over the world are to be found in every part of Israel excavating ruins that tell the story of the earliest efforts of man to establish and develop a better organized life for himself, absolutely nothing had been done at the time of our arrival to extend their search to the waters which border its western coastline.
>
> Off these shores had passed the sea traffic of the earliest peoples known to history. From its ports had come and gone the ships of the Egyptians, Phoenicians and Persians, followed by those of the Greeks and Romans. Later came Crusaders from a Europe in the throes of a struggle between church and state. Here they had battled for almost a century to secure the Holy Land for the Christian faith, although submitting at last to the superior power of the Turkish empire which then held the battle-scarred lands in thralldom until the end of the first World War.
>
> There are few seaports along the clean-cut shores of Palestine, and these are exposed to stormy seas whenever the winds blow from any direction except leeward. A few of the ancient cities had fashioned twin ports, so that shipping could take refuge in whichever port was sheltered from wind blowing either from the north or south, but none of them offered much protection.
>
> Consequently the water traffic over the centuries came to be concentrated around a few focal points from whence stemmed the ancient roads leading into Mesopotamia and the interior cities of the east. Our minds and our emotions reacted to the exciting music of their names — Ashkelon, Joppa, Appolonia, Caesarea, Dor Tantura, Athlit, Shikmona, Acre, and Zib.
>
> We had flown to Israel with a limited amount of diving gear and no salvage equipment, desiring only to size up the possibilities of these waters for a future expedition. We did not propose to uncover any buried

artifacts, but instead wished only to ascertain the most promising locali-
ties for search, the type of bottom, clarity of water, depth and distance
from shore, weather conditions at various seasons of the year, and the
availability of divers and boats.

We were put in touch with the leading archeologists of the country,
all of whom showed a great deal of interest in our quest. To our surprise,
however, we found that they knew as little in regard to the methods and
possibilities of underwater archeology as we knew of the land archeology
of Israel. They were enthusiastic over the prospects that such a search
promised. We, on the other hand, were overwhelmed to discover that in
spite of all our previous experience in our part of the world, where we
had dealt only with sunken ships and cities that had lain underwater less
than five hundred years, these men of science talked in terms of thousands of years.

In outlining the prospects to us, they seemed scarcely interested even
in the period of the Crusades more than eight hundred years before. They
indicated instead that there was much to be learned about the Roman
world at the time of Christ, and if we could ascertain anything about the
earlier civilizations such as the Egyptian, Assyrian, Persian, Phoenician,
Canaanite or Greek, they would be much obliged. They even deigned to
smile politely when we mentioned the time of Columbus in the fifteenth
century, or the disappearance of Port Royal in the New World some two
hundred years later. ~

"Our arrival in Israel in 1956," she went on, "marked the beginning of an
intensive course in ancient history." Ed and Marion both were acutely aware of their
own lack of historical background in this part of the world. Their church and school
studies suddenly seemed insufficient to their understanding of the rise and fall of
ancient civilizations in this tiny country.

Everywhere they went, as friends and guides attempted to bring them up to
date in a short time, they both admired the "intensity of mood and quiet determination to accomplish," which was so prevalent in the fifties in Israel. Marion wrote:

~ We found ourselves almost automatically absorbing a vast amount of
information as to the building of a new nation, the settlement of its huge
immigrant population, the development of its debilitated lands, and the
attempt to integrate dozens of various nationalities into one loyalty.

Never in ten days' time have we crammed our minds with such an
assortment of knowledge, from the discovery of the remains of Early
Stone Age man in the caves of Wadi el Muzharah near Mount Carmel to

present day problems of a small nation seeking to establish itself in spite of constant pressures of an alien Arab world on its heavily guarded boundaries. Only the seacoast remained free of the ever present threat of sniping Arabs on its four hostile frontiers. ~

* * *

ED AND MARION HAD ARRIVED IN ISRAEL at Lod Airport near Tel Aviv at 4:30 in the morning. Looking up into the silent starlit sky as she stepped from the plane Marion observed that the stars seemed closer and more incandescent than any she had ever seen, and she wrote in her manuscript of that lasting first impression of the Holy Land:

> ~ I knew then how the Star of Bethlehem must have looked two thousand years ago. If these ordinary stars were so magnified in the clear air, I could imagine how in that ancient time, with the added power of two planets, Jupiter and Saturn, coming together in one tremendous burst of light, the beholder must indeed have been awed. ~

She had jotted in her notes that they were met at the airport before dawn "by the secretary-general of the Israeli-American Friendship League, from some 15 miles away at Tel Aviv," and by "A. Yaffe" of the United States Division of the Ministry of Foreign Affairs who had driven from Jerusalem more than 40 miles away.

Marion described their route through the countryside, writing of how they were deeply impressed by the efforts of the people to restore a land which had long since been "completely stripped of its soil right down to the hard rock." They saw evidence of labor in the fields everywhere, "and thousands upon thousands of tree plantings covering the hillsides, in an ambitious attempt to reforest and thus reclaim the eroded slopes." She wrote of their deepening admiration as they passed through "woodlands of older plantings, providing shade and cover for birds and low-growing vegetation." "We were seeing for the first time some of the restoration that is taking place as the Israelis transform a worn out land to the fertile country that it was in Biblical times."

Approaching Jerusalem they witnessed the stark reality facing the people of Israel, which was evidenced all around them. Marion's writings register how moved they were by the sudden appearance of "carcasses" of wrecked and burned trucks scattered along the road outside the city as they followed its curve up through the steep hills. This was Ein Karem pass, where bloody battles were fought by the Jews to break through Arab forces that had surrounded Jerusalem during the war of Liberation in 1948 — only eight years before — to get water and supplies of food and arms to the besieged people of the city who were threatened with starvation. Marion's journalistic instincts were aroused by the broken vehicles, and she wrote:

~ The presence of these wrecks made vivid the recent struggle between Arabs and Israelis, which even now rested on a United Nations cease fire agreement that was constantly being threatened by marauding expeditions from across the border. ~

Their guide pointed out a town on a nearby hillside, saying it was an Arab town, to which he added, "The Jordan border lies between it and this road."

"At this point," Marion observed, "the corridor keeping Jerusalem from being an isolated city is only a few miles wide."

Taking in the historic city from the outskirts, she was impressed with its stone, "ochre-toned" buildings. These provide a visual background to Jerusalem's unique sounds heard above the ordinary hum of traffic; Arab calls to prayer over loud speakers, the cries of roosters, donkeys, goats and camels blending with the sweet ring of church bells floating over the hills. These usual sounds are punctuated on certain Jewish Holy days by the blowing of the shofar, or ram's horn.

They saw "new architecture hardly distinguishable from ancient," and were fascinated with "the turrets and towers of churches and mosques ascending above flat-roofed synagogues, houses, and modern buildings." They could see in the distance the Moslems' Dome of the Rock hovering near the remains of King Solomon's Temple. These ruins constitute the ever-present and most sacred of Jewish shrines, the "Wailing Wall," a poignant reminder not only of the last destruction of the Temple by the Romans but of the mysterious persecutions of all Jews that have tended to erupt at various points of the world since the beginning of known history.

The YMCA, a center of intrigue during the 1948 War of Liberation, stands across the street from the King David hotel where Ed and Marion stayed. The hotel, they learned, had been bombed in 1946, resulting in the loss of many lives. Their room on the third floor had a balcony overlooking the old walled city, a part of Jordan then inaccessible to the Israelis as well as to most Westerners. Reliving her first enraptured impressions from their balcony Marion wrote: "Centered about the Dome of the Rock, which just showed above the ancient wall, the spires and towers of the many religious places of worship formed an irregular horizon of great beauty," to which she added on a depressed note:

~ Between the old wall and our hotel grounds we could see "no man's land," now cleared and designated by the United Nations to divide the Jordanian and Israeli sectors of the Holy City. It was strung with barbed wire entanglements, the road along its western edge lined with barricades and tank traps.

How sad that this city of Peace should be today symbolic of the strife which tears our world apart. We were soon to find that it was more than a symbol, for we narrowly escaped being included in one of the many shooting incidents that were occurring constantly on this long and irregular border.

We had arrived on the last day of a congress of international archeologists that had met in Israel. Had we timed it sooner, we would have been included in many of the field trips being made to excavations in all parts of the country.

The previous day, while more than a hundred of the archeologists and students were gathered around listening to a lecture at the excavations at Kibbutz Ramat Rahel, just south of Jerusalem, there was a sudden burst of fire from the Arab side of the border. Three of the archeologists fell dead on the spot; eighteen were wounded, one so badly that he later died. In spite of this incident, the visiting scientists spent their last day on a tour to the Negev desert to inspect other diggings there under the guidance of Dr. Mazar, president of Hebrew University and Israel's leading archeologist. We had dinner with Dr. Mazar that night and heard at first hand the story of the shooting.

That same day Israelis had been aroused at the killing by invaders in Jordanian uniforms of a young mother who was picking olives on her own property a half-mile from the Jordan border, and the murder of a farmer driving his tractor who was picked off by snipers from across the border. That evening while we dressed for dinner we heard gunfire from the direction of no man's land. Edwin warned me more than once to stay away from the open balcony windows when the light was on.

These incidents lent realism that day to our explorations about the Israeli city in a car provided by the foreign ministry. We returned to the hotel late in the afternoon along the Mandelbaum Gate, the sole location designated by the United Nations Mixed Armistice Commission for leaving or entering Israel from Jordan. There is no other place of access to Lebanon, Syria or Egypt, the other hostile Arab nations bordering little Israel. ~

The Gate was described in 1972 in the book *O Jerusalem* by Larry Collins and Dominique Lapierre:

~ For nineteen years after the end of the 1948 hostilities, the Mandelbaum Gate, next to the ruins of a wealthy Jewish merchant, was the symbol of the Holy City's division into Arab and Jewish halves. It was the only open door between Israel and the hostile Arab states surrounding her who refused to acknowledge the existence of the new state. ~

Marion wrote that they expected the Mandelbaum Gate to be an "imposing aperture," but found it to be no more than a wooden gate, the door standing open next to a plain wooden guardhouse on the Israeli side. On the other side of no man's land stood a similar Arab guardhouse. A team from the United Nations were meeting nearby, no doubt discussing the latest border incidents. She continued:

~ We were beginning to wonder whether we should carry out our plan of visiting Jordan and Syria by way of the Mandelbaum Gate when we finished our survey in Israel. The whole Near East was aroused over Egypt's seizure of the Suez Canal. England had withdrawn her nationals from all Arab countries where there was danger of mob violence, including Jordan. It was reported that American citizens had been molested by unruly crowds of Arabs in many of these countries. Still it was unthinkable to be so close to the Holy City and not visit its sacred and historic sites. ~

On making inquiries regarding a visit to the other side they learned that Jordan would refuse to honor its own visas on the grounds that the Links' passports were also stamped with Israeli visas. Stymied, Ed and Marion determined to see the next morning if the American consul could somehow obtain permission for them to continue their journey as planned.

With characteristic optimism, on waking early in the morning, Marion wrote of "breathing in that special clear air of the Judean hills to the sounds of Jerusalem; the musical dissonance of the Christian bells and the muezzin's voice calling his people to prayer." Jerusalem, she recalled, next to Mecca and Medina, is the third most holy place of the Moslem religion. "But," she added, "there was no audible note to draw my attention to the presence of that third great religion, Judaism, which belongs even more closely to Jerusalem — the very cradle of its faith — yet all around me I am conscious of its impress." She then looked over the balcony to the wide strip of no man's land and thought:

~ This barren strip is here because, in spite of the faith and teachings of three great religions, all accepting one God as their Creator, there is no brotherhood of mankind. What no man's land proclaims for all the world to see is that at this phase of human development, neither Church nor State has yet found a way for people to live together in harmony.

It also proclaims that Edwin and I cannot cross to the other side of that vacancy because Israel has set its seal upon our passports, and Jordan will not accept a passport even with their own consular visa if it also bares the mark of the hated state of Israel.

The glorious glow of love and faith and happiness that I felt on first awakening and looking over the Holy City has deserted me. How is mankind ever to find its way to peace and happiness except by worshipping God and loving one another. ~

Of course, many of the conditions the Links found then in the Holy Land have since changed, among the most significant being that under the Israeli government the whole of Jerusalem is presently open to the world, to Arabs and Jews and Christians alike. Not so in the fifties. The consulate assured them that it was "absolutely impossible" to help them out, that Jordan would under no consideration allow anyone to cross the border in both directions. "If we were able to get into Jordanian territory, we could not return, but must go instead to one of the neighboring Arab countries," Marion reported. However, the consulate did commit to trying to get their visas reinstated so that they could possibly utilize their airline tickets back to America by way of Jordan and Syria, "though," she noted, "they would make no promises; it was very doubtful, we could only hope."

Another obstacle in the way of researching Israel's history was the existing situation with the Dead Sea Scrolls. Apart from the fact that certain scholars held jealously to the bulk of the material, which could reveal so much to other researchers and interested parties the world over — particularly new evidence about certain sects of Judaism and the earliest days of Christianity — Ed was told at the time that these were inaccessible because there was no safe place to display them in Jerusalem, about which Marion wrote:

~ We were disappointed to learn that one of the choicest sources of information, the Dead Sea Scrolls, which have created so much interest and comment all over the world since their finding by Bedouin tribesmen in the Judean Hills near the Dead Sea, were not available to the public. We were told this was because there was no building to house a museum except the crumbling, dusty, makeshift quarters of the Department of Antiquities which we had visited the previous day. Instead the scrolls were being carefully treasured and guarded in one of the few newly-built government office buildings which had been erected since the partition of Jerusalem. ~

In truth, the Israelis themselves had little access to the full content of the scrolls since they had begun to appear in 1947. Israel held only a minute portion of those that had come to light, which did eventually end up on public display in a

Jerusalem museum, the Shrine of the Book. However, most were held back from other scholars as well as the public, and were monopolized for 40 years by French catholic archeologists and scholars. Dominican Monk Father Roland De Vaux, in particular, who had spent five years digging at the Qumran caves near a Jewish communal site that was destroyed by the Romans in 69 AD, dominated the scrolls. Arguments arose in the academic community, accusing those in charge of assigning too much material to too few scholars, while the majority of the scrolls unearthed by then, as well as material yet to be discovered, fell under the jurisdiction of the Jordanians. These were housed in the Palestine Museum (now the Rockefeller Museum) then on the Jordanian side of the border. Israel only finally gained access to what in all rights was their own material long after the land on which the Jewish writings were then located, the West Bank, became occupied by Israel following the 1967 War. Even then it was academic pressure that at last got the Israelis involved in the rightful distribution of the contents of the scrolls. In fact, perhaps owing to some extent to the publicity given the situation by authors Michael Baigent and Richard Leigh in the their popular book *The Dead Sea Scrolls Deception*, it was only near the end of 1991 and early in 1992, after years of bitter academic and political struggle, that photostats of the body of these rare treasures were at last made accessible in their entirety to the public.

Finally, Marion wrote in 1956:

~ It must have taken almost an act of the Knesset to accomplish it, but it was our good fortune to be allowed to view the famous scroll of the book of Isaiah, coiled loosely at either end, carefully preserved in a protective glass casing, its creamy leather sections carefully sewn together, bearing the painstakingly wrought Hebrew characters in orderly rows. The official in charge told us these were obtained from a dealer in Bethlehem at a time when it was most dangerous for an Israeli to venture into that Arab-held territory, and then turned over to Hebrew University to be examined and interpreted. ~

Marion noted that the Book of Isaiah was three to 4,000 years older than any part of the Bible known to exist, probably written between the years 200 BC and 200 AD, and that they were allowed to see it only because it was the best preserved of the Israeli-held Dead Sea Scrolls. (Authors Baigent and Leigh contend that the Israelis having possession of certain ancient scrolls was tolerated by the Christian scholars only because they were too old for their contents to be of any threat to cherished beliefs about the beginnings of Christianity. Other Qumram materials, still hidden by the French at the time, suggest decidedly Jewish and perhaps militant sects of "Christianity" in its earliest days, which may have existed even before the advent of Jesus and his followers. Furthermore, some scrolls seem to indicate that the people who wrote them and who possibly founded Christianity may not have been the esoteric and monastic Essenes at all, as commonly supposed, but a sect of Saducees.)

Perhaps more fortunate than many biblical scholars at the time, the Links were also shown photostats of two other manuscripts, in a much poorer state of preservation: the Psalms of Thanksgiving, written in the first century BC; and the account of the Battle Between the Sons of Light and the Sons of Darkness, from the same era.

That afternoon Ed and Marion were privileged to have tea with General Yigael Yadin at his home, where they discussed at length the excavations he was conducting at Hazor in northern Palestine, an ancient Canaanite city. Yadin was a famous scholar and son of another noted Israeli scholar who was head of Hebrew University's Department of Archeology, Professor Eleazer Subenik, and who negotiated the clandestine purchase of certain Israeli-held scrolls. General Yadin, former chief of staff of the Israeli Defence Forces, the Haganah, was also an archeologist by profession, and was current guardian of the Israeli held scrolls. He was then engaged in a study of the Battle of the Sons of Light and the Sons of Darkness, the only first hand account of the ancient Hebrew military forces.

The Links were duly impressed with this remarkable Israeli. Marion wrote of Yadin:

~ We found him to be a man of wide and varied interests, a man of tremendous imagination and intelligence, a man of great vitality. He was still under forty years of age, yet already wearing the accolade of a successful leader of the Israeli forces and outstanding in his chosen field of archeology.

We were surprised to find that he was also an ardent skin diver, although he had never sought after underwater artifacts. He was most interested in our plans and promised to spend time with us when we would return to Israel with our own vessel [in 1960]. ~

General Yadin filled them in on much of the historical background of the coastal cities of old Palestine, then arranged for a visit to the Fishing School at Michmoreth, under the direction of his brother-in-law, Raphael Rupine. On leaving Jerusalem for their first inspection of the seacoast areas where they hoped to dive, they visited the Fishing School with much curiosity. They found this to be a cluster of neat buildings for housing teenagers, who were, with the use of a scattering of dories out in the bay, actually learning to be fishermen. "It is thus," Marion wrote admiringly, "that Israel is rebuilding an economy to weather any storm, for in every field of activity the same amount of careful planning and effort is being expended to train her future citizens."

Yadin's brother-in-law gave them a tour of the school, then took them to his small beach house where they saw a remarkable collection of amphorae [two-handled Greco-Roman jars], "...of many shapes and sizes, their varicolored sides patterned with the twisted white wormshell deposits from centuries in the sea," as Marion described them in her text. According to Rupine they had been dragged up from the bottom of the Mediterranean in the nets of his fishermen, at depths of 30 to 40 fathoms and more. One of the instructor/fishermen was then called in for Ed to question at length while Rupine translated. "Could he tell them where they were found? Were they all from the same locale? Had any been found in shallow water? Could he go back to the same spot again?" Marion then wrote:

~ We learned that the fishermen dragged their nets in deeper waters at least two miles off shore. He could not be sure that all the amphorae had come from the same place, as they were not discovered until the nets were pulled, sometimes many miles from where the objects were scraped up. Even though the nets dragged and caught, it was not known if they were caught on wreckage from a ship or on rocks strewn on the bottom.

We questioned him about the possibility of finding wreckage in shallower waters nearer shore. He talked of Caesarea, the abandoned Roman city a few miles up the coast, with its mostly submerged ancient port. He described having seen sunken marble pillars in six to seven fathoms about 400 yards from shore near Caesarea. Yes, he was sure he could go to them again. The bottom there was rough and rocky. Nearer shore he thought he had seen a large anchor on the bottom, jutting out of the sand, the iron covered with sea growth. He reported that the contour of the bottom was apt to change considerably due to shifting sands in time of storms.

That morning in the Rupine living room, Caesarea was just a name to us, the name of a city built by King Herod nearly two thousand years before in honor of Augustus Caesar of Rome; a city that existed when a man called Jesus taught the multitudes; and later that same century after the destruction of Jerusalem by the Romans, a city that became the ruling city of Palestine.

That same afternoon, however, Caesarea became a living city to us, even though what we were seeing — once beautiful buildings, spacious temples and imposing harbor — was now but crumbling ruins, partly excavated on the land, and piles of rubble at the edge of the sea. In its place stood the later ruins of a Crusader city long since abandoned by the invading Christians, and more recently occupied by the Arabs. Now, these decaying, empty buildings presented a forlorn appearance, ravaged as they were by time and the winter storms of the Mediterranean. ~

They drove along the sea to the fishing and farming Kibbutz Solat-Yam to meet the village elder and director of the Caesarea museum, Aaron Wegman. He too oversaw a "spectacular" collection of amphorae, and many other ancient seagoing artifacts dating back to the earliest known marine history, which had also been salvaged in the nets of kibbutz fishermen.

Ed and Marion were given their first taste of kibbutz life during this visit, the voluntary communal way of living not entirely unlike that of similar communities whose people wrote and preserved the Dead Sea Scrolls. More secular than religious in recent times, communal life had now become a highly practical way to absorb the broken and lost survivors of the Holocaust and thousands of other homeless Jewish refugees who came pouring into Israel. They also harbored any number of zealots who simply wanted to go "home" to live and participate in building a new land. The seafaring couple, accustomed as they were to "communal" living on a small scale aboard *Sea Diver*, were pleased with the opportunity to learn more about kibbutzim. She reported:

~ Aaron Wegman took us to his home where we found his wife and two young boys taking their afternoon siesta in the little one-room cottage. It was a holiday or they would have been absent——Mrs. Wegman at her job in the fields and the boys in the school-home at the end of the village. This follows the pattern of living in most of the kibbutzes, for the children from six months of age take up their abode in these school-homes where they eat and sleep and study and play under the supervision of trained personnel, often including their parents who may alternate duty as teachers. Otherwise, only on holidays and for several hours at the end of each day do they spend time with their own parents.

We learned that the people of the community share everything, the products of their labor going into a general fund. Besides their subsistence they receive only a small allowance during the year...."From each according to their ability, to each according to their need," we were told. There is a community dining room, kitchen, laundry and infirmary, and in most cases an assembly hall for cultural programs. The school-homes and in this case, the museum, are owned and supported by the community as a whole, which is governed by a General Assembly of all its members. ~

They learned at Solat-Yam that kibbutz life is not suited for everyone and is not taken lightly by anyone. Those who choose this lifestyle may do so only on a trial basis, generally for the first two years, and may not pool their resources with the holdings of the community until it is mutually agreed that they fit into the community as kibbutzim. It was also pointed out that though the children only spend several hours every evening at home, they receive the undivided attention of their parents during this "quality time." The Israelis compared kibbutz progeny to children in conventional homes, where individual family members come and go on differing schedules, and said that kibbutz children very likely spend more waking hours with their parents than the other children do. In addition, they said that for whatever reason, students on kibbutzes all over Israel won the highest grades in the country and won by far the greatest percentage of the national scholarships. Marion continued to observe:

~ Many of the 223 kibbutzes now in existence were established in the early days of Israel's settlement and are now, like this one near Caesarea, comfortable villages with excellent farming equipment and facilities, and, at Solat-Yam, a fleet of fishing boats that cruise as far as the Straits of Turkey.

We found that the people of the kibbutz take a personal pride of ownership in Caesarea and the excavations which break the even pattern of its fields. The museum is their special pride, for it is their own. Financed and built with the work of their hands, its shelves are filled with the finds of their fishermen at sea and farmers upon the land. They were most cooperative as we carried out our searches off the shores of the old town.

Two days later at lunch in the dining room of the kibbutz we were waited on by a personable young man who turned out to be Joseph Amorai, principal of the local school system. He was taking his turn at this aspect of the duties of communal living. Later he sat down and told us the story of the founding of Solat-Yam.

In 1938, he with nine other men and two girls made camp on the shores of the then arid land. They lived in tents pitched on high bluffs overlooking the northern portion of the port of Caesarea while they made their first attempt to cultivate and plant a small portion of the neglected land. Both day and night they found it necessary to stand guard duty against the hostile and thieving Arabs who dwelt in the nearby ruins of the Crusader city. Theirs was a tremendous task, for over centuries of neglect, the fertile lands of this area behind the sea coast had wasted, while heavy winds, sometimes the khamsin from the east, and again the winter storms from the south, had lifted and carried away the soil. At the same time the useless sands along the shore had crept gradually inland, despoiling the land and covering the Roman ruins.

First they planted trees and crops to pin down the drifting soils, and then provided irrigation to keep the crops alive. How well they succeeded could be seen by the lushness of the fields surrounding the kibbutz, even to the grassy acres where well-fed milk and beef cattle grazed at pasture. Even the little cottages along the village streets were almost lost in the heavy shade of trees that had grown up around them, their small garden plots blooming with flowers of every description.

We went from the Wegman home to the old harbor at Caesarea through the hot, dry air of late September, our feet kicking up clouds of dust in the unpaved streets. As we neared the port, we saw that the road was lined with stone structures erected in Crusader times from the ruins of the old Roman city, for Caesarea was one of the three important seaports that held the Crusader kingdom together through the years of its stormy history. These structures had later been patched together to serve as living places for nomadic Arabs who garnered a precarious existence from their goats and the barren soil. It was not many years prior to our visit that these buildings had been abandoned by the Arabs who had battled the coming of the pioneers of the Israeli state.

We came to the jetty at the end of the Crusader-built road extending straight out into the sea. This was fortified on the left with stone bulwarks strengthened here and there by lengths of Roman columns protruding from its construction. To our right, overlooking the harbor, was a two-story stone ruin. The jetty ran straight out into the harbor for a distance of perhaps four hundred feet and then made a right angle to the north. A seawall on the outer side kept the breakers from dashing over the escarpment.

As we faced shoreward from the jetty we could see what remained of the ancient town, heaps of stone pillars and rubble lying in the water close to shore, the stone floors of former structures now partly inundated by the sea.

"This right-angle section of the jetty was built in recent years," Wegman explained. "We believe it follows the outline of the Crusader port, but we have reason to believe that the old Roman port was of much greater dimensions.

"If you would solve that one for us," he said, "it would help us greatly in reconstructing the areas of the old city," a challenge which Ed accepted and would act on in the future by orchestrating a complete reconstruction with a team of divers and Israeli scholars. He then spoke of Josephus Flavius's description of Caesarea written in the century of its founding, detailing the size and structure of the port. ~

After Ed and Marion had their first glimpse of the Mediterranean waters where they were to dive, they left the area to set up headquarters in Haifa and returned two days later with diving equipment, ready to board what they had expected to be a fishing boat Wegman was to rent for them. In Haifa Ed had picked up an air compressor and a diving mask that he had shipped ahead before leaving Binghamton. Supplementing these with face plates, flippers and a heavy iron bar from the workshop of the kibbutz to use in investigating whatever he might find on the bottom, he and Marion were ready to set out on their first survey mission. It seemed they were prepared in every way, except for what they would find on their return to Caesarea:

~ We arrived on the breakwater at the port just as an open fishing boat with sails, manned by a dozen teenage boys and girls, rounded the end of the quay and tied up to the dock. With much lighthearted chatter they got the sails down in workmanlike fashion under the direction of an athletic-looking man at the tiller.

To our dismay we learned that this was our transportation for the day. We were hard pressed to figure out what use a sailboat would be in maneuvering about the confined waters of the harbor, particularly as there was a strong wind blowing offshore from the east. We were assured that our crew did not intend to use the sails but would row the boat instead. I looked at Ed, then did a double take in the direction of the boat. Sure enough, there in the bottom was a pile of the largest and heaviest oars I had ever seen.

At their leader's command, the boys began arranging themselves mid-ships, each with a long-handled oar. The girls perched on the gunwales, presenting a pretty picture in their sailing clothes and typical Israeli hats. A place was cleared on one of the broad seats for the compressor, and their leader, Ilan Hartuv, Ed and myself placed ourselves as best we could about the stern. There were at least fifteen of us in the craft.

The minute we cast off the wind caught and carried us back against the dock, so we pushed and shoved along until we cleared the end and got underway. The boys then fell to with a will to row us across the harbor toward some reefs that we had been told might mark the northern dimensions of the port. However, they scarcely made any headway against the wind, and whenever the awkward craft got broadside we found ourselves being carried out toward the sea and away from our goal. Finally after a long struggle, which failed to take us where we wanted to go, we indicated that they should anchor, figuring it would be easier to swim the intervening distance than to try to get the boat into position.

At last the three of us went overboard and for an hour combed the waters in the vicinity. During that time we found only what looked like the remains of a wall completely covered with sea growth. We went back to the boat and after much struggle succeeded in getting it moved to the new spot, where Ed went down with the air hose.

It turned out to be a fruitless day's work, for meanwhile the wind had begun to blow with a stronger force and the harbor had become rough with waves. Ed swam back to the jetty, examining the bottom as he went, while our young crew got the sails up before turning back to the kibbutz to the south. Our first day of searching was a great disappointment.

"We've got to have a more maneuverable boat," Ed said, "or we will never be able to accomplish anything." In the end it was decided to get in touch with Rupine at the fishing school and arrange to have the fisherman who saw the marble columns in the sea meet us the following day with a motor boat.

We said goodbye to the merry group of boys and girls who had worked so hard to aid us. They were orphans, Ilan Hartuv told us, who had been adopted by the kibbutz, now as much a part of the community as the children of the settlers. To see these healthy, happy youngsters, it was hard to realize that they were homeless waifs who had survived the concentration camps of the world. They and hundreds like them will be a solid buttress to the future Israel, nurtured as they are by a wholesome and extended family life plus substantial academic educations in addition to training in both farming and fishing.

Our second day in the waters at Caesarea proved much more successful. The fisherman from the fishing school met us at the dock with a roomy, open power boat. He had as an assistant one of the pupils from the school.

A scorching hot east wind was blowing again, carrying fine particles of dirt through the air with stinging velocity. This was the khamsin which occasionally blows from the desert lands to the east, creating the most unpleasant weather conditions that are known in Israel. We were glad that our kind of archeology carried us into the cool waters of the Mediterranean rather than the dust-laden, scorching air of the inland excavations.

Ilan Hartuf left us that morning to return to Jerusalem, and later in the day we were joined by Emmanuel Amati, a well-informed young archeologist and skin diver from the Ministry of Education's Department of Antiquities. Before his arrival our guide from the fishing school ran us out to a spot about four hundred yards offshore and anchored. Here, he indicated, was the locations of the pillars he had seen.

We were soon overboard surveying the area from the surface. Not only did we see a few scattered pillars in the clear water some twenty-five feet below, but there was also a vast collection of odd and interesting shapes extending in a wide area and surrounded by the white sand bottom. I continued to scout from the surface, while Ed went down with the diving equipment to investigate at closer range. To complete our day's exploration he searched with great care the waters between this spot and the Crusader jetty near shore. We ended the day's activities with a survey of the shallow waters near the shore to the south of the jetty.

This time we felt we had succeeded in establishing some positive facts regarding the original Roman port. Ed now felt certain that the main jetty of the port had run directly out to sea several hundred yards beyond the present one. At a depth of twenty to thirty feet he had measured a row of fourteen heavy stone slabs about five feet long and one-and-a-half feet square. He had seen two huge, rectangular objects, perhaps fifteen feet long or more, resting in the sand along with many columns, broken stone walls and shapeless, unidentifiable objects.

Also in his search he had discovered a pile of ballast from a sunken ship lying on the sandy bottom just beyond the line of rubble; and in still another spot, a claw-type anchor such as has been used in the East for many centuries, half-buried in the sand. When he tugged at the anchor ring, it came off in his hand and he brought it to the surface. The degree of corrosion, judging by standards in our western waters, led him to think it might be two or three hundred years old.

That afternoon from shore we investigated the possible north side of the harbor with Wegman who pointed out where he thought the jetty wall should lie. It was too late to investigate further that day, although having outlined the south wall of the Roman Harbor, we were now most anxious to find its northern limits.

As we stood on the sandy bluff overlooking the port, we looked down upon a scattering of eroded and broken columns lying in the shallow water near shore. To our right at some distance, just covered by the lapping waves, could be seen a flooring of handcut stones, where it was said the Roman Temple had once stood. The curving, sandy shoreline at our feet cut deeply back into the hillside, and it was obvious that over the centuries wind and waves had gradually nibbled away at the original shoreline, so that today, where once stood proud buildings at the edge of the harbor, there were only ruins lying in shallow water.

Returning to the hotel that night, we were able to secure a copy of Josephus Flavius's description of Caesarea as recorded in his *Wars of the Jews*, written in the first century AD and probably the only on-the-spot record of the old city. We were tremendously excited, for as we read of the magnitude of the harbor and the construction of the jetties, we found that much that we had seen could easily fit Josephus's description. We could hardly wait to return the next day to determine for ourselves whether the north side of the harbor also fitted this account.

Josephus had written: "When he had measured out as large a space as we have before mentioned, he let down stones into 20 fathom water, the greatest part of which were 50 feet in length, and nine in depth, and ten in breadth, and some still larger. But when the haven was filled up to that depth, he enlarged that wall which was thus already extant above the sea, till it was 200 feet wide; one hundred of which had buildings before it, in order to break the force of the waves...On this wall were very large towers, the principal and most beautiful of which was called Drusium, from Drusus, who was son-in-law to Caesar.

"There were also a great number of arches, where the mariners dwelt; and all the places before them round about was a large valley or walk, for a quay (or landing place) to those that came on shore; but the entrance was on the north, because the north wind was there the most gentle of winds. At the mouth of the haven were on each side three great Colossi, supported by pillars, where those Colossi that are on your left hand as you sail into the port are supported by two upright stones joined together, which stones were larger than that tower which was on the other side of the entrance."

It went on to describe the white marble buildings which bordered the port, and the narrow streets of the city leading down to it. "And over against the mouth of the haven, upon an elevation, there was a temple for Caesar, which was excellent both in beauty and largeness...."

We had seen enough beneath the water and on land to be able to visualize the whole setting—-the beautiful white marble buildings on the shore dominating the wide, colonnaded way which led to the imposing towers at either end of the quay surmounted by three impressive Colossi on either side of the harbor entrance. And within the harbor, the varied and picturesque ships of the Roman world gathered here from all parts of the Mediterranian. ~

A third day of diving filled out and completed the Link party's picture of the harbor. Without a boat, Ed, accompanied by Emmanuel Amati, swam from shore while Marion remained in town catching up on her records. The two men were successful in outlining the north jetty. Then Ed continued to dive and managed to locate a sarcophagus described as three by six-and-a-half feet and to find a perfect amphora of the Roman period which was cemented to a section of the old wall standing above the sandy bottom. Clearly, the area offered vast possibilities for further exploration. Marion commented that Josephus's detailing of depths, and the size of the objects to be found were "doubtless exaggerated," but, she added, "it would remain to be seen."

Ed had noticed that though there were certainly tremendous differences between the 20 fathoms of water Josephus described as originally at the mouth of the harbor and the four or five fathoms presently seen by himself, there were huge stone blocks lying on the bottom partly buried in the sand. He concluded that had all of the structures Josephus described at the end of the quays collapsed into the water, they would have consumed a great deal of space, which once filled in with sand could have altered the depth greatly.

What aroused Ed's curiosity was how the 20-foot wide jetties with buildings ringing their outer sides had collapsed and sunk beneath the sea to such a depth, since it was evident that there had been little or no change in the level of the Mediterranean in the intervening years. And he thought he had an answer: In examining the huge building blocks visible on the bottom, he discovered that a number were split in irregular sections, and separated in many places by several feet. Marion documented his conclusion:

~ "Only an earthquake could have thrown that masonry into the sea and
shattered it in such sections. There have been many violent earthquakes
in this part of the world in the past. One of them must have been responsible for destroying the port of Caesarea." ~

Then she added her own observation: "It was evident that much further research was needed before we could even begin to solve some of the puzzling mysteries of this ancient port."

(Ed's intuition regarding an earthquake was very likely on target. On their next trip to Israel he would find evidence of an earthquake in that area, which pinpointed the probable date of the destruction of the port of Caesarea to be 130 AD.)

On leaving Caesarea the Links visited dozens of "interesting" little museums scattered around the country. At the Department of Antiquities in Jerusalem they saw ancient artifacts; at Michmoreth, another "wonderful" collection of amphorae; and yet another collection found by kibbutz fishermen, in the hills behind Acre.

They also felt they gained some insight into what perhaps sets Israelis apart from so many other peoples of the world who live off the land. Marion remarked with wonder at the kibbutzim in particular, who, she said:

~ ...did not accustom themselves only to the limited life of fields and barns.
Almost all of them supplemented these healthy and strenuous activities
with challenging interests of their own. Whether their work carried them to
the fields or on forays into the Mediterranean with their fishing boats, they
varied their tasks at home by their enthusiasm for hobbies ranging from
wide reading and study to music, art, archeology and science. ~

The Links next met with Arie Ben-Eli, founder and director of the Maritime Museum of Haifa, who showed them rooms full of ancient ships models. Here they took the opportunity to study the museum's collection of charts and prints comprising a varied picture of maritime life in the Mediterranean over the centuries. "We looked them over with interest," wrote Marion, "because here we were able to find portrayals of the old-time ports we were planning to explore, the appearance of the cities that had lined their shores, and indications of changes that might have occurred in the coastline up to the present day."

From there they drove to Acre at the northernmost curve in the shallow bay of Haifa. Marion remarked with mild surprise at the peaceful life of an Arab community, the residents evidently perfectly happy to be living on Israeli soil. She learned the same was true of other Arabs in other Arab villages throughout Israel, a fact, she noted, that was little covered by the news back home. She wrote of Acre:

> ~ The present-day city, superimposed upon centuries of previous construction and destruction by various peoples, was built by the Turks in the sixteenth century. It replaced what was left of the stoutly-created Crusader town, headquarters for the feudal Kingdom of Acre established here during the western European invasions several centuries previous. Today Acre is inhabited chiefly by Arab people who chose to stay in Israel when the new state was formed in 1948 rather than to join their countrymen in the Arab states across the border. Here they live comfortably and happily in sharp contrast to the lot of those who left Israel and now many years later are still dragging out a sad existence in UN-supported refugee camps, having never been assimilated by the Arab nations. ~

Ed and Marion preferred walking through the narrow alleys of Acre as a quicker and easier way of getting around than taking the alternative, which meant circling the town by car, going out at one gate and in at another because the streets in the heart of the village were too narrow to drive through. And as Marion said, they liked wandering through the old city on foot:

> ~ Here we found much of the color of the Near East which had hitherto eluded us in modern Israel — men in flowing robes and white headgear, crowded street bazaars selling exotic and unknown articles, tall old houses with slits of shuttered windows bordering narrow streets, their balconies almost meeting overhead in the stone canyons paved with ancient blocks. There was even the wailing music of the East, although I am sure more times than not it came from phonographs behind the mysterious-looking walls....

Acre is one of the oldest ports in Israel, there being documentation of
the presence of a settlement here 2,500 years before Christ, when Egyptian
ships used the harbor to trade with Syria and to obtain fresh water. ~

She commented that the ancient port city, known as Ptolemais during the
New Testament era, had acquired various identities over the centuries. Acre was
once an important Phoenician harbor; was occupied by Canaanites; was evidently
under the jurisdiction of the Romans after the fall of the Maccabeans; and became
the center of the Kingdom of Acre during Crusader times. In relation to their work
there she wrote:

~ During this time, the sturdy walls of the present city were built, the
whole surrounded by the deep moat which still exists today. The Crusaders
also constructed the long jetties to protect the harbor along the southern
shore. It was this area inside the jetties which most interested us, as we
gazed across from the Fishermen's pier on the south side of the city wall.

A wide expanse of water at this point was bordered on the shoreward
side by a sand beach. Some distance out from shore a broken heap of
masonry, known locally as the Fly Tower, was visible above the surface
of the water. To our right could be traced a line of capsized wall reaching
out from the corner buttress of the sea wall, so that it was fairly clear that
this had marked the confines of the inner harbor. The entrance we found
later had been guarded by the Fly Tower on its left.

The morning we were to dive, there was the customary confusion and
scurrying about to obtain a boat for our use. We went first to the Acre
museum, housed in a most interesting old Turkish bath in the heart of the
walled city, where the director made arrangements with one of the local
fishermen to take us out.

That day we were accompanied by Emmanuel Amati, the young skin
diver from the Department of Antiquity, who was interested in studying
our methods of approaching marine archeology; Arie Ben-Eli; our driver,
who had lived in Iraq and was familiar with the Arabic tongue; and the
Arab owner of the boat and his youthful assistant, neither of whom spoke
Hebrew or English. ~

Ed spotted a cannon and a possible shipwreck a short distance offshore as he
explored the ocean floor near the Fly Tower, following the deep water along the
outer side of the seaward jetty. These, he conjectured, were of that period of history
following the Crusades when Acre, then a Turkish city, was under siege by
Napoleon's troops. The Israelis agreed with his hunch, and told them how Napoleon

suffered defeat by the British in Egypt and then attempted to secure Acre as a fortified place from which to fight the Turks. They said Napoleon was finally forced to
return to Egypt because he could not hold out against the combined forces of the
British and the Turks at sea. Marion, taking it all in, mused again about the strange
history of this beleaguered land:

> ~ Was there ever a major war in all of man's history that this little strip of
> land bordering the east shore of the Mediterranean has not been involved
> in? As long as the memory of man, Palestine has been fought over, coveted
> by the eastern nations as their window on the Mediterranean; by the west-
> ern powers as a gateway to the east; and after the time of Abraham also
> desired by one or more of three world religions, Judaism, Christianity, and
> Mohammadism. No wonder every acre of its soil bears testimony to the
> dozens of civilizations that have occupied and fought over it! ~

All of the divers agreed that Ed might have seen the remains of a battle
between Napoleon, the Turks and the English; surely beneath the waters would
be more evidence of this raging battle. And so the search was on, in spite of
building weather conditions that would soon catch Ed in a serious quandary
underwater and bring about disappointment in the face of a tantalizing prospect.
Marion recorded the incident:

> ~ Except when the khamsin blew from the desert lands to the east, we
> found at this time of the year the winds came gently from shore during
> the morning, creating a condition of calm along the coastal waters.
> Toward noon there would occur a sudden switch, and from then on we
> could count upon a strong offshore breeze from the northwest, making it
> very difficult to handle our awkward boats and keep the positions which
> we wished to search.
>
> That day at Acre we had just set out to explore the deeper water off-
> shore from the seawall when the wind shift occurred. Ed had gone over
> the side at the end of the air hose, instructing the boatman to follow him
> slowly in the general direction of Haifa to the south, while he swam close
> to the bottom, carefully examining it as he went. Amati and I fanned out
> on the surface from where Ed was, watching for his signals and mean-
> while inspecting areas just to his right and left. The water here was prob-
> ably about thirty feet deep.
>
> Then the wind came up, and the boat was moving too fast. It had soon
> overridden Ed and was actually towing him. As I approached the boat to
> warn the others, I saw that the exhaust fumes from the engine were being

carried toward that section of the boat where the compressor was pumping air to Ed underwater. This was very dangerous.

I made Eli understand me after a bit, above the noise of the motors. He relayed the message in Hebrew to our driver, who in turn passed it on to the boatman in Arabic. The boat engine gasped and quit. The compressor still continued its put-put. I indicated that the boatman should take the oars and guide the boat; that there was sufficient wind to carry us, but he must steer in the right direction. He signaled back that he could not use the oars. This meant that we would have to drift with the wind.

I swam away from the boat to resume my position only to discover that we had drifted into much deeper water, probably seventy-five to a hundred feet, and that Ed was trailing out at the end of the air hose some distance above the bottom. I started back to the boat to tell them that somehow they must get it under control and change its course. We were getting too far out to sea. I was struggling to relay this information through the "international language exchange" when Ed suddenly appeared at the stern.

Panting from his exertions as he pulled the mask away from his face, he gasped, "Turn around, quick! I've found something important. Turn back! Turn back!"

There was much confusion. The boat, adrift without power or steerage, was being carried rapidly away from the spot. We had no marker buoys. Again, his words had to be translated from English to Hebrew and then to Arabic. The boatman's protests that he could not use the oars were renewed. The compressor was still running, adding to the din. There was a chorus of voices in English, Hebrew and Arabic.

Meanwhile the boat continued to drift with the wind. I looked down into water so deep that I could just barely make out the bottom.

Then I looked back at Ed, and heartsick, watched his eager expression as it turned to puzzled wonder and finally to despair. Pulling off his mask and signaling to shut off the compressor, dejected, he climbed into the boat. Reluctantly, Amati and I followed.

"I saw a stone on the bottom," he explained. "It was almost buried in the sand, but I could see characters written on it. I came up as quickly as I could to tell you to stop. Now it is too late. We'll never find it again with this boat and in this wind." ~

Only one day had been allotted for the survey. "How fervently I wished for *Reef Diver*," wrote Marion, "with its 'on a dime' steering, its efficient equipment, glass bottom and handy marking buoys." Her mind and Ed's were one, for as if he read her thoughts he said, "We'll come back here with *Reef Diver* next year."

On their last day in Israel they went to the Sea of Galilee, where Ed thought they might possibly find evidence of very old types of boats, since it was so rich in history and wooden craft might be expected to survive indefinitely in the fresh water.

Marion stood transfixed as she gazed upon that inland lake, recalling reading of the various settlements on its banks over the centuries, of Jesus of Nazareth ordering the wind and waves, "Peace, be still." She thought of how his disciples described his coming to their rescue in the fourth watch of the night, walking upon the water. She recalled the bloody battle within the first century after Christ, between the Romans and the Jews. "Yes," she wrote, "Galilee must have its share of history under the sea."

On their way to the Sea of Galilee Ed had set out from Haifa with officials in one car while Marion traveled in another with Dan Ben Dor — whose brother, she commented, was an archeologist with Harvard University — and a "Colonel Jaffe," who was with the Israel Defense Forces and was an ardent skin diver. Jaffe was to secure a boat for the expedition from a police precinct near Tiberius. Driving through the hills she remarked how the vicinity of Nazareth made her think of Biblical times, as they passed men in flowing robes on the backs of small donkeys and women in ancient dress carrying jugs on top of their heads. At that moment Ben Dor brought her thoughts to present-day reality by speaking of his 19-year old daughter, an only child, who was stationed with the Israeli land forces on the Syrian border just below Galilee. She marveled that Israeli girls not only served their country in the military for two years, from age 18 to 20 as did the boys, but that they were also under exactly the same orders and would pull the same dangerous duties as the boys. Colonel Jaffe volunteered that many of the best fighters and leaders in the War of Liberation six years before were women.

Of cresting the last hilltop Marion wrote:

~ My first impression of the Sea of Galilee was breathtaking. A long body of soft blue water, about fourteen by five miles at its widest, it lay ringed round by golden hills, steep and barren on the eastern shore. Below us on the nearest shore sprawled Tiberius, pristine white against the blue water and the golden fields.

We found the patrol station near the south end of the lake hidden in trees and fronting on a quiet river of greenish water. I learned with a thrill that this was the famous Jordan. At the dock we were ushered aboard a roomy and powerful cabin cruiser (made in New Orleans, I noted). The captain and his assistant quickly maneuvered us clear of the dock and we were on our way up the historic river. A bend soon hid the docks from sight, and we cruised an area of rushes before emerging into the Sea of Galilee.

We circled the lower end of the lake heading toward the eastern shore, where only a narrow strip of land was Israeli soil. Back of it rose

the barren hills of Syria. Farther along the shore to the north, the Syrian
boundary was set only twelve yards from the edge of the water. Here, as
in all parts of Israel where unnatural boundaries separate the hostile
states, it has become necessary to maintain a constant patrol of the lake to
prevent Arab marauders from sneaking down from the hills and attacking
the people of the countryside.

Our boat captain searched the hills with binoculars as we neared the
farther shore. Inside the cabin on the seat where I had placed my bag lay
pistols and a Bren gun. No one seemed to pay any attention to the conceivable dangers of the situation, however, for each one was too
engrossed in the underwater possibilities of this body of water. And I,
too, soon forgot the menace of our surroundings. ~

Ed spent a great deal of time on the bottom offshore in an area the guides
felt may have been an anchorage for some ancient town. He was encouraged by
what he had seen, including the remains of two well preserved sunken boats
which, though not ancient, did indicate that the water acted as a natural preserva-
tive. The bottom was clean and hard with only a shallow covering of mud. He
reasoned that because the Jordan flowed through the center of the lake, most of
the sediment from the country to the north would be carried in its path and probably also deposited more at the upper end. On their return, Marion wrote of her
thoughts, "It would be quite a problem to decide just where to dive on this blue
inland sea," then she added:

~ There were differences of opinion over the site of the ancient city of
Taracheae, though it was believed to be north of Tiberius. Christ's ministry had been centered at Capernaum, at the northern end of the lake. We
would have to do much more research before attempting any further
exploration of the waters. ~

While cruising down the Jordan they had found their way blocked at one point
with two heavy ropes strung across from one shore to the other. A group of soldiers
"with full packs," practicing commando tactics, were making water crossings. The little group aboard the cruiser watched awhile then went back to the mouth of the stream
to wait for the lines to be removed. "Thus we were conscious everywhere we went of
the careful preparations that were taking place all over Israel for protection from self-
professed enemies, which surrounded it on every side," Marion commented.

The Sea of Galilee was their last scheduled visit. Their time in Israel was running out. At the end of their sojourn she wrote:

~ That night in Jerusalem we met with several interested archeologists and historians at the home of Hebrew University's president, Dr. Mazar. Among those present was Dr. Abi-Yonah, a specialist in Roman and Byzantine archeology, director of the land explorations at Caesarea. Reminding us of a second Einstein with his benign demeanor, his long, white hair and ruddy complexion, he was most helpful in supplying us with information about the area.

We left Israel the next morning to make the long flight back to the United States. We had been forced to give up our plans to return by way of Jordan and Syria; the American Consulate had finally succeeded in obtaining permission, but not until the preceding day. It was too late, for it had been necessary to change our plane reservations several days before to insure our being able to make our next connections in Rome.

We left Israel convinced that it would be most worthwhile to organize an expedition and return with the proper equipment for a thorough search. Not only would this result in the recovery of objects valuable to marine archeology, it would also supplement the intensive land archeological explorations which are now taking place all over Israel.

Ed and I believe we are the first to definitely survey and establish the boundaries of the ancient Roman Harbor at Caesarea and to explore the underwater ruins of its great jetties. How much more lies beneath the sands which have drifted into this area in the past nineteen centuries can only be conjectured....No wonder we are eager to return for further search. ~

* * *

BACK AT HOME ED'S STATE-OF-THE-ART *SEA DIVER II* had been built, and Marion had completed her book, *Sea Diver*. They had sailed the new vessel to Jamaica in 1959, again in response to invitations from the Jamaican government, and conducted their second archeological survey on the sunken city of Port Royal, even while Ed laid plans for his return to Israel with an appropriate vessel. Meanwhile he had made history in underwater circles for the work carried out on the final mission at Port Royal with his well thought-out and fully equipped vessel.

The first and second missions in Jamaican waters had been conducted at the frontier of underwater archeology. Therefore it is perhaps not surprising that he not only drew praise but was also criticized for his efforts, particularly by competitors who saw themselves as the legitimate experts in the field, and who may have coveted the distinction of being first to conduct a thorough survey of the old city, which in itself meant little to Ed.

Without recognizing that Ed was perhaps the only person sufficiently equipped to conduct those first surveys, Robert F. Marx, in his book, *Port Royal Rediscovered*, is somewhat uncomplimentary towards Ed and his work of 1956 and 1959 (prior to Marx's work beginning in 1964), which is brushed off, apparently as insignificant.

A segment of *Port Royal Rediscovered* is included along with a chapter from Marion's book, *Windows In the Sea*, in Hillary Hauser's anthology, *The Adventurous Aquanaut*, published by Best Publishing Company. In the Marx chapter he spins a web of entrepreneurial and political intrigue that puts Ed in the heart of a scheme to thwart his own ambitions of managing the research investigations at Port Royal; however, in studying Ed's life, there seems to have been neither the time, the concern, nor the temperamental inclination for such covert operations. In fact, though *Sea Diver* with her unique capabilities and her highly experienced skipper were undoubtedly in demand by the Jamaicans — and Ed may well have had hopes to return to the work one day (though not evidenced in the records) — over the time period in question he and his vessel were committed to work in the Mediterranean and the Bahamas, and he was serving on oceanographic committees with the United States Government. He was by then also busy designing the world's first lockout submersible. While it was said that Ed and his dive vessel were involved in future tourism plans for Port Royal made by the Jenkinsons, owners of the popular yacht club at Port Royal, and other Jamaicans, Ed in fact only returned to Port Royal one time with *Sea Diver*, and that was to make a brief stop in passing only, on the way home from British Hondurus. He did no underwater work at the time and never returned again.

What Marx fails to recognize is that Ed, who never claimed to be an academic scholar or a certified archeologist, did, with his cutting-edge underwater systems, open the doors for all future marine archeology at Port Royal as elsewhere, even as he was about to do in Israel. Marx does, however, concede: "The Link expedition, which received international newspaper and magazine coverage, made the world aware that the sunken city of Port Royal is the most important marine archeological site in the Western Hemisphere."

Following their second and only other expedition at Port Royal, the Links were ready to return with a fully equipped vessel to Israel in 1960. Once there, they found that the political climate in the Holy Land had changed enough since their 1956 visit to allow them, before returning home, to at last pass through the Mandelbaum Gate to visit the Jordanian side of the border, including the old walled city of Jerusalem.

This time there would be no reliance on others to obtain small fishing boats — or sailing boats manned by teenage kibbutzim — in order to carry out their explorations. Instead Ed and Marion and crew would arrive from the States fully equipped aboard their own 93-foot marine archeological research yacht, the all new *Sea Diver*, with *Reef Diver* placed in her davits and *Wee Diver* resting on an upper deck.

Bound for Israel, the party finally cast off after much preparation, research, and the inevitably frantic, last-minute rush in Miami, which included a late decision to hire a female cook for the expedition. "Don't know how Ed stands the pace," Marion jotted in her journal, "he's been going day and night for weeks now."

Both sons accompanied Ed and Marion to Miami to help get the ship underway, after which Clayton made the crossing to Nassau before returning home to finish out his school term, now at Colgate, then rejoining the ship later in Israel. (Eighteen-year-old Clayton had recently graduated with honors from Millbrook, a college preparatory school located on the Hudson River where his father sent him after he picked up such bad habits from his peers at Binghamton High as smoking and letting his grades drop.) Much to their parents' disappointment, and as Marion complained in her journal, Bill, now in his early twenties, had plans of his own and would not be joining the expedition.

"It seems in retrospect to have been not so bright on my part to have missed that wonderful opportunity in Israel, just as I had missed going to Port Royal when I went out West and hired on as a ranch hand," Bill now confesses, "but I wanted to earn my own way in the world then. I really regretted it later."

Perhaps an additional factor keeping him at home was that he was strong-willed like his father, which could make living in close quarters difficult. In any case, Bill had real reasons for not going along to Israel. For one thing he didn't want to leave behind his girlfriend, Juliet Ridley, who would eventually become his bride; for another, he had a problem with the way his father must always be in charge of everything involved with handling the ship. Then too, he had his own service station to run in Binghamton. If these weren't reasons enough, he had yet another problem. He was socially uneasy and something of a loner, much like his uncle George Theron had been in his younger days and even as Ed was to a mild degree. Unlike his outgoing younger brother Clayton, Bill imagined he would be awkward and uncomfortable with the streams of reporters, guests and dignitaries who would undoubtedly come pouring across *Sea Diver's* decks throughout the entire journey. Finally, there was a problem with seasickness, which he had never fully overcome.

One problem that Bill and Clayton did not have was being on their own as much as would seem from the various publications and journals. According to Bill they were well looked after at home by several responsible "housemothers" over the years when their parents were away, but he points out that they were not separated from their parents that much to begin with. Published material on their sea-going adventures generally covers only those seasons of the year when the sailing was good, and he and Clayton were out of school during the better part of those periods. They always had the option, and were even strongly encouraged to join the expeditions during the summers, and their parents were usually at home during much of the school terms.

So it was that Marion sadly noted in her journal, "Bill was a wonderful help, but just was not interested in going along." However, she added that her brother and his wife, Larry and Laura Clayton, would accompany them as guests as far as Puerto Rico.

* * *

## The Israel Expedition, Part II

AT LAST THE SEA-GOING MISSION TO ISRAEL was underway, leaving Miami at 4:20 in the afternoon on Monday, March 28, 1960. *Sea Diver* was loaded to the gills with everything Ed thought they might need in Israel, including a Volkswagen that was "slung aboard and tied securely to the afterdeck." Dorothy Soubiron from Miami, who had just completed a stint on a sailing charter, had hired on as cook at the last minute. The captain would soon be 56 years old, and Marion, his first mate, was now 52. Other crew members included Ed's old friend and retired naval officer, Capt. P.V.H. Weems, who happened to be the only man aboard experienced at ocean crossing. Among other crew members were George Cassidy, director of the America-Israel Society, who had been responsible for most of the arrangements for the expedition; Chet Brandon, described by Marion as a "brilliant" electronics engineer associated with GPE, who would serve as ship's radio officer; George Jones, carpenter and painter who traveled only as far as Puerto Rico; divers Curt Scott (who had also been a crew member in Port Royal) and Jay Elliott; and engineers Philip "Flip" Armstrong and Paul Caudell. Jack Ellis from Washington was to join them at Gibraltar.

But first they had business in Haiti, where they were met by *National Geographic* photographer Dean Conger and spent time over the Easter holidays diving once again on reefs in the area of Cap Haitien. Ed had gone ashore on arrival to inspect the Columbus vintage anchor they had retrieved there in 1954, which had been in the custody of the Army. During this eventful layover, on a foray with *Reef Diver* they spotted a freighter, the *Trolla*, which they assumed was heading into the harbor but later realized had gone aground. On April 14 Marion recorded the bad news: "Watched *Trolla* on her reef all day as she gradually sank stern first into the deep water until only her bow and hoisting gear remained above. Still the lights burned on, although she was abandoned, and the Norwegian flag still fluttered from her rigging."

On April 21 a presentation ceremony took place at the Hotel de Ville on the Square, in which the Haitian government presented the anchor to the Smithsonian Institution. Then, Marion wrote, "All government officials and ourselves were invited to upper chambers for a champagne toast, while Dean Conger took pictures." When it was over, *Sea Diver* could at last get underway for Puerto Rico, from where Ed had to make a quick foray to New York for a GPE stockholders meeting. Marion then saw the carefully packed anchor off at Puerto Rico for possible restoration at the Smithsonian Institution in Washington. Ed called afterwards from New York, to report a delay in his return as he had discovered on visiting a doctor that he had developed diabetes and would have to undergo more tests to determine his medication dosage. Then on Wednesday, May 11, he was back aboard in Puerto Rico and *Sea Diver* got underway at 5:00 o'clock that afternoon.

The crossing was relatively uneventful. One day Marion observed that Ed hadn't been feeling well, having "ups and downs" with the diabetes as he learned to gauge his medication according to his diet and how fatigued he became. At last Ed made the final crossing entry in the log and then commented: "Fifteen days and more than 3,000 miles and we only had to correct our course once, just before we entered the straits of Gibraltar. I'd say that's pretty good navigating, Capt. Weems."

But if the crossing to Gibraltar was uneventful, fate more than compensated for it following their departure from the rocky fortress on the first of June. By noon the seas were pounding and a strong wind had picked up from the southwest. As the night wore on the wind increased and swung around to the northeast, creating seas so steep that *Sea Diver* was constantly riding to the top of one crest and then plunging into the deep valley of another. Crew members up and about found it difficult to keep to their feet. Then, in the middle of the night, Marion wrote that the lights suddenly went off:

~ I was safe in my bunk and stayed there, but I could tell from the sound of the engines as they were slowed down and the stopping of the generator that something unusual was happening....I braced myself once more, clinging to the wildly careening bunk and attempting to go back to sleep.

Later, when I saw Ed his expression startled me.

"What happened," I said.

"Only a fire in the engine room," he replied. "Flip and Paul were right on the job when it happened, and fortunately no serious damage was done." They had quickly put out the fire with the extinguisher, he said, then explained that the overhead door onto the aft deck had been left ajar to help ventilate the engine room. A huge wave breaking over the bow swept down the deck, inundating it and spilling over the eight-inch door sill and down the hatch. Saltwater drenched the fusebox and shorted some of the lines, which caused the fire. ~

Another milestone was passed on the continuing journey to Israel, and Marion jotted in her journal:

~ Monday, June 6, 1960. 29th Wedding Anniversary. We've had a little rough weather again but nothing like the storm. I had a late watch last night so spent the morning in bed which was a luxury. Late watch coming up again tonight.

Unfortunate happening; the fuel tanks aft were not tightly stoppered at the top and in the rough weather they leaked. The oil sloshed up into the cork decks and bulkheads of the hall and adjoining rooms. No wonder the smell of fuel oil has been strong. ~

At last, on June 12, Marion wrote of their arrival in the Holy Land: "Got up at 4:30 this morning to have a first glimpse of Mt. Herman and the shore of Palestine. We came in close to the Lebanese border and then coasted down to Acre until our scheduled arrival time in Haifa, 9:30 a.m." By the 14th of June she was writing: "So happy to have Clayton here," and adding again with a note of disappointment, "if only Bill could be with us also." Clayton had arrived just after the usual confusion that accompanied landings in new ports. Only the day before Marion had written:

~ Such a busy time with many arrangements....Ed went to Caesarea and didn't get back until evening. Our representative from the foreign office has not shown up, and we are having trouble unraveling red tape regarding the Volkswagen, Chet's lack of a passport, obtaining anchor from Navy, etc. Ed is impatient and irritable due to his illness, and also his usual impatience with delays. ~

Once on Holy Land soil, Marion again took up the narrative on Israel which she had begun in 1956, still hoping to write an entire book but realizing soon enough that she was too busy living Ed's and her adventures to have the time needed to write about them extensively. She began her second attempt by describing the ship's arrival at its destination at Caesarea:

~ I was ashore when *Sea Diver* smoked her way down the coast from Haifa and edged in through the ruins of the ancient port to a berth along the inside of the narrow quai, which has been built in recent years for the local fishermen. I watched her first through an arch of the old Roman aquaduct that follows the shoreline north of the port. ~

The ancient city with its famous port was built by King Herod just before the time of Christ and was famous throughout the following centuries as headquarters of the Roman government in that part of its empire. Later it was used as a base by the Crusaders. The port, entirely man-made, was the only shelter for sailing ships along that whole stretch of coast and is described in the historical accounts of Flavius Josephus who lived at that time.

Marion continued her narrative:

~ When Ed and I were in Caesarea four years before there had been no
sign of the stone aqueduct, only a high bank of windswept sand perhaps
50 yards from the water's edge leading off to the north. There were other
changes, too. Important ones, for the state of Israel had determined to
restore the Crusader city that had been built upon the ruins of Caesarea.
And as we drove down the road leading to the kibbutz we were startled to
come upon the steep walls of the fortress city slanting down into the deep
sandy moat surrounding it. Mechanical shovels were at work there, and
hundreds of men with hand shovels were attacking the long-buried walls
of tumbled towers and keeps. ~

Marion and Clayton stood waiting for Ed on the very walls they meant to
study, once breached by the Turks when they brought about the final downfall
of Christianity in its birthplace. They felt the seabreeze as they waited, imagining the history recorded in the stones beneath their feet. Marion shuddered at
her thoughts:

~ And still the everlasting stones form a monument to that strange
upsurge of religious fervor that had sustained the Crusaders for a span of
centuries in their indefatigable attempt to wrest the Holy Land from the
'infidel.' Thousands on both sides fell in that last battle, and history
reported that the waters of Caesarea ran red with blood. ~

Clayton began to explore while his mother watched for Ed. Her text continued:

~ I looked out across the sea from the highest piece of land in the walled
city toward the north. Far on the horizon I could just make out a trail of
black smoke from *Sea Diver*. The ship was still below the horizon, for
she was traveling very slowly because of fouled engines. Just in front of
me stretched the narrow road leading to the jetty, lapped by the waves on
its southern rocky edge and bordered on the right with a row of abandoned Turkish huts. ...A pencil-thin minaret of the past century knifed
the sky. The road led out onto the jetty, which was supported by a mixture of Roman and Crusader constructions and ended in an L-shaped turn
around a small harbor. Here *Sea Diver* would be tied up while her crew
made preliminary investigations of the larger Roman Harbor with its now
buried outlines deep beneath the sea. ...Later, as we stood looking
through the arches, *Sea Diver* was seen heading toward the jetty on a cir-

cuitous track to skirt dangerous piles of stones beneath the surface. ...We hurried to the jetty, to be there when she arrived. ~

That night the crew was invited to a picnic on the beach where Israeli boys and girls sang and danced to the tune of what Marion, hearing it at a distance, described as "a strange sounding instrument." She continued:

~ Ed and I did not go to the party. We were too tired, but I'm not sure that the sights and sounds of that gay gathering on the shore will not linger in our memory longer than in the memories of those who participated. As if to climax our first night at Caesarea, as we sat on the quiet aft deck our eyes suddenly caught the brilliant flash of a large comet as it shot across the sky behind the sleeping ruins of the town. Like the stars that greeted us on our first arrival by air some four years before, it seemed a promise of things to come. ~

But good omens are not always instantly realized, and new problems soon developed. On the third day, Shabat, the Hebrew sabbath, the previously empty beaches filled up with crowds of bathers. Wegman had to put up a guard at the entrance to the jetty to prevent *Sea Diver* from being overrun with visitors. Bill Link's premonitions of crowds to come were justified. As it was, enough people got through, bearing gifts and invitations of all kinds, to keep the Links busy all day answering questions and showing visitors through the ship. All work had to be called off for the day. Then on Sunday, the Christian sabbath, the same thing happened, but where they had Israeli visitors the day before, they were now inundated with American visitors. Most of the crew had disappeared for the day, leaving only Ed, Marion, Clayton and Dorothy, the cook, to mind the ship.

As the morning advanced, a strong southwest wind came up and the sea outside the breakwater commenced to pound. Big rollers charged into the inner harbor through the entrance, creating a surge in the otherwise protected area, which kept *Sea Diver* working at her lines. As the day wore on, the sea built, the surge increased and the boat jerked violently. Several times the little crew heard sharp cracks announcing a line that had snapped under the strain. By nightfall they had lost six lines. It was a constant race to man the fenders, which were being chewed to bits against the rough cement dock, and their starboard side was scraped and blackened by the constant chafing.

The other crew members arrived after dark, too late to cast off and move the vessel outside to anchor, a delay which was a harbinger of unpleasant things to come. Ed was worrying about carelessness and a possible lack of responsibility on the part of some of the crew members, and was concerned about the weather.

Though at this time of the year one could generally count on a period of calm seas, the weather report indicated that a bad storm in the vicinity of Crete was building up the seas, which were not likely to calm down for several days. Ed was strongly advised by local fishermen to leave Caesarea for protection at Haifa, meaning delay and disappointment.

Meanwhile Marion observed in her journals that Clayton was adjusting well, having a good time with the crew and the Israelis. She and Ed were happy to have him along, though Clayton would bear his share of mishaps on this adventure. He had already badly gouged a leg that was finally healing, and now, just before leaving Caesarea, the morning after Ed had been up battling with the seas until 2:00 a.m., Clayton had the misfortune of getting an insect in one of his eyes. Once the carcass was removed, Ed discovered with a magnifying glass that it had left a deposit of larvae, described by Marion as "little white worms with black heads and eyes." Clayton was in much pain. Ed got him on the navigation table and begin removing the larvae one by one until at last, four hours later, a doctor arrived on the scene, just in time to remove the last one and administer cocaine drops to relieve the pain.

*Sea Diver* and her crew waited out the weather in Haifa, returned to Caesarea, and this time anchored well outside the jetty but still inside the circle of the ruins of the old Roman Harbor. However, in a period of nine days they never once got the needed calm to begin operations. On the first day they had optimistically called a press conference to accommodate the dozens of newsmen and photographers who had been besetting them for a story on the expedition. In spite of the seas, they were surprised to find that between 30 and 40 people had shown up on shore to be ferried to *Sea Diver* by *Reef Diver*, getting drenched along the way. Almost all of them suffered at least some degree of seasickness before returning to shore.

*Sea Diver* was already gaining a reputation for having a unique gait in certain kinds of seas, which left many a seasoned sailor — with the exception of those who had grown accustomed to her — heading for the rail, the bunks, or preferably for shore whenever possible. At times even Ed suffered from seasickness, though it wouldn't hold him down. (A future crew member, Pete Knight, tells of Ed working on a problem in the engine room late one night in terribly rough weather with a coffee can tied around his neck so he would not have to run to the rail when the urge so demanded, which Pete says was customary when the seas were that bad.)

Even the skin diving archeologist, General Yigael Yadin, former leader of the Liberation forces whom Ed and Marion had met on their first trip to Israel, had to cut short a visit aboard the rolling, bobbing *Sea Diver*. However, he did not escape before witnessing a harrowing episode. He had been aboard only a short time when *Sea Diver*, struggling to free herself from her restraints, snapped one of her lines and swung perilously close to a dangerous outcropping of rocks. Fortunately Ed got the engine going in enough time to run the vessel up on her anchor chain to what he hoped would be a safe distance from the rocks. Soon it was obvious that he couldn't stay there either, and he was forced to move the ship and reset her anchors.

At last, after a practically unbroken series of frightening incidents in continuing bad weather, he and his crew held a council of war in which it was regretfully decided to give up the struggle until the seas subsided.

In the interim they went with *Sea Diver* to Haifa yet again, and from there trailed *Reef Diver* to Tiberius to work in the Sea of Galilee. But as Marion remarked, "...not before "Old Man Sea took one last wallop at us as we prepared to leave that morning." While trying to get *Reef Diver* onto the davits, a job which Marion likened to handling an unbroken maverick, a surge raised the little cruiser six feet in the air then slapped her against the ship as she slid to the trough below. Her bow planking was smashed, a hole was stove in her side, and her lines jammed in the blocks and slipped out of their rings. The attempt to get her onto the davits obviously had to be abandoned. Fortunately the puncture was high enough to allow her to be towed safely behind *Sea Diver* to Haifa to undergo repairs before continuing on to the Sea of Galilee.

Once again Carl Jung's theory of synchronicity seemed to be evident in Ed's affairs. Due to the unusual circumstances of the weather — and at one point, quite by chance, when *Reef Diver's* engine happened to die — they would make several highly significant finds at this inland site. It was as if something behind the scenes had predetermined what it was that Link and his crew must unveil in the Holy Land.

But first the crew members had to find quarters nearby, which they managed to secure at Harts House, a YMCA hostel just north of Tiberius, which, Marion wrote, "appears to be ideal for our meals (eight of us at present)." There she and Ed found a small room as a temporary shelter for themselves while Clayton and the boys bunked outside at the bath house. Eventually she would move with Ed to the Scotch Mission nearby, where they had more comfortable quarters overlooking the lake. Still they continued for some time to take their meals at the "Y" where the crew kept their quarters for a while longer.

Ancient pottery, stone anchors such as used in primitive times, metal bowls and jars, and the remains of an ancient wooden boat along with many other precious artifacts began to show up almost immediately after they began digging in the mud bottom of the Sea of Galilee. At one point they checked out a site where a mosaic floor was said to be on the bottom, but laid that conjecture to rest when they found only a cracked, hard clay bottom dotted with small stones. These, Ed surmised, had misled the archeologists who had only seen the sea floor from the surface.

After suffering various and sundry little accidents and other medical problems, including Ed's bouts with diabetes, they were happy to welcome to their crew at the

Sea of Galilee their friends Barney (the medical doctor from Ohio) and Jane Crile, and in addition, U.S. Naval specialist, Charles Aquadro, MD, and his wife.

Marion recorded in her journal shortly afterward that Ed and Aquadro were soon investigating a mysterious stretch of ancient cement that the divers had found just off the shore. "It was approximately 15 feet below the surface," she wrote, "below the Horns of Hattin, at the foot of the mountain near Magdala." She said that it appeared to be paved and about 30 feet wide by 300 feet long. Wondering if this was a road, dock, jetty, fish-drying platform, or what, Ed looked it over thoroughly and described it as "a very straight line parallel to the shore but irregular on the sea side, about 150 feet from shore." He took samples of small cobblestones imbedded in a clay-like cement. On board ship he saw that the cobbles were round on the bottom and flat and smooth on the surface. Though it would be left to professional archeologists to determine, the pavement seemed to be evidence of the ruins of ancient Magdala. A committee report in the "Year Book of the American Philosophical Society, 1961," said that many ancient artifacts were found on that site, and concluded that the find gave clear evidence that the "'Lake of Galilee' was considerably lower in Roman times that it is now."

But the most important find at the Lake came about by chance, when *Reef Diver* one day developed engine trouble and died, leaving her occupants with nothing to do while they waited to be rescued but to dive. Right away they discovered two perfect and beautiful Roman cooking pots dating from about the first century AD. With more equipment on the site during the next few days they found other prize artifacts, including seven perfect specimens of the same type of pottery and 22 others of similar type. (While working with Marion Link on this biography, she once asked the narrator to take down a small, round clay pot from a top shelf in her den, then said, "You could be holding a pot once used by Jesus of Nazareth.")

On July 29 Marion wrote that Dr. Mazer, renowned archeologist and president of Hebrew University, visiting the site with friends, "exclaimed eagerly over our finds," and credited the diving party with collecting "a whole museum already." He was particularly taken with a group of well preserved jars, which were, he assured them, "Herodian, from between 100 BC to 100 AD, and a rare collection indeed." He said that until then there were only two of these in the Department of Antiquities, both in poor condition and much mended. He too was intrigued and puzzled over the location of the paving Ed had taken him to see, which he and other experts would eventually say they believed may be where Jesus's disciples, Peter and Paul, dried their nets along with other fishermen.

Marion then wrote that George Cassidy of the America-Israel Society and Ed went to the airport to meet Ken and Carolyn MacLeish and John Bullett who would do a story for *Life* magazine. All of the action was suddenly stepping up, with less than two months to go in the diving season. On August first she wrote:

~ We are now working two sites, Ed is cutting out a chunk of the paving below Hattin with an electric hammer, and the others are rigging an air-lift on the site where the pots were found....We are fortunate that the spot is so close to shore. The water is not clear, and it will be difficult for Ken to get underwater pictures that *Life* can use. ~

Soon another *Life* photographer, Pierre Boulat, joined them, bringing the number of their party now staying at the Mission to twelve, including the rest of the crew who had since moved from the "Y". Now all shore operations were located at the Mission, where the underwater archeologists were given a kitchen in the hospital to use for cleaning, cataloguing and storing artifacts.

The weather seemed to calm down at last. On August 6 the team returned to Haifa to prepare again for work at Caesarea. On the 9th, large blocks were found at the entrance to the Roman Harbor, which were thought to have something to do with the colossi at the port entrance. On Sunday, August 14, Ed and Marion were joined by their friends Connie Wolf (a famous woman balloonist, even into her eighties, from Philadelphia) and General "Abie" Wolf (U.S. Army), one of the founders of the Aircraft Owners Pilot Association (AOPA). Abie Wolf was also an editor of the *AOPA* magazine, to which he contributed a monthly article on aviation law.

Then once again the team went back to Tiberius, this time to be set up with film producer Ben Ozerman to do a picture on the project at the Sea of Galilee. This time Marion, skin diving in the Sea of Galilee, made the startling discovery that land animals were not the only species interested in making practical and decorative use of discarded shells and even rare artifacts from the bottom. On August 18, she recorded a find of fairy-tale proportions:

~ Spent another morning at Magdala. I found an area of the bottom that was riddled with fishes' nests. The cover was formed in the sandy bottom by rocks that had been cleaned out by the fish and shored up with broken Roman pottery and mussel shells. The fish had decorated entryways to their holes with a facing of tiny mussel shells. The large fish, golden yellow, guarded the entrances, where inside were hundreds of swimming babies. I wonder if the rocks beneath the sands of this nursery are part of the ruins of Magdala, for the water is only about ten feet deep. ~

As the days grew hot and there would be little time left for sight-seeing, the crew went off on holidays in different directions. Then on Monday, August 22, Marion wrote of their last week in Tiberius. The crew once again gathered together and they moved the airlift to Magdala to use the metal detector off shore, then took it to an area where they already had metal indications, all of which was documented by the Ozerman film crew.

*Sea Diver's* own crew was getting down in numbers when, on August 27, Clayton left for school (planning first to spend a few days with a friend in London on the way home.) "We will surely miss him here," Marion wrote, "but guess we are lucky to have had him with us all summer at this age. He has been a pleasure this year; adult enough to get along without difficulty." The crew was now down to seven.

Once again, on August 30, they returned to Caesarea. Then a significant crew change took place on September 4, which seems to have lightened Ed's load considerably even though it left him temporarily shorthanded. Marion had indicated off and on throughout the journey that Ed was edgy with one of the diver/engineers who appeared to lack a sense of responsibility, and on this day for whatever reason he let both of the engineers go. She wrote the very next day that the mood of the ship had changed for the better. Within the week Israeli divers had joined them, as had one Danny Eden who was initially to serve only as a temporary engineer but who became a regular. By the 7th, yet another Israeli diver, recorded only by the name of Saul, joined them to bring the crew number back up to ten.

Then on September 14 Luis Marden of *National Geographic* surprised them by showing up at Ceasarea. The next day Marion wrote: "Saw a comet-like object hurl across the sky tonight about 7:00 p.m. and wondered if it were a space missile reentering earth's atmosphere."

This time her comet was a positive omen. Good news came with the weather report on a Jewish holiday, September 22, and Marion wrote:

~ Happy New Year and a change in the weather! Calm, clear and wonderful for picture taking and for work. Much was accomplished today. We went in by the pillars close to shore for pictures early and then the boys worked the colossus site the rest of the day. ~

The next day:

~ We took *Reef Diver* to the Roman bath this morning to use the jet hose on the shore where a mosaic floor was said to be buried under sand and rubble. Sure enough, we uncovered a very interesting pattern in black, red, yellow and white mosaics. Also found the base of a fountain and pool with marble rim and lead pipe leading in - stone steps, etc. General Jaffe was there to assist, as was Wegman. ~

On September 24 Marion found her second coin and a seal from a ring on the bottom. "We now have several coins," she wrote, "including one found by a diver that none of the experts have ever seen before." That day they brought up a Byzantine lamp, bits of glass, a lead sounding weight — "very little," to her mind, "for all the effort put forth." However, she had grossly underestimated the value of the one odd coin.

On the 25th of September she wrote of a visit she and Ed had made in Haifa to Ben-Eli at the museum:

> ~ ...He was very excited about the coin which is silver and depicts two ships at the entrance to a harbor as well as the Greek letters "K" and "A". On the other side is a Triten - two holes punched in coin. We will have a photo enlargement made. ~

The next day Ben-Eli visited *Sea Diver* with blow-ups of the coin, still very excited about it.

By the 28th of September, Marion was complaining about the decreasing number of crew members again. Evidently she was growing tired and homesick, perhaps in particular since Clayton had left them. Maybe she even had a premonition when she wrote, "Everything is ganging up, and I will be glad when it is all over," because on the 29th, with a still shaking hand, she recorded a near disaster:

> ~ Typed out a slew of mail this morning then went for a dive by the air-lift. I was all alone waiting for Ed to come down with a camera when air suddenly went off. I coolly waited for it to go on again, rising to the surface and trying to unhook my belt. But it did not come back on. I could not get the hook unfastened and by this time I was very short of air. I popped my head above the surface, looked toward the boat and could see no one on deck. Then I saw Ed under the awning fussing with his camera. At that moment I panicked and instead of coolly removing my mask I tried to shout. I was stifling. I knew I was about to sink under water with the mask still on and die. I was desperate. Just then I got the belt loose. At the same time, miraculously the air came on and I paddled madly to the boat, sucking in great gulps of air. Jay met me as I came up the ladder and took off my mask. "We've been having some trouble with the pressure," he said. "I tried to signal you on the hose." Without any breath left to answer him, I swished below and collapsed on the bunk. ~

For several days she was bothered in her chest from the quick ascent, and finally visited a doctor who at first thought she was going to have to decompress at the hospital, but after taking tests found that fortunately all was well. After writing on October 3 that they had obtained about 3,000 feet of very good footage for the film being made, she added that they heard *Life* magazine was planning six color pages, four black and white, and two texts covering their work.

"Only in the last days of the last attempt," wrote *Life's* Ken MacLeish, "did the air-lift work its way down to the earliest Roman level, 15 feet below the sea floor....But the few hours of dredging at the deep level produced more of historical interest than did all the wind-hampered work at Caesarea." He continued with his description of the finds:

> ~ A complete storage jar appeared, then a beautifully scalloped lamp unlike any found before. There were also several carved ivory hairpins, match-thin and perfectly preserved; a metal seal bearing an image of the god Horus; bronze nails and coins. At the very end Gad Asher, an Israeli diver, picked up a tiny black disk which he tossed in with the coins. It was not a coin, however, but a tessera or commemorative medal. On the one side, under the Greek letters KA (for Caesarea), it presented a picture — the only one in existence anywhere — of Herod's great port." ~

Marion wrote on the 4th of October, "Ed is terribly tired and no relief in sight," and on the 5th, "Ben-Eli still believes our coin to be the 'one and only,' but suggests Ed take it to London to the British Museum." Then the work at Caesarea was wrapped up and they left for Jerusalem on October 6. Before leaving the country, they made arrangements to dock *Sea Diver* at Kishen fishing port near Haifa Harbor for the winter. Ed was already making plans for the following year, intending to add the waters of Greece to their agenda. Meanwhile, they had begun negotiations once again to try to visit Jordan, and after a long delay were finally given the go ahead, with just one day's notice. Then again, in a last minute visit to the Department of Antiquities with their prized (though still unrecognized) coin, they created a great stir. Happy with the results of their mission in the Holy Land, Ed and Marion congratulated themselves that they had long ago decided to pursue underwater archeology rather than treasure diving, even if it meant foregoing filling their coffers with gold and silver in favor of contributing to the growing body of historical knowledge.

On October 8, 1960, Ed and Marion Link passed through the Mandelbaum Gate with no trouble, free to set out in a car arranged by the US Consulate for the Dead Sea and Jericho. At last they would follow "the Way of the Cross," the Via Dolorosa in the old walled city where Jesus completed his earthly sojourn, winding his way on the cobblestone pavements to Golgotha, a site whose location is bitterly disputed today by various factions of his followers. Ed and Marion both were in many ways disappointed and disillusioned in old Jerusalem. She wrote in her journal that she missed the beautiful countryside of Galilee with longing in comparison to the cluster of holdings by religious groups who obviously competed vigorously with one another not only over the magnificence of their edifices but also over their claims for the authenticity of these structures as historical sites. And there were the inevitable hucksters selling religious relics.

By making that side trip when they did, the Links had unknowingly accomplished yet another "first." This time, they learned on their return, they had been the first people to cross both ways through the Mandelbaum Gate on a simple tourist passport. Still thinking like a reporter, Marion conjectured: "Perhaps Hussein's presence at the United Nations and Jordan's turning to the West is responsible."

Ed then flew to London with his prize coin, while Marion stayed behind to give a report on the results of their expedition to no fewer than 800 members of the Israel Exploration Society. "I gave my talk in the exalted company of Yadin, Biram and other archeological celebrities," she wrote, adding, "What a relief to have that over!"

Later, after flying to check out other areas in the Mediterranean and Aegean Seas for archeological research in the coming year, Ed and Marion returned for a final wind-up of their affairs in Israel. This time Ed's sister Marilyn joined them with a friend, Mauri Furbay. By then, Marion wrote on the 21st of October, she was tired and wanted to return home. On the 23rd they were joined in Haifa by friends Maurice and Anice Duriaux. They picked up the couple at the Zion hotel and brought them back to the ship to stay. "Had quite a time getting past the breakwater and finally had to leave the car at the entrance as the Navy was having night maneuvers," Marion observed.

Then a whole new problem occurred, one which almost prevented Ed from leaving *Sea Diver* at Kishen for the winter, after all the necessary arrangements had been made: "It suddenly developed that there were three sets of high tension cables over the channel entrance and our mast is too tall." After planning on making an emergency foray with the vessel to Greece for winter dockage there, they instead got unexpected assistance from an Israeli official:

~ Immanuel Ben Dor came along and the next day had things humming....The powers that be finally ordered the light company to cut the cables if necessary to get *Sea Diver* through, but by all means, to get us in to Port. So we'll stay. Danny Eden and Jay will stay with the boat this winter. ~

Meanwhile, the mysterious coin continued to arouse interest to the last, about which Marion wrote:

~ Much later, when the coin had gone the rounds of numismatists in Israel, the British Museum, and the Smithsonian, the consensus was that it was a tessara or commemorative coin of the first or second century AD, and that it very well could have been struck to celebrate the construction of the port at Caesarea. Furthermore, as far as is known, it was the only one of its kind in existence. ~

"That little thing cost us about $100,000," MacLeish quoted Ed as saying in *Life* magazine. "I guess it was worth it."

CHAPTER IX

# AN ARREST IN GREECE

**1961**

*The world is not small. It is large, so large
that a coincidence, a chance encounter between people
who share a bit of history, can seem intentional.*

—*Fannie Peczenik*
*"Antenati," Fellowship in Prayer*

"John the Greek," born John Margetis in 1936 at Sikinos, a small island south of Athens, had never heard of Ed Link and could not speak a word of English; nevertheless, he was destined in 1961 to join *Sea Diver* as cook and crewman and to become the next thing to a member of the Link family for life. It was as if the same unseen hand that guided Ed had prepared John specifically for the job; he had picked up a certain degree of savvy growing up on the streets of Athens, had gained experience at sea in the Greek Navy, and had then been forced by circumstance to give up the Navy for a better paying job as a cook to help support his parents and siblings. As it turned out, this former seaman just happened to be employed as second cook at the Plaka Restaurant near the Acropolis when a patron who knew the Links, a local architect and former member of the Greek Congress, told him of the Americans who had just passed through Athens that April on their way to Israel. They were, he said, in search of a cook who could also serve as a seaman for their archeological research yacht.

Although John was on his way up in his second career choice, making a good living for a young, unmarried Greek, he loved diving, missed working at sea, and was particularly intrigued to learn that the famous Americans intended to conduct archeological dives in his own home waters. Hardly giving it a second thought, he packed a few things, picked up a letter of recommendation from Ed's friend, and took a boat directly to Israel to see Ed. Now, more than thirty years later, he can say: "Wherever *Sea Diver* has been, I've been."

By the time John arrived at the dock at Kishen, the well-protected inner port near Haifa where *Sea Diver* had wintered, he knew a little about the famous million-

225

aire inventor and industrialist he had come to see, but was not at all prepared for his first impression of Ed: "I couldn't believe he was so simple, so humble," he says. "The first time I saw him he was in the engine room working, dirty and sweaty. It was hot on the ship and there was no air conditioning in the engine room, but he just worked on as he interviewed me, ignoring the heat."

Marion had much to consider on meeting this stranger who would work closely with her and eventually take over her galley, but because of the language barrier she could learn little from their first confused interview beyond surface impressions. John's credentials looked good, he had managed somehow to convey that he was crazy about diving, and that was all she had to go on. Though the ship had lain at port all winter and Marion was busy doing her part in only a few short days to help prepare for going to sea again, she took a moment to record in her journal:

> ~ Thursday, May 25, 1961 - Expected our Greek cook this morning and Jay went at 6:30 to pick him up, but couldn't find him although he was on the passenger list of the Atlantia. Meanwhile, I went marketing and on errands, and when I came back he had arrived, speaking not one word of English. Of course this is a real problem and I am going to have to spend a great deal of time to accomplish anything, laying out materials and going through the processes of doing things. I am discouraged, but think we can make it work. ~

The ship drew away from the dock at Kishen on Saturday, May 27, heading for an anchorage outside a Haifa shipyard for routine maintenance the next day. At the suggestion of Israeli authorities Ed had deliberately chosen to cast off on the Jewish sabbath so as not to make too great a disturbance to the country, since the power had to be cut off to let *Sea Diver's* mast through three sets of high tension lines. Meanwhile, Ed kept a speaking engagement in Jerusalem at the Department of Antiquity. Afterwards Marion recorded that though his lecture on their first expedition in Israel went well, and there was an excellent turnout, they had to cancel all social engagements connected with it because he was feeling poorly with recurring sugar problems.

On the 30th she went marketing with John for fresh fruits and vegetables before leaving the next day for Greece, after which she mentioned in her journal:

> ~ It was quite a struggle getting John to understand, but I like him; nice personality, very clean and a good cook, though slow to pick up on English. When I tell him the word in English, he repeats it in Greek. ~

After some delay — and irritation on Ed's part with workmen who put the base bottom paint on without scrubbing the bottom or thoroughly removing all of the barnacles — on May 31 the ship went back into the water, the Volkswagen and *Reef Diver* were lifted aboard, and *Sea Diver* headed out to sea. Marion wrote that everyone on board was at last able to relax, including Ed in spite of a nagging problem with maintaining a stable blood-sugar level which was still making him edgy at times.

It was a calm and beautiful day. Leaving the others to their duties and dreams, Ed and Marion stood together at the rail, feeling overjoyed to find themselves at sea again and eagerly anticipating their next adventure. They talked of how Greek waters were bound to be abundant with ancient artifacts which they alone were best equipped to bring to the surface and turn over to the appropriate Greek officials. Ed already anticipated several more visits over the years, and even voiced high hopes of making at least one major find there.

So it was that these "innocents abroad" approached that ancient land of myth and legend without the slightest notion that the same kind of cordial working relationships they had shared with scholars and officials in Israel, Jamaica and the Bahamas would not be enjoyed in Greece. Instead Ed found himself facing frustrations such as he had never dreamed of, which finally culminated in a jail sentence.

The entire episode might have taken on the dimensions of an absurd comedy if it hadn't been such a source of grief to Ed. Even so, the untrained artist produced a series of seven roughly-drawn cartoons based on his misadventures in Greece. Perhaps these, coupled with two beginnings to a lighthearted story he tried to write about them, served as a kind of catharsis for his true feelings, for despite the superficial humor, he suffered greatly from the experience. He had never before been in trouble with the law and it shamed and embarrassed him to suddenly be confronted with arrest and conviction, not to mention his outraged sense of justice at being falsely accused. By the end of the summer he left the country so upset and bitter that his dreams of future work in Greece had vanished forever. He would appeal the verdict and eventually clear his good name, but would never return even though he knew the waters to be scattered with priceless historic artifacts. In a brief description of their work in Greek waters for her book, *Windows In the Sea*, Marion pointedly omitted the painful experience as if it were not intricately woven into the fabric of the entire expedition.

Numerous and varying accounts exist of what happened to the Links in Greece. These include Ed's stories, Marion's journals and a diary by a guest aboard ship, Fred Maytag II — a good friend of Ed's and owner of Maytag Dairy Farms in Newton, Iowa, and son of the founder of Maytag Washing Machine Company. Other versions spilled from the pens of a multitude of biased Greek and confused American newspaper writers. Maytag's chronicle contains insights of special interest that are included here, not the least of which was a closing comment concerning Jacques Yves Cousteau showing that Ed had been in contact with Cousteau before going to Greece and that Cousteau had not had an easy time there either. Maytag wrote:

~ Last night at dinner Ed said he learned that when Jacques Cousteau was here with his ship Calypso, a couple of years ago, he also ran into so much trouble that he departed. Ed said, "I now understand what Cousteau meant when he said to me, 'I hope you get along all right with the Greeks.'" ~

It's difficult to tell which of Ed's two preliminary drafts on the mishap came first, but since both were unfinished and unpublished, they have been edited, in part combined and included here as perhaps the best documentation of his own thoughts on the subject. It all began, he says, in this way:

### IT'S GREEK TO ME
### "An Amazing Experience of an American Yachtsman"
### by Edwin A. Link

~ We had been pioneering for a number of years, developing equipment and techniques for finding and recovering underwater archeological artifacts, which finally resulted in designing and building our new boat, *Sea Diver*.

This year we were very excited, as we had been in contact with the Greek antiquities authorities and were assured that if we went to Greece we would have no problem working there and would be welcome. We were full of high ideals and delusions, fired up with such lofty thoughts as, given the chance and with the experience we had gained, maybe finding something comparable to the Venus de Milo which we could contribute to their museums for posterity.

But first we needed a rest after two years of hard, serious work at Jamaica in the Caribbean and at Isreal. [Covered by *National Geographic* magazine, February, 1960; and *Life* magazine, April, 1961.] We looked forward to a nice, leisurely cruise with several good friends through the Greek Isles on our way to Athens.

Our troubles began at Rhodes, where one of the seven wonders of the world, a collosus through whose legs ships were supposed to be able to pass, turned out according to modern researchers to be fictitious.

...We had finished a most wonderful cruise with *Sea Diver* from America to Haifa, Israel. In 1960 we had done an expedition to the ancient biblical city of Caesarea, built by King Herod the Great just before Christ died, from where Christ's disciples Peter and Paul departed to preach their gospel of Christianity to the world.

We had on board a striking pamphlet, printed in color and issued by the Greek tourist office, describing the simplicity and beauty of yachting in Greek waters. But we were due for enlightenment the moment we reached Rhodes.

No sooner had we dropped anchor than a rather imposing group of men in white uniforms filed aboard. They were the Navy Police, in quantity. Little did we know at that time that they were to be our constant companions. We were overwhelmed at their numbers as they came and demanded to take inventory of almost everything; our cameras, provisions, and even our decorations. We were then introduced to Greek red tape and rubber stamps. This rather shocked us, as it was so unlike the expectations we had built up from the picture painted by the lovely brochure. But it did not dismay us; after all, weren't all port officials the world over in love with rubber stamps? Of course here we had to make visits ashore as the Greeks had devised a few more requirements than usual, but, we thought, this could be a lovely collection of rubber stamp "art" that in the year 3,000 would be a treasure just as ancient Greek coins are today.

After a day and a half of that slight annoyance, armed at last with a long document, an inventory of almost everything we had on board, including our lounge decor of old guns, swords, armor, and an imposing document in Greek with a beautiful collection of rubber stamps that we had been required to obtain, we felt that we were well in Greece and on our way.

A Greek crew member we had engaged had failed to appear, so being short handed, we were happy to have a young American military man aboard as a volunteer, but alas, this would cause us to learn still more about the simple means of yachting in Greece than our fine booklet outlined.

Upon arrival at the next port, another, larger delegation in white uniforms filed aboard demanding a crew list. This was a surprise for which we were not prepared, but we willingly complied, thereby bringing about more problems and several hours of questioning. Why did we have an extra man aboard? Where was he from? Where was our certified crew list? Didn't we know we were subject to jail and fine because this man wasn't cleared from Rhodes? Finally, we learned another lesson quite well, that each island clears you like going from one country into another. So, thinking that we were now well informed, with expressed regret at our stupidity, we were cleared and proceeded on.

We thought then ...that our troubles were over — but alas, we had to realize, "we ain't learned nothin' yet;" we were only just beginning. At the next landing, tying up stern first in a typical small, overcrowded Greek harbor, we cut a fisherman's anchor line. Not wishing any more arguments we promptly paid him double what the line was worth and got

settled in. Then we were visited by the usual array of men in white uniforms and we collected more autographs and rubber stamps, which took
several hours time and necessitated another shore visit.

We got underway in the morning. The next port again being small,
and not feeling flush enough to buy more line for another fisherman, we
decided to anchor out in the harbor. Also we had noticed on the way an
unusual vibration and a leak in our starboard shaft seal, probably caused
by the line caught in the propeller. However, this didn't bother us too
much, for didn't we have aqualung equipment aboard which could allow
us to make repairs underwater quite easily?

We hardly got into the water when our friends the Navy police came
out ten strong in a launch and subjected us to an hour of questioning,
then informed us that we couldn't dive, even to make repairs, without a
permit from Athens.

Another lesson learned; we couldn't dive or swim so as not to cause
more trouble, but we were not dismayed because the water was cold anyway. We felt much like the old American nursery rhyme:

Mother may I go out to swim?
Yes, my darling daughter,
Hang your clothes on the hickory limb,
But don't go near the water.

More rubber stamps, a crew list, and the necessity of taking a taxi
across the island to collect more autographs and rubber stamps, then we
proceeded the next morning through several other islands.

Now we could not help but notice that we were accompanied by a
gunboat, which followed us from island to island for the next several
days. We joked about this for a while; after all, we must certainly be
"VIPs" to have such an escort, but after following us port after port, it
became annoying so we hailed the Captain and asked why we were being
followed. His amazing reply was that he wasn't following but only
accompanying us in case we needed assistance. Incredible! How lucky
we were to cross the Atlantic and the Mediterranean without his aid!

At Mikonos one of those winds that blow frequently through the
Greek Islands greeted us, and after anchoring several times, with the
anchor dragging each time in the small, overcrowded harbor, we decided
that we had to anchor outside in the shelter of a nearby point. This we
did, and though I was in the habit of diving down to inspect or set the
anchor whenever we were in an exposed place, after our previous sad

experience, not wishing to excite our friends again, I dispensed with this safegaurd and posted an anchor watch for the night instead.

A good precaution, for just past midnight the watch sang out, "Dragging anchor and headed for rocks!"

All hands were soon on deck to avoid shipwreck, and after trying unsuccessfully to find our anchorage again (...safe anchorages outside of harbors are scarce), we put on the radar, and having to run all night anyway, gave up the rest of our trip and headed for Piraeus. We'd had enough of playing "robber and pirate" with our gunboat escort anyway, and wanted to get to Athens to clear up our status.

Our gunboat crew must have been terribly annoyed when they couldn't find us the next morning as they had no radar to follow us with. They must have also been quite surprised that we turned up at Piraeus the next morning instead of skipping the country, as I am sure they had expected.

This, however, didn't dismay them much, though their minds were full of international smugglers who come to rob them of their antiquities. Sophia Loren, with her beautiful figure, had recently played the part of a lovely, sexy girl in the "Boy on the Dolphin," so named after a rare Etruscan artifact, which had somehow translated to us, convincing every Greek that we answered the description of the American yachtsman who came to smuggle antiquities out of Greece. [A UPI story about Link, dateline Dec. 24, 1961, by Jack V. Fox says the movie with Sophia Loren and Clifton Webb had just been shown in Greece. Fox described it as "... the story of a millionaire archeologist who sailed his yacht into Greek waters and was apprehended trying to get away with the Etruscan figure."]

On arrival at Piraeus we were again boarded eight or ten strong by the Navy police and endured the necessity of getting long endorsements and rubber stamps on our documents. We were then invited, or rather told, to go to Athens and explain our actions to the Greek "FBI." After three grueling hours we finally felt well assured that all was now understood, or so we thought.

But it seemed that no one was to be trusted in Greece, not even the Greeks, as was proven in subsequent events. Only for a while did we think all was well. Mr. Papadimitrio, head of the Department of Antiquities, was aboard for lunch and was greatly interested in our boat and equipment and what we could do for him. We met [Greek Navy] Admiral Voutsaras, head of the Hellenic Subaquatic Federation sponsored by the Queen [Frederika], who was designated to act as liaison and who proved to be a staunch friend to the end. [Before leaving

Athens Ed was assured that all of his papers (in Greek) were in order, and he was told to go Perachora to await Voutsaras.]

We were asked to do some diving at Voula Bay, and also to check out a site where sunken ruins were reported. We weren't particularly enthusiastic about these assignments as they were dull and the drags of what was possible, but we did them just the same, for we felt we must cooperate and take the bad with the good that we hoped for in the future. There were members of the Greek sport divers aboard, a fine group of young men which we welcomed, fed and berthed. We did our assignments willingly and well, mapping, photographing, and reporting in detail at considerable effort and expense to ourselves.

And then, through a small error, the roof fell in and the police "threw the book at us." ~

* * *

SO ENDS ED'S TALE. Just as the intrigue mounted and the situation worsened, he seems to have lost interest in writing about it. Meanwhile, Marion had been recording her own observations in her journal as they traveled through the Greek Isles. Optimistically, while still on the way to Rhodes, she wrote on leaving Cyprus:

~ Tuesday, June 6, 1961 (Our 30th Anniversary) - Went to market and did some final errands this morning, then took off for Rhodes right after lunch by way of the southern shore. The weather and sea were perfect and we enjoyed every minute of it. This is our 30th Anniversary, I can't believe it! ~

That entry was to be one of the last optimistic notes for some time to come. On June 7, as the seas kicked up in a storm and everyone on board was suffering from a touch of "mal de mer," the left engine had quit and the automatic pilot was down, she wrote: "Very happy, soon after I went on watch at 6:00 a.m., to see the coast of Rhodes."

But as Ed had observed in his story, it was at Rhodes that they ran into their first sign of trouble, and by the time the confused ensemble reached Athens, Marion was writing:

~ Wednesday, June 21 ...Ed and I were requested to appear at the Customs Research and Investigation office (Greek FBI, I guess) and Ed was interrogated under oath as to our movements and plans. This is getting to be a regular cloak and dagger operation. Costa [a Greek friend who was providing assistance] and the ship Chandler went with us to translate ...two other men sat idly at their desks, who Costa is sure understood English. ~

Still the dogging continued, with little understanding of what was happening on the part of *Sea Diver's* party. Marion had also written that earlier, outside Athens on June 16, Clayton, now out of school for the summer, had arrived on an island boat at 4:00 a.m. That day they had taken off for Patmos after Ed cleared with the authorities. The Coast Guard set out soon afterwards, arriving in Patmos just as they were dropping anchor. She then commented: "...queer doings and Ed is mad at their following us."

On the 21st in Athens they went to the Archeological Department to see Papadimitrio's assistant and learned that their proposal for permits was due to come up the following Tuesday. Then Marion mentioned that they met with an Admiral Alexandrous, "who was helpful." On the 22nd she wrote of the mounting tension:

~ Small frustrations all day and Ed is fit to be tied! Then this evening John brought aboard Sergeant Wood [the American military man Ed had mentioned in his version] who has organized a skin diving club within the armed forces here and has dived on many interesting spots. He gave us new hope that we can establish permission to dive through another channel, a Confederation of Skin Diving Clubs, sponsored by the Queen. He brought along the confederation's chairman, who is also on the Archeological Board, Admiral Voutsaras, who became very interested in our ship and its possibilities.

There is more intrigue in this land. Would love to go diving with Bill Wood but don't dare move until we are in the clear. ~

On another occasion, after sight-seeing at Mycenae while awaiting the longed for permissions, Marion wrote of their being secretly shown small pieces of artifacts from Mycenae by the proprietor of a lodging there, who tried to sell them on the black market.

Finally, on Monday, June 26 they received the good news: Bill Wood had come to visit with Admiral Voutsaras to say arrangements had been made for the Link party to dive under the auspices of the Hellenic Federation of Sub-Aquatic Activities, also sponsored by the Queen, first on one of their own established dive sites near Athens then at a choice site off the coast of Crete. On Tuesday they scurried to leave for the beautiful harbor of Vouliagmena east of Athens. Ed, as usual, had more difficulties with customs, more crew lists were demanded, and then at last they were off.

Meanwhile Marion and Clayton drove in the Volkswagen to meet the ship, arriving at the new port in time to help tie up their hard-working vessel between an elegant British yacht and an extravagant American yacht. They were cleared to dive on the following Friday. She wrote on Wednesday that customs agents demanding to see a crew list were included in their list of visitors to the ship that day. "Ed is so fed up," she continued. "He drove into Athens to the Greek Tourist Office to complain, and was rewarded with the assurance that this was completely unnecessary at each port as long as we stayed in Greece."

In spite of their troubles a number of friendly dignitaries continued to flow across the decks of *Sea Diver*, including, on June 28, the American Vice-Consul, Bill McGrew and his wife. At least to some extent things seemed to be going their way. On the 30th they anchored over a 4th- Century BC amphorae wreck, near a long reef offshore from Vaula, with, as noted by Marion, "the whole beautiful panorama of Athens - Piraeus, mountains, islands and sea about the horizon."

At last the divers began to breath easier. Evidently possibilities for expanding their operations were opening up. They learned that arrangements were made allowing them to dive on a series of sites around Greece, including Methanan, a sunken ancient town of the Peloponnesus; Marathon Bay with approximately 200 wrecks of ancient ships, where they hoped to find bronze statues; Navarino Bay, where Greece was at last freed from Turkish domination; and elsewhere in the Bay of Corinth.

Meanwhile they were joined on the first wreck by Greek skin divers who began photographing and mapping amphorae with Ed. *Sea Diver* and crew were finally at work doing what they came to Greece to do. Marion wrote that Bill Wood and Admiral Voutsaras appeared almost every day.

On their last day at the first wreck site they were met by Greek acquaintances Costa and Julia Tanes, as well as by the same Admiral Alexandrous previously referred to in the journal. Then well-known American marine archeologist Peter Throckmorton arrived. All were particularly delighted with an almost complete amphora that Bill Wood had produced. Artifacts collected were ultimately moved to shore and catalogued, and a complete report for the authorities was prepared by Ed. Then they moved on. Numbers of amphorae were found as the party cruised from site to site. On one occasion Marion wrote: "We have a beautiful, complete amphora which Jay and Clay dug out with our hammer today. Dimitrio [a Greek archeologist aboard] thinks it is Roman 1st century B.C." On the 19th of July she wrote: "Found the remains of a Greek shipment of tiles (Laconian, according to Dimitrio, 5th-century) and brought up samples."

At Vouliagmena, on Sunday, July 23, Bill Wood arrived at *Sea Diver* to tell Ed that Papadimitrio, with whom he had been trying to make contact for some time, could see him that day at one o'clock in the city. Donning their street clothes in spite of the oppressive heat, he and Marion left the ship and drove into Athens. Afterwards she happily jotted down the results:

~ Had a nice visit. He was very cordial and practically gave us the keys to Greek waters. Told us to make out our itinerary and he would okay it. So we are going to the Gulf of Corinth next week: Perachora, Heliki, Phea, and Navarino - later, perhaps to Delos. ~

On July 24 she received a letter commissioning her to write a story on Navarino for *National Geographic*. "They will send a photographer," she recorded, adding, "They said my Port Royal story had been one of their most popular features [February, 1960]." Perhaps it was a harbinger of things to come when, breaking into this peaceful lull in her recorded events, she continued on the 27th:

~ *Sea Diver* set out for more work in Voula Harbor this morning while John and I headed for the market. When we returned two hours later, they were still there, our anchor and chain all snarled up with two other boats next to us. In this harbor everyone drops their anchor in the middle and ties up stern-to. It is not a very good system when there are lots of boats. Our boys dived all morning, untangling the snarl and it was noon before we got away. ~

She wrote on Saturday, July 29, that they were joined by visiting American guests, the Fred Maytags and the Hugh O'Briens, following the departure of their friends Barney and Jane Crile who had accompanied them for several weeks. On the 31st Marion's journal shows that the party cruised through Saronic Gulf and Corinth Canal, then anchored for the night at Loutraki. She mentioned on the same day that their Caesarea story finally appeared in *International Life* the previous week. The next day *Sea Diver* cruised out of Loutraki early in the morning, then because of high seas and rough winds, continued on to Perachora instead of going back to Loutraki. They attempted for more than an hour to tie up at Perachora, but without success. "We then retreated down the shore and anchored," Marion wrote, but evidently the anchor did not hold because she added, "We finally returned to the cove at Perachora and by lunch time had lines out to the rocks, and an anchor down." Finally all seemed well enough in spite of the winds. The afternoon was spent scouting the bottom, diving and bringing up intriguing amphorae from a depth of over 100 feet and described as having unusual mouths.

Party members at that time, as told in a report by guest Fred Maytag, were, in addition to himself, his wife Ellen, and the Links:

~ ... a paid crew of five, consisting of Jay [Elliott], a 25-year old Texan who has been with the ship since it left the States over a year ago. He came originally as a diver, but Ed has taught him seamanship and navigation so that now he is a very competent mate. The engineer is Danny, a 40-year old Englishman who has an Israeli wife and 3-year old daughter, and who shipped on in Israel. The cook is John, a pleasant, slightly chubby Greek who knows only two or three words of English but prepares deliciously indigestible food, cooked in olive oil. ...A handsome young Greek seaman named Tony who fortunately speaks both English and Greek, whose usual attire is khaki shorts and a crucifix. The fifth member is Clayton, Ed and Marion's handsome 19-year old son who is a student at Colgate University. In addition to the Hugh O'Briens and the Maytags, who are classified as guests, we also have Bill Wood, about 30 years old, who is a Technical Sergeant with the Air Force Communications Base at Athens....He is officially assigned to the expedition by the Air Force as diver, photographer and radio man.

It is a very harmonious and happy crew, although the unmarried boys wish we would stay long enough in one spot so they could get better acquainted with the local girls. Clayton had a beautiful 20-year old Greek goddess aboard for dinner this evening. ~

Though offhand references to the dating activities of the crew are laced throughout journals and diaries devoted to *Sea Diver's* travels, none are so pointed as the comments made about the above mentioned girl. John Margetis refers to "poor Clayton," who according to all accounts had been temporarily bewitched by the stunning young college student from Athens.

Wednesday, August 2, started off innocently enough. Marion walked with Ed up to the light house at Perachora that morning to take pictures, and later wrote: "Saw Clay and Jay diving far below on the rocks, bubbles showing their location. They brought up and showed us a beautiful amphora from a ship wreck."

However, on their return to *Sea Diver* they found none other than the Navy police aboard. Between gesticulations and translations, they soon understood that for some unknown reason the police wanted to take away all the amphorae that were on the deck, but Ed, who had been warned to deal firmly with local officials, told them he was to meet Admiral Voutsaras in Loutraki the next day and would take them there himself. He then sent a crew member to shore with the police to telephone the Admiral and explain.

However, the crewman returned to say that the Admiral had sent word to Ed: "No more diving." But by then the boys were already back in the water with the small boat. Meanwhile, the police reappeared and said *Sea Diver* must leave immediately and return to Loutraki. Ed, who was photographing antiquities at the time, suddenly made the decision to put them all back into the sea, as retrieving them was evidently causing trouble. "We asked the police on shore to please observe," Marion wrote. At that point the boys returned with another big amphora, which was photographed and also lowered overboard. Refusing the escort, Ed then proceeded to Loutraki, where, she reported:

~ The Admiral arrived and seconded the desire of the police to search the ship. Much confusion! We were finally cleared of harboring illegal antiquities and were told we could go ashore, but without packages. ~

On Thursday, August 3, her log continues:

~ Went shopping and marketing this morning and had lunch ashore. Mr. Howey arrived in the afternoon from the Embassy. The Admiral was busy all day. The police informed us that we are to be tried for being at Perachora illegally, and asked Ed, Clayton, and Jay for statements. We are more and more aware that we are in trouble. The trial is set in Corinth tomorrow morning. Such sadness, after two wonderful days at Perachora.

The Admiral now says we should not have been there; that when he said we could go to Perachora, he thought we had wanted permission to visit the little town up in the mountains. ~

On Friday, August 4, her only comment was: "The evil day!"

Ed had been arrested on Thursday, and with no time for preparation, had been tried the first thing the next morning and convicted of diving at Perachora without permission. As soon as the trial was over, he and Marion tried to piece together just exactly what had happened. Meanwhile Maytag had written:

~ Instead of being an informal hearing as was expected, it turned out to be a full-blown trial which lasted three hours, before three judges with four or five Coast Guardsmen, the district archeologist, and the temple keeper at Perchora all testifying....There was a competent interpreter who gave Ed a highly condensed version of the testimony and proceedings. ~

The day after the trial Marion wrote:

~ We spent most of the day drafting a letter to Mr. Papadimitrio, explaining our position and how the misunderstanding originated. A friend from Athens took it personally to be delivered. We are all pretty low and pretty sad, and we are very unhappy over keeping our guests twiddling their thumbs. ~

Monday morning found Ed and Marion caught up in a montage of events. "Were at the American Embassy this morning," her entry in the journal reads, "and from then on things roared." It continued:

> ~ Consulted with the Embassy lawyer, Deloukas, meeting with the minister of the Prime Minister in the Parliament Building, Haggerty, Papadimitrio, the Admiral - a visit to lawyer Papaspirou about filing an appeal. We had a quick lunch at the Haggerty's, and moved our things from the hotel to stay overnight with them. More conferences at the Embassy. ~

In one of the conferences the Admiral asked Marion to write an explanatory letter to *National Geographic* and the *Smithsonian*. He further offered to help in every way, and in spite of all that had transpired, made it known that he still wanted them to continue with the plans for Navarino. Though Ed thought better of it, he agreed on the chance he could still clear himself.

Marion's sometimes enigmatic notes jotted during these sessions are testimony to their agitation and to the atmosphere of intrigue in which she and Ed were entangled:

> ~ - Permission canceled Sat. following trial.
> - P. is waiting for orders from T. to proceed. Will not be offended if orders come from higher up but welcome it.
> - Keep trying to see P. and be friendly to show no ill feelings.
> - Y. does not like P., Y. is on another board and has different policies.
> - Thinks permission will be put thru immediately after meeting with T.
> - Wants us to write letter to embassy protesting our treatment by port police to be forwarded to certain government offices.
> - Says reason for treatment is that policy is new this year of allowing boats freedom of ports except for ports of entry and departure.
> - Wants photostats of Smithsonian letter.
> - Wants last report on M. which we gave to P.
> - Wants copy of my book *Sea Diver*.
> - Admiral visited Press Minister this a.m. 8:30. Government now ripe to act. Tell Embassy to press diligently for settlement. T. back today in office later this afternoon. P. Tues. a.m. (Link to see him 10:00 a.m. if possible.)
> - Admiral will accompany us to Navarino - told them we would go not for science but to vindicate our honor -
> - P. caught in bad position - made mistake by hasty action - We should try to continue our original friendly contact. ~

John Margetis, the ship's cook, who saw himself acting not only as a character witness but as a defense attorney, tells now how the Links were deeply discouraged by their treatment before the trial, particularly because Ed, as he said, "was taken right away to court, with no time to call the Embassy or lawyers." He describes how Ed tried to defend himself without knowing the language and without a lawyer. According to John's report, Ed was completely abandoned by all of the Greek divers who had been on the ship — most of them Greek Navy personnel who were evidently afraid to defy the authorities.

Anything to do with archeology in Greece, then as now, is highly political and competitive among various factions, and Ed Link was unwittingly caught in the intrigue in his trial. Adverse publicity did not help his cause. Furthermore, it was not easy for John to defend Ed against popular opinion, and because he tried, he received numerous threats from officials and even from his acquaintances as well. The Greek press automatically assumed Ed to be guilty, making John's position awkward at the very least.

"Everyone asked me," John says today in his still halting English, "how come a Greek young guy like you defend Americans who steal artifacts from under water?"

In the UPI story inserted by the biographer in Ed's version of events leading to the arrest, reporter Fox saw humor in the situation and wrote: "Link was arrested earlier this year in what to him is a most irritating but to others a rather hilarious misunderstanding over where he was permitted to look for underwater treasure near the Bay of Corinth."

Afterward the Links went over the trial with John and read translated transcripts, and only then did they understand fully all that had taken place in court. As John tells it, they learned that John had gotten angry and had said that the judge didn't know what he was talking about, for which he was threatened with punishment. Nevertheless, John went on to point out that whatever was on *Sea Diver* was listed by Link with the American Embassy and with the Greek government. He told the judge, "You go and search *Sea Diver*, and then if you find anything you can talk about it," knowing full well there was no damaging evidence to be found. He reminded the court that at all times when they were diving they had people from the Greek archeology department aboard, that whatever was found was listed in inventory documents and photographed. He also told them that all of the retrieved objects were finally taken to the Greek museum in Athens, and further stated that the only thing of national interest that the Links had kept on board was a large amphora, which the Greek government had given Ed as a souvenir.

"People like the Links are interesting, and very valuable people who work in countries like ours, to bring Greek underwater history up to date," John assured the court. He then told the judge: "You do not know who Link is, what an important inventor." Evidently the judge wasn't impressed, and he again threatened to punish the young Greek for interfering. Finally John said: "You're the judge, but whatever the decision, we are going to appeal."

Despite John's loyal and heartwarming attempts in Ed's behalf, which probably did help reduce the charges, Ed was convicted and given a six month jail term, but was offered an opportunity to pay the sentence off for a fee set at an astonishing $750.00. Ed responded immediately by writing a check to free himself, but then ran into yet another snag, for no one wanted to cash it. At that point a frantic search for a bank willing to accept the check began by phone, while John ran around Corinth trying to convince bankers that Ed was a legitimate American businessman whose checks, including his own paychecks, were always good. At last the check was cashed late that day and Ed was freed from jail, however unhappy at being wrongly convicted in the first place.

Maytag wrote that the original charges were: attempting to illegally export artifacts; exploring without a permit; resisting arrest; and - [reportedly alleged by a *Sea Diver* crew member] threatening to throw a Coast Guardsman overboard. "The judges," he summarized, "found him guilty of exploration without a permit and dismissed the other charges."

After turning the case over to the Embassy, Ed appealed the verdict and eventually won, almost two years later, but in his mind the damage was already done. Afterward the Greek government apologized to him, returned his money, and even wanted him to carry out another expedition in Greece to fulfill his formerly extensive diving plans, but Ed refused to do so. He had had enough; particularly with what followed after he was freed and given permission to conduct his final mission in Greek waters at Navarino.

And by now Ed also had other things on his mind. He saw more and more the need to find ways of carrying out underwater work without having to constantly worry about air hoses or running out of air with scuba gear. His mind was drawn again and again to the submersible decompression chamber (SDC) he had designed and was having built at home. On his way to Navarino he thought about his coming trip to Monaco, fervently wishing that the SDC could somehow be ready for experiments there. Even as he carried out archeological dives in Greece he had begun to lay careful plans for new equipment and systems that would allow man to remain underwater and work for long periods of time. He had begun to outline what he called his "Man-In-Sea" program. He had seen the need for university programs in underwater archeology, and was writing to and negotiating with Tufts University and other colleges about his ideas. He told UPI writer Fox even as late as 1961, "There are not more than 10 qualified underwater archeologists in the world and not more than three or four who also know diving techniques of marine extractions," adding, "and after all, you can only spear fish for so long." (Some time later Ed was awarded an honorary degree by Tufts University.)

With the SDC on his mind, Ed headed for Navarino Bay but his heart was no longer in the expedition. As Maytag had observed immediately after the conviction:

~ Ed is completely shattered by the experience. His reaction is to pay the fine and immediately leave for Italy where he has been invited to collaborate with a Tufts University archeological expedition. However, we persuaded him instead to file an appeal bond (interestingly, only $500, which is less than the amount of the fine) in order to gain time in which to try to clear up the misunderstanding. ~

And so *Sea Diver* remained in Greek waters. Marion wrote that at one point on the way to Navarino the boys wanted to spear fish but Ed insisted that they get clearance to do so with the port police, "who, at first, were cordial and then, on second thought, refused." Then she remarked: "Everyone upset again over this, as this prohibition is not enforced against other boats."

Throughout all of the intrigue and irritations, in spite of drawbacks and moods of despair, Ed's spirits could still rise when the occasion warranted, as evidenced by an entry written by Maytag on Wednesday, August 9:

~ ...It has been decided that we will make a leisurely cruise of the Ionian Islands along the west coast of Greece. However, the government has requested us not to visit Corfu, because the royal family [King Paul and Queen Frederika] are there aboard their yacht vacationing and attending the international sailing races which are in progress. Ed remarks with a wry smile that this is the first time he has ever been in a position of embarrassing a king. ~

But he was uncomfortable all the same, and so disgusted by all that had happened that he canceled the visit from the *National Geographic* team scheduled to join them at Navarino. Even after meeting with the resident archeologist at Olympia, who was in charge of Navarino and that whole part of the Peloponnesus, and who Marion says "commiserated with us on our troubles," they were not free from suspicion. August 17 found them at Patras, once more being invaded by Navy police and customs who demanded to search the boat. Ed, outwardly polite but seething with anger, refused to allow it unless they produced orders and called the American Consul to be present. The police returned to shore leaving three guards aboard. At Ed's insistence they took along one of his crew for them to show him their orders, though none were ever produced. An hour later, after placing a call to Athens, one of the Greek officials returned to the ship, made apologies, and told the guards to leave.

Marion reported another hectic day on August 18, talking with the Embassy, lawyers, etc., but says there was definitely a better climate in the press. At this point, public opinion had begun to sway in the Links' favor, though the matter would never be set at rest because intrigue was evidently such an ingrained habit indulged in by the Greeks. Marion says one of the dive federation members, "shocked, up in arms, and with tears in his eyes," apologized to them for all they had been through. She also wrote on the 18th that two of the key figures Ed tried to reach by phone were mysteriously "unavailable," that everywhere he tried to call he was turned away with excuses. "There is much intrigue behind all this," she remarked, "stemming chiefly, we are told, from violent schisms in one of the concerned departments and its council." Those who would help were often caught in the middle.

On August 19 they were visited by a cordial Greek Navy general who told them that the Coast Guard had orders from the archeological department to keep them under surveillance from the time *Sea Diver* reached Rhodes; that these orders had never been canceled. "What gives?" a perplexed Marion asks in her journal, and then adds, "He will use his connections to find out more."

If it were true that the movements of the stars actually had an influence on human affairs that allowed for prediction, Ed might have had a horoscope drawn before entering Greek waters and saved himself some grief. Surely such a reading would have warned him to stay away, for yet another incident was to aggravate him. This time one of their Greek social acquaintances, who had forwarded their mail, made some appointments for them, and otherwise been kind enough to give them an occasional hand in small ways, suddenly presented Ed with a bill of $4,000. He said it was "for services [supposedly as an unauthorized agent] from the first of the year." Marion's only recorded comment was: "Our faith in humanity...is sorely tried." The bill was later retracted, but once again the damage was done in Ed's mind.

On August 24 *Sea Diver* was still waiting for permission to work in Navarino in compliance with the Admiral's wishes. Anxious to get on with it, and to get out of the country, they were told by the Admiral, typically, to wait until the permit was in his hands, and meanwhile not to talk with any Greek divers.

Still wanting to be understood and to clear his good name, Ed had seemed to put up with all the cloak and dagger business rather well for a man known to be impatient with bureaucracy. But Marion knew him better than anyone and she knew that he was barely containing his emotions. Therefore she was not surprised when he finally began to boil over:

> ~ Ed completely fed up and almost hysterical after the Admiral left. I had
> to go to the Admiral's club and tell him we simply have to get started or
> he will have a breakdown. ~

She was quite serious about Ed's state of mind. His health had suffered ever since he began to show symptoms of diabetes. As always, he had only a limited amount of time for the mission, and he was in no condition to handle the constant stress and tension imposed upon him by the often ridiculous posturings of certain

Greek officials. Finally the permit came allowing them to go on with their mission. At last they headed for Navarino — perhaps best known to Americans from the movie, "The Guns of Navaronne," which documented the dramatic arrival of allied troops on Greek soil to roust out the occupying Germans near the end of World War II. *Sea Diver* sailed into the southwest Peloponnesus on August 27, about which Marion wrote in *Windows In the Sea*:

> ~ Navarino Bay is the site of an early nineteenth-century battle between the Turks, who had occupied Greece for 300 years, and the combined strength of British, French, and Russian ships. When the battle was over, the Turkish fleet [of 60 warships] lay at the bottom of the bay, and Turkish dominance [of Greece] was at an end.
>
> Because of the depth of the harbor, no successful salvage of these ships had been possible in the past. Now with the more advanced tools for underwater salvage offered by *Sea Diver*, Greek officials hoped to ascertain the present state of the sunken ships and the prospects for recovering them. ~

As *Sea Diver* sailed into the long narrow harbor between what Marion describes as "high guardian rocks pitted with caves," she says they saw one of the loveliest panoramas in all Greece:

> ~ Slender, rocky islands formed the western border tapering off into the distance while grape-clad hills sloped steeply to form the eastern shore. To the right, the little town of Pylos lay on a crescent hillside encircling a small port dominated to the south by a hilltop Venetian castle. ~

At first Ed and his crew barely noticed the tiny fishing boat in their midst. Then they began to realize that wherever they went, the same fisherman was always somewhere nearby. They were being followed. Granted, this time it was not a gun-boat, but nevertheless, they obviously were not out from under the cloud of suspicion that had hung over them from their initial arrival at Rhodes.

On Wednesday, August 30, Marion wrote that Peter Throckmorton arrived that night, followed by Mike Papadagonis. On the 31st she recorded in her journal a scene that reads like a paragraph straight out of a Le Carre novel:

> ~ We began to realize we are being spied on - man in a small rowboat, posing as a fisherman, has been hanging around us ever since the first day. Last night he followed us into the dock, put on a white shirt, combed his hair, looked at his wrist watch, and headed for town. This noon, when the

Admiral and Papadagonis accosted him, he said he was just fishing and refused to give any information, but headed for town shortly afterward. ~

On the following day an alarming event of another kind temporarily broke the suspense. Marion recorded on the first of September:

~ Peter gave everyone a thrill while being towed by dropping off the tow when the boys were not paying attention. When he got to the surface, they were far away. He finally decided to swim ashore and had disappeared again by the time they discovered he was missing. A good lesson for them all, as long as he was safe. ~

On Thursday and Friday, September 7 and 8, the work was winding down and she wrote:

~ I guess our diving activities here are over, as the Admiral failed to send us more divers. He wired that a Dr. Muros will be here on Saturday, but, as we are going to Athens on Sunday, this is no help....We felt pretty low at seeing Clayton off [to return to school at Colgate], as we still have a couple of months before returning to Binghamton. ~

The water at Navarino Bay, ranging from 40 to 80 feet deep near shore to 135 feet offshore, was too deep for any great success on this part of the mission. Divers were unable to stay underwater long enough for careful surveys without having to undergo long periods of decompression. Marion wrote that Ed had thought longingly of the SDC back in the United States, which they had just heard was completed and ready for inspection, much too late in the season for it to be of any use until the coming year. Had it been available in Navarino Bay, the divers could have conducted thorough investigations of the buried ships. As it was, Marion wrote with a mixture of relief and resignation: "Faced with so many handicaps, it was reluctantly decided to cancel any further attempts that year."

Although Ed's name was to be cleared of any wrongdoing in Greece, he never did reach a definitive conclusion as to why *Sea Diver* fell under so much suspicion on cruising into Rhodes. He thought it was possible that the Greeks had made an imaginary connection between his expedition and the movie, "The Boy on the Dolphin." Another party member thought he saw an indirect connection in the presence of Peter Throckmorton. Throckmorton was a young, famed, itinerant American archeologist who had worked two summers before on a Bronze-Age shipwreck (dated circa 1600 BC) found in 120 feet of water off Cape Gelidonya, Turkey. The wreck was considered to be the oldest ever explored until that time. Throckmorton had conducted his underwater work with an American yachtsman who unfortunately smuggled a sampling of the raised artifacts to the United States. The yachtsman had then exercised further bad judgment by talking about the smuggled artifacts on television, thereby causing an international scandal that surely reached archeological interests in Greece. In that case, it is conceivable that Ed was unjustly categorized by the wary Greeks, ignorant of his sterling character, as yet another deep-diving American yachtsman who was only out for himself.

On September 15 the Links received an official permit to keep one amphora, 5th-Century BC, which had already been unofficially given to them at the second wreck at Voula. Bearing only one artifact as they left Greece was hardly what the Greeks had suspected of them, and it was a gift at that. Marion commented: "I am very pleased, as it will be our only souvenir of Greece."

They left the country with the opportunity for Ed to clear his name still pending, on September 16, 1961, but not without one final dramatic surprise. "Woke up this morning," Marion recorded, "to find a destroyer and a gunboat in the harbor. As we were to leave for Italy that day, we said this must be our escort." And again officials did not not make it easy for Ed. After passing customs he was held up for hours by immigration officials who would not let *Sea Diver* out of the country without clearing through the government in Athens. Marion said:

~ Ed hounded them all morning, fearful that they would close up the shop for the weekend and we would be stuck in Navarino until Monday....We all breathed a sigh of relief when we were finally out at sea where the ornery Greek officials could no longer reach us. ~

Summarizing the extraordinary mission, she made her final journal entry:

~ Our summer in Greece has been a bitter-sweet experience. Never have I been in a country which appealed to me more - the landscape, the climate, the people, its antiquities, and the wonderful sea with its thousands of caves and harbors. But our experience, from the moment we arrived in Rhodes until now, has been one of constant hounding by the law, and as far as we can ascertain, there was nothing in the beginning to trigger such surveillance. ~

# CHAPTER X

# MAKING HISTORY
# IN MEDITERRANEAN WATERS

**1961–1962**

*If we encourage the use of alternate realities, as in meditation, play,*
*serious music, and so forth, we increase the ability of human beings to reach*
*toward new potentials. If we prevent it, we damage these people.*

*— Lawrence LeShan & Henry Margenau*
*— Einstein's Space and Van Gogh's Sky*

*ea Diver* left Grecian waters for new horizons. Her ultimate destination was now a winter berth at Monte Carlo near the French Riviera, where the International Hydrographic Office was to sponsor her stay and where the world famous underwater pioneer, Commandant Jacques-Yves Cousteau, headed the International Oceanographic Museum.

*Sea Diver's* first port of call on the way was the historic harbor of Siracusa, Sicily, where, long centuries before, Greek had fought Greek as well as Roman and Carthaginian ships of war. Ed wondered on entering the harbor if with his equipment aboard *Sea Diver* he could find the remains of any of the lost warships. Though this was to be only a brief stop, coincidence once again had a role to play in his affairs that would commit him to a later dive mission there. This time, while visiting the local museum, he came across an archeologist he had met the year before in the United States who grew excited to learn that Ed had future plans to dive in the Mediterranean. He urged Ed to consider diving in Sicilian waters, and introduced him to Marchese Piero Nicholas Gargallo, honorary superintendent of antiquities for Southeastern Sicily, Department of Underwater Archeology. Gargallo was a diver who had located and salvaged several ancient wreck sites there with much success. His own exciting collection of artifacts, including an ancient Greek warrior's bronze helmet, helped convince Ed — who hoped the helmet and other bronze finds might lead to an early Greek warship — to return to Sicily the following year.

From Sicily they eventually moored near Capri, where on September 24 Marion wrote that John "did a fine job" for a dinner party on board ship that night, then added, "He is getting better and better every day. If only he would learn English"!

They traveled on the next day to Naples where other contacts were made, and where Marion remarked: "We are rejoicing in the simplicity of arrivals and departures from Italian ports after the red tape and perils in Greece."

Though prospects for work in the Mediterranean were looking far better than those in Greece had turned out to be, it was a long season and the Links were getting anxious to go home. With Clayton back in school, Marion was feeling homesick and ready to leave John, Jay and Danny in charge of the ship for the winter. In addition, she and Ed were particularly concerned to see Bill, whose wedding they had attended before leaving for their latest journey, and his wife, the former Julie Ridley. Bill had only just written that after he and Julie had settled down in a new apartment in Tucson and he had registered to attend the University of Arizona, he had been given notice to rejoin his Army military unit in Georgia.

At that time Ed and Marion were still in Naples, where days had yet to be devoted to making arrangements for the following year. Ed then met his sister Marilyn, vacationing in Geneva, and she joined them for their journey to Monte Carlo. *Sea Diver* at last put out to sea for the final leg of the season, but not without still another escapade involving police. This time Marion wrote on October 9: "Set out for Monte Carlo about noon. Exciting start today, with seven police aboard before breakfast, hunting an escaped convict."

On October 10 she was on watch in the pilot house with Marilyn as *Sea Diver* approached her destination for the winter, and documented the arrival:

~ In order to kill time until daylight, we headed for light near San Remo then along the coast, entering the harbor at Monte Carlo about 7:00 a.m. We have a fine berth at the end of a long line of beautiful yachts on the south breakwater, so that our port side is open to the promenade. It is such a beautiful harbor with steep surrounding hills, built up with tall buildings and fine gardens - the waterfront is so clean and tidy and full of boats. ~

At last *Sea Diver* was secured for the winter. Ed and Marion drove with Marilyn along the Riviera before leaving Europe for Binghamton and home, but not before receiving an unpleasant reminder during a stopover in Geneva of the misadventures in Greece. Marion's October 13 journal entry reads:

~ I walked to the American Consulate this morning for mail. Found a letter from Deloukas saying he thought things were set up for the appeal hearing. They had talked to Papadimitrio and he was willing to have Hadjicosta and Papathanosopoulis testify. I don't want Ed to go back, however. It is too hard on his nerves, and as we have no intention of returning again with *Sea Diver*, there is no need for going through it. ~

But later, on February 2, 1963, Binghamton "Sun-Bulletin" staff writer Lewis Grossberger reported:

~ Edwin A. Link, founder of Link Aviation, was acquitted yesterday by a Greek court on a 1961 charge that he conducted illegal underwater archeological research in Greek Waters. ..."I'm happy to have it cleared up," Mr. Link commented. ..."I was terribly embarrassed."

Mr. Link said he [had] expected [that] the higher court would reverse the conviction, "when all the facts were brought out."

"It was really sort of a farce," he continued. "We never should have been convicted in the first place...." ~

\* \* \*

TODAY MARILYN LINK RECALLS that "Ed always joked afterward, `It is Greek to me.'" But with the theatre of the absurd comedy of errors in Greece behind him, he could once again get down to serious work. Heretofore he had given much attention to archeology, but now, working on new ideas at home, as always with his beloved classical music in the background, he was about to experience an explosion of creativity in the field of underwater engineering. In fast and furious strides he brought into being some of the most significant advances in underwater technology that had yet been made. These were covered extensively by *Life, National Geographic*, the *Smithsonian, Popular Science*, and many other national and international publications. A more thorough documentation of his extraordinary accomplishments was made by Marion in her long-selling book, *Windows In the Sea*, Smithsonian Press, 1973, the last available copy of which sold at Harbor Branch in 1992.

Ed's newest direction had a beginning, of sorts, already, when, while cruising, he meditated on the design of the submersible decompression chamber that was now a reality ready to be tested. Over the previous few years he had clearly defined to himself the problems of working at depth, including nitrogen narcosis (the narcotic effect of nitrogen in the blood that can cause a euphoric diver to remove his mask and drown), the bends, caused from staying down too long and coming up too fast, and oxygen poisoning that can be brought on by breathing too much oxygen for too long a time. Working with the military, he had learned what the U.S. Navy Experimental Diving Unit had already done, which included proving that nitrogen could be replaced with helium in the air breathed by divers to overcome the problem of narcosis. He had learned of the Navy's study of the length of diving times, which showed that if the ascending diver remained at certain depths for prescribed periods of time, gases could be absorbed by the body and eliminated harmlessly, and thus the diver could avoid the problem of the bends.

At home Ed studied all the research literature he could get his hands on, steadily developing his Man-In-Sea plans while also working on a proposal for additional support for future work. Marion wrote in *Windows In the Sea* that he explained his ideas to the National Geographic Society:

> ~ ...Ed described the three main essentials in his Man-In-Sea concept — the pressurized underwater house from which divers could work for unlimited periods of time, the submersible decompression chamber (SDC) that would act as an elevator to carry divers from the surface to the shelter on the bottom, and the large and comfortable deck decompression chamber (DDC) where the divers could be transferred upon returning to the surface for decompression which might require days. ~

When Ed was ready to return to *Sea Diver's* winter dock on the French Riviera at Monaco, Marion described how he explained his SDC to the National Geographic Society committee:

> ~ I figure I can use this SDC in all three capacities for the time being. That is, I can send a diver down in it to the bottom. He can use it while there as his underwater dwelling for several days. We can then bring it back on deck still at bottom pressure with the diver remaining in the chamber as long as necessary for him to decompress. ...It won't be very comfortable, but it will be safe. ~

After much preparation, Ed and Marion returned to a freshly painted *Sea Diver* at Monaco on Saturday, March 3, 1962, her crew ready and eagerly awaiting their arrival. "Danny and Jay," Marion logged, "were both on hand, and we sent up to town for a late dinner delivery, as we had many things to talk about."

Marion wrote of settling in over the next few days and shopping with John for the season. Then a remark of special interest appears in her journal on March 8: "The Cousteaus came by tonight for a drink, and we made some plans for next week." Then again on the 13th: "The Cousteaus came aboard for a drink tonight and we went back to their house for dinner." On the ˌ18th: "Ed and J. Cousteau had a conference this morning."

There was an interlude in these notations when Ed flew from Nice to England for what Marion described as, "a busy few days: Naval officers [involved in shipping his SDC overseas], GPE, Mohawk Airlines [Ed was a stockholder and director of Mohawk], Lord Kilbracken [English writer and photographer who had already covered their work and would cover more], etc."

Then appears another notation on March 24: "Jacques Cousteau came for a drink with us tonight and stayed until 9:30 p.m. Simone [Mrs. Cousteau] had family visiting and could not come." Next she wrote that Ed and Cousteau had a date at noon on Sunday, the 25th, when Piero Gargallo of Siracusa unexpectedly arrived. Evidently the others shared Ed's love of great music, for the three men went to the opera together that afternoon.

It was of course inevitable that two such dedicated undersea explorers would eventually come together; both Cousteau and Link were driven with a relentless will to make the seas accessible to man, and both were systematically engaged in undersea exploration and experimentation. However, where Cousteau was more inclined to reach the public, Ed was much more concerned with concentrating on his designs and engineering developments. Cousteau was particularly interested in Ed's proposed Man-In-Sea program, as well as his innovative genius for designing underwater systems that would allow man to work deep in the oceans for long periods of time. They would attempt to combine their interests in a joint endeavor, Cousteau linking with Ed's Man-In-Sea program. Marion had added to her Sunday notation in the journal on March 25:

~ Ed and Cousteau are planning an experiment to be carried out this summer. They will build a small "house" and lower it to the sea bottom, then send a couple of divers down to live in it for two weeks. The divers will eat and sleep there, doing a spell of work outside for so many hours a day. No decompression until they end their stint. Should create almost as much interest as the astronauts. ~

Then again, in *Windows in the Sea*, Marion described the potential joint endeavor and what led up to it:

~ ...Both [Cousteau and Ed] realized the time had arrived for man to be able to go deeper and to spend longer periods of time on the bottom.

Ed told Commandant Cousteau of his Man-In-Sea concept, describing the submersible decompression chamber that would be arriving almost any day. Together they discussed the possibility of carrying out part of Ed's plan later that year by using the SDC as an elevator and decompression chamber to carry divers to an underwater house. ~

The Links now had a copy of the documentary film that Ben Ozerman had made about *Sea Diver's* Israel expedition, and were showing it to the usual troop of visitors aboard, which included the Cousteaus. Typical of Marion's entries regarding these touring/social visits is the following string of comments:

~ Prepared most of the day for a cocktail party on board tonight for about twenty people. Also showed our film. Think it turned out most successfully.

Later dinner with the Knoxes.... The Feinbergs from Boston came aboard for lunch today. He is president of the US Underwater Archeological Group.... Had the Dales with a friend and Commander Anderson and his wife, with Mrs. Grosvenor, daughter-in-law of the National Geographic Grosvenors, for the evening and showed one film of Caesarea. ~

In the midst of these social engagements, which Marion had graciously adapted herself to over the years as the price she must pay for Ed's fame, Ed took time out to hire a young Dutchman named George Krashman as assistant engineer. Marion said it was a good thing, as there were a million things to do before leaving for their first mission of the year. And it turned out to be a particularly good thing since right afterward, Danny, the English crewman, injured his back and was laid up for a time undergoing surgery and suffering through a somewhat prolonged recovery.

Ed too had to play the role of congenial host while at dock, although his mind was constantly on his plans and he was anxious to get on with his experiments at sea. Then, at last, Marion made a notation of a most significant kind; essentially about the practical beginning of one of the most exciting highlights of Ed's singular career, which would lead to the invention one day of the world's first manned lockout submersibles:

> ~ Thursday, March 15, 1962. Well, the long-delayed shipment of the diving chamber, etc., finally arrived. It came in a corrugated iron box, half the size of a freight car, and was quite a problem to unload and get aboard. A near tragedy when the whole case slipped over the edge of the dock and was saved only because it was attached to *Sea Diver's* boom. We had to get a harbor crane to come and raise it. The men were exhausted when it was over, and so were the spectators. ~

But Ed had to wait for more equipment to arrive and clear customs before the real tests could begin. And he must also fulfill his commitment to work over the early summer months with Piero Gargallo in Sicily. After several eventful delays, he set out for Sicily on a beautiful day, Saturday, April 7, in a smooth sea. *Sea Diver*, with the SDC — looking like a large aluminum cylinder with small, fish-eye-like portholes jutting out on an angle on each side and a lockout hatch at one end — and resting in a cradle on the stern — left the Cote d'Azure behind, the snow-capped Alps in the background. Just before dark they passed Cap Corse and headed past Elba and Ponthe. Eventually they passed the Aeolian islands — Stromboli, Lipari, Vulcan, went through the Straits of Messina, and arrived in Siracusa Harbor at 1:30 a.m. on the 10th of April. On the 11th they were visited by the usual diving scholars. "Van Johnson surprised us," wrote Marion. "He is here with a classical group from Tufts and they all came to visit *Sea Diver*."

Another event gave the Links the impression that Mediterranean operations just seemed to go hand in hand with police matters. This time they had been away from the ship most of the day, taking a Sunday drive in the country with Piero Gargallo, visiting his citrus farm, an ancient fortress, and a deserted fishing village he partly owned and wanted to acquire fully to develop. That evening they went out for dinner and came back to *Sea Diver* to find that during their outings Ed's new electric watch had turned up missing from its place in the chronometer box. The police were there all of the next day, taking finger prints and eventually arresting, to the sorrow of everyone aboard, a young English-speaking Italian boy who had been hanging around the ship on the day of the theft, and who was caught with the watch still in his possession.

Late in April the ardent Belgian diver, Robert Stenuit, with his wife, Annie, joined the Link party at a sunken wreck site of Gargallo's. Ed's sister Marilyn Link joined the crew shortly afterward, as did Tom Ambercrombie, *National Geographic* photographer. Ed's proposals the previous February had made the expedition possible; he had obtained full backing and a substantial grant in funds for his Man-In-Sea project from the National Geographic Society in Washington, after convincing the committee of the importance of his conception of how man could one day conquer the ocean environment. Ed and several others were to publish articles for a coming (May, 1963) *National Geographic* magazine on deep water work, which featured Ed's missions that summer.

While still awaiting more equipment to arrive and clear customs, the dive team worked Gargallo's wreck site at Ognina in southeast Sicily. Many unique amphorae were found at the Ognina site. Marion wrote that they also waited for the second part of Gargallo's project to get itself better organized, and that Ed's patience was "tried by not knowing from one moment to the next just what was going to be in the offing." Important finds included a marble altar and other sections of a Byzantine church dating back to around 600 BC. They raised a sunken cargo of carved marbles half-buried in the sand near Marzamemi, also at the southeast tip of Sicily. Marion took advantage of lapses in their work to study Italian so that she could better act as a liaison when needed while Ed worked on developing tools and John was kept busy cooking three meals a day at sea for twelve people.

In spite of being at loose ends at times, Gargallo's diving project hit pay dirt, and on Friday, May 18, Marion wrote:

~ This was a big day, culminating in the raising of seventeen large and heavy marbles, four columns, six bases, three capitals, three straight, long sections and a crowning piece that must have weighed four or five tons. The men worked like slaves all day, getting them packed aboard. ~

A large crane moved the pieces at a loading dock the next day. Then everyone came down with colds all at once and the work came to a standstill, which more than pleased Ed because it gave him an opportunity to work with a newly acquired piece of equipment whose potential fascinated him. The "mud pinger" was designed for locating non-metallic objects buried in mud on the sea bottom. "He is concentrating," Marion observed, "on getting Dr. Harold Edgerton's mud pinger to work, and also trying it out with *Reef Diver.*" (Edgerton, an innovator like Ed, Professor at Massachusetts Institute of Technology, was perhaps best known for his high-speed photography, including his famous image of a bullet stopped in action.) (NOTE: photo pg. 175, #13).

On May 22 Marion mentioned that Ed was building a small sled to tow the mud pinger along the bottom, adding, "If it works correctly, it can be very valuable for locating ... statues, stone blocks, etc., underneath the mud bottom." At another point she said: "Ed is working on a new device to use with the mud penetrater that will shoot out a buoy when an object is detected."

Eventually the Stenuits left the group and were replaced by another couple, Skip and Claudine Marquet, from Princeton, New Jersey. Skip had volunteered to come aboard and work with Ed for several weeks on the electronic gear. Then on May 25 Marion made a personal notation that she and Ed left the ship to go to Agrigento. "We drove as far as Gela, where we spent the night. It is good to get away from the boat and responsibilities now and then, and have a little more time with each other."

On June 5 Ed had the diving chamber in the water for the first time, checking it for pressure and practicing entering and leaving it underwater. "It will require much practice," Marion observed, "to have everything worked out precisely."

Ed and Piero were at loggerheads from time to time, over work Piero wanted done which Ed insisted could be done by any boat and did not require *Sea Diver's* special capabilities and time. He had the pinger working and was now busy designing a gun that would shoot a buoy forth from the pinger, bury itself in the mud, and mark the spot accurately. When all was in working order, he wanted to let someone else pick up the remaining marbles at Gargallo's dive site while he tried to turn up a Greek ship or something equally important back at the main harbor of Siracusa, a project he saw as essential for Ambercrombie's *National Geographic* picture story.

Furthermore, it was indeed apparent that Ed's interest in archeology for its own sake was giving way to an even greater interest in underwater engineering and scientific research, or how to make underwater archeology work. According to his pattern of following a wandering star, he was right on target, doing what he did best — breaking ground in a new field then letting experts take over while he moved on to an even newer interest.

On June 6 Ed and Marion's 31st wedding anniversary was documented in her journal: "Tonight we had a special celebration with all the crew. Dan and Jay provided champagne, Piero roses, etc. It was fun."

Clayton, out of school for the summer, joined the mission on June 13, while others left and Marion noted that the crew was rapidly dwindling even as Ed's work and interest in developing new systems was intensifying. On the 16th she mentions that she went ashore with Ed for an hour before dinner, then commented: "...his first visit ashore since we've been working in the harbor. He is really wedded to the ship and the job."

Finally Gargallo got his wishes and Ed took *Sea Diver* to raise more of the sunken marbles, which they thought to be the last until, with his own new equipment and Edgerton's device, he discovered many more pieces under the mud bottom. On June 21st Marion observed that after finishing the job and with about 20 tons of marbles aboard, "surprisingly," as *Sea Diver* headed for shore, their speed was much greater on the calm sea, "with the stern heavily weighted and the bow riding high."

They still waited for certain equipment necessary to Ed's SDC project. The equipment had arrived but now customs refused to release it because Ed refused to pay what he thought was an unwarranted duty charge of $200. Marion at last solved the problem by having the equipment forwarded to the next country on their agenda, where they could pick it up without paying the fee in accordance with Ed's wishes. But she stated her mind on the subject:

> ~ July 3, 1962 - We made final preparations for leaving today. ...I spent the morning trying to arrange to have the oxygen analyzer and compressor, which have been held up in customs, reshipped to us at Monaco. What a hassle! I felt that, in spite of his principles, Ed should pay the $200 and get his hands on them. But, no. ~

Next came hints that Ed's plans with Cousteau were beginning to go awry. Cousteau would alter the plans, push forward, and conduct an experiment in relation to the Man-In-Sea project without Ed. Ed became disappointed and very annoyed with Cousteau. Marion reported on the 10th of July:

> ~ Ed is not too happy over the way Cousteau has arranged the "week under sea," as Cousteau plans a large house containing a light decamper chamber which can be raised and transported ashore rather than the original plan.
>
> However, Ed is anxious to get to work on his tests with the diving chamber and will plan to go to Villefranche tomorrow where the water is the right depth. ~

On the next day, July 11, a successful test dive was made with Ed's dive chamber in Villefranche-sur-Mer Harbor, headquarters of the U. S. Navy's Sixth Fleet, on the French Riviera. Marion wrote in *Windows In the Sea*:

> ~ The 4,200 pound aluminum chamber was lowered over the side, where it floated upright, the head riding about a foot out of water, with

several hoses trailing from it to the deck...

Ed dove over the side and disappeared beneath the surface. Soon his voice could be heard over the SDC's intercom talking to the engineer on deck, as he experimented with opening and closing the hatches and varying the air pressure. At times, clouds of bubbles came popping up to the surface as gases were released from the chamber.

Finally he announced himself ready to lower the chamber to the harbor bottom 15 feet below; then there was the slow steady clunk of the chain riding through the winchgate as the cylinder disappeared beneath the water. ~

At this point Marion was becoming quite edgy about the entire operation, and on July 12 she wrote in her journal:

~ The crew made two dives today. The morning one was very successful, but by afternoon we had wind and surge to complicate things, and Ed decided to make some changes in procedure which resulted in his popping up and down in the chamber from the bottom like a rocket. I was really concerned, for I still am not used to Ed's shutting himself in that chamber under water for hours at a time. ~

By July 14, however, she was becoming somewhat accustomed to the idea, and had to admit, "I am so proud of Ed and the imaginative, yet painstaking, scientific fashion in which he approaches things." After writing that he had various groups aboard at intervals all day on the 18th to see his chamber and equipment, including French, Italian, Belgian and Swedish visitors, she wrote: "I think Ed is really off to a good start in a new and exciting field."

Ed continued to work out his ideas. Marion's next notation was about one of his greatest media admirers:

~ August 8, 1962 - [England's Lord] John Kilbracken arrived today to observe the diving and write it up for the papers. He will stay aboard for a while. Ed is very busy this week constructing a mixing tank with gauges for controlling the atmosphere of the chamber for oxygen and helium diving. ~

Then on a wistful note she added: "The washer is broken down, and two refrigerators, but no time for anyone to fix them." On August 14 she wrote: "Ed is having difficulties with the mixing tank and has not had it in operation yet - he has so much patience! But he was very tired tonight."

Then Ed suffered the final disappointment with Cousteau. Marion wrote on Monday, August 20:

~ Cousteau was aboard, and this time there was no pretense of Ed having a part of their underwater house program. It has been postponed...making it impossible for us to participate - so we have decided to go it alone and conduct our own series of experiments in Villefranche harbor....Cousteau said he had no idea Ed was so advanced in his tests. ~

The two men would go their own ways. John Margetis offers his opinion that Cousteau and perhaps the French government did not like to see Link being first with the Man-In-Sea program in their own home territory. There was Link with the backing of the U.S. Navy, with the Sixth Fleet transporting his dive chamber across the Atlantic and continuing to help by contributing divers, expertise, and supplying all the helium and oxygen for the dives. The fact was, Link had the resources, the Navy, and the ideas, and was able to go ahead and carry out his ideas by himself.

Marion wrote on August 26 that she and Ed had planned a day's outing off the ship with Clayton but that Dr. Harold Edgerton and his wife arrived that morning. Then the two like-minded geniuses spent a good part of the day working with Edgerton's mud pinger. Afterwards, she added:

~ Late in the afternoon, we drove to Venice and then to St. Paul where we had dinner. Clayton's time is getting very short as he is leaving us to go to Germany on Tuesday where he will spend a couple of weeks before going home and back to school. Would think he would want to stay for the dives, but he had planned this trip far ahead and has really seen very little of Europe. ~

Clayton, however, did manage to stay for his father's most spectacular dive, in which Ed accomplished a stunning first in underwater history. Harbor Branch engineer Chris Tietze refers to this event as but one instance demonstrating why Ed Link was such a hero to him as well as to many others, because he was willing to experiment, and, as he says, "Link would never ask anyone to do anything he wouldn't do himself." Before trying out his dive chamber or his saturation diving ideas on anyone else, on August 28, 1962, 58-year-old Ed Link had himself lowered in his SDC chamber to carry out the world's first sustained helium-oxygen dive. The dive was made at a depth of 60 feet. He remained submerged for a period of eight hours in waters off the coast of Villefranche-sur-Mer. Marion documented the event in her journal:

~ Ed made a record-breaking eight-hour dive at 60 feet today, using oxygen-helium gases. Everything went fine. He emerged from the chamber several times to hunt for a buoy anchor and to work with Dr. Edgerton, who was using the mud pinger overhead. Ed ate two good meals delivered to him in the chamber including a chicken dinner. The chamber was brought on board before dark and he finished decompression at about 11:00 p.m. after a total of almost 15 hours in the chamber. He had no ill effects and was very jubilant at the success of it. Took Clayton to the airport in the afternoon. Clayton made a couple of dives in the morning to see his father in the chamber. ~

Ed proved his point. Man could work at depth breathing heliox (mixture of helium and oxygen) for long periods of time, a point at the crux of his difference with Cousteau, who was to carry out his experiment in shallow water with divers breathing ordinary compressed air. Marion then made a reference to the plan that had originally been made with Cousteau:

> ~ Thursday, August 30, 1962. Ken went to call on Cousteau this morning and reported he is planning his underwater house experiment early next month. The publicity is all sealed up for a special coverage. He says *Life* is not interested in paying a big price. ~

Immediately after Ed's first saturation dive he turned his mind to orchestrating the next longest, deepest dive, which originally was intended to last a week. As momentum built in preparation for this, Marion maintained a steady stream of notations in her journal:

> ~ ...Friday, August 31. The Marquets are here and will be aboard for a couple of days. Skip was delighted to find Dr. Edgerton with us and will help with some of the pinging program. ...Sunday, September 2. Robert Stenuit and Annie arrived...Robert is keen to make the dive - Annie full of trepidation. Bates Littlehales of *National Geographic* is here to take Tom's place as he is going to Turkey. ...September 3. ...Ed visited Captain Chenault on the *USS Springfield* to ask help from the Navy and, later in the day, heard the Navy submarine tender *Sun Bird* had been detailed to us for TWO DAYS. We also sent a cable to Admiral Anderson, inviting observers to be present. ...Tuesday, September 4. Robert and Ed did some practice dives here today at 60 feet. Robert is very collected and careful and catches on very quickly. Annie [French speaking] is her usual cute self but we still do not communicate very well. ~

On Friday at 6:00 a.m. they moved out to the mouth of the harbor and anchored in over 250 feet of water. Then a stiff wind came up and prevented the dive. Marion says the seas were so bad that even the chamber started shifting on the deck and had to be additionally secured. The men worked all night evacuating the air from the chamber after Ed welded in an extra heat unit. Then they stocked the chamber with supplies for Robert, and started filling helium. She further document-ed the memorable event in her journal:

~ Thursday, September 6 - Ed went to bed at 1:30 a.m. and was up at 5:00 a.m. Completed filling the chamber and put it overboard while the sea was calm. They began preliminary tests at about 9:00 a.m. to 200 feet. Robert made out fine. Many photographers and newspaper people were there.

The real dive began with compression at 11:00 a.m. The *Sun Bird* arrived at 8:00 a.m. this morning to stand by in case of trouble, and the officers came aboard this afternoon to observe the dive. Captain Sloatman also arrived from London to represent Admiral Anderson, and stayed for dinner with us.

We sent food down to Robert on a line just before dark. He reported the water was so cold he would rather have a diver hand it in to him than to don the rubber jacket and get out himself. Dan has built a container to send down that can stand the pressure. ~

Stenuit was down on the bottom in the chamber at a depth of 60 feet, Friday, September 7, when the day began overhead with an altogether different adventure. Marion and Annie had escaped the tension by going to Monaco for the mail, but when they returned to the dock the seas were so heavy the boatmen refused to take them out to *Sea Diver*. Then a certain Mr. Seymour volunteered to take them out in his speed boat. "We were drenched in huge waves when we got to *Sea Diver*," Marion logged, adding, "but it was impossible to get aboard. Learned that in the rough seas *Reef Diver*, under a load of 15 helium bottles and passengers, had just sunk!" Fortunately the passengers were safe, but the helium had sunk with *Reef Diver*, which unfortunately meant that the dive would have to be cut short so as not to overextend the supply of helium on board. However, by then the record had already been set for the world's longest, deepest dive: 26 hours at a depth of 200 feet. Marion continued her narrative:

~ We dried out ashore, had lunch, and went to Nice airport for a package. We then stuck around the waterfront, waiting for word. We were advised to stay ashore overnight, but eventually were able to get aboard. It was 10:30 p.m., SO TIRED.

In the meantime, the chamber had been lifted aboard. Decompression had started at about 2:00 p.m. while it was still below. We were unable to get food to Robert. Fortunately, he had enough. ~

Another run of notations covered the event the following day:

> ~ Saturday, September 8, 1962 - We moved into the inner harbor this morning where it will be calm. ...Dropped a buoy in an attempt to mark where *Reef Diver* went down and hope to retrieve it later. ...Have been cramped with TV and reporters and photographers all day. ...Robert had slight signs of the bends during the night and they had to reverse decompression. He will have to stay in the chamber until Monday morning. It seems a long time. ...Ed is so tired out, I'm worried about him. ...We have to keep two people each on a 24-hour watch to stay with Robert. ...The helium was replaced aboard this morning. ~

Sunday was a day of rest. On Monday Marion took up her running account again:

> ~ We got up at 5:30 this morning to welcome Robert out of the chamber. Several photographers and TV men were present. Robert looks fine and is very happy. ...a big breakfast was served for Robert ...there were more interviews . ...I went to Monaco for the mail and when I returned found *Sea Diver* at dock for water. ...John Kilbracken is getting wonderful series of stories and pictures. ...Had a "coming out" party for Robert this evening (about 24 people). ...Too many late hours! ~

Ed had written in a paper found in his files some years later:

> ~ I have been asked a number of times the difference between Comm. Cousteau's experiments this year in Marseilles and mine in Villefranche. In brief, the Marseilles experiments were carried out to test environmental conditions, while ours were based on deep diving techniques and the use of mixed gases. Comm. Cousteau put two divers down in an underwater house for a week at a depth of approximately ten meters where it was possible to utilize ordinary compressed air. At any depth greater than this, it is unsafe to use air for long exposures as serious consequences might result. For instance, nitrogen narcosis could occur, or concentrated oxygen produced by pressurization of air at greater depths could cause lung congestion, pneumonia and death.
>
> On the other hand, aboard *Sea Diver* this summer we conducted a series of experiments using helium-oxygen mixtures for prolonged deep dives in a heavily stressed aluminum diving chamber designed especially for the purpose....
>
> The value of helium-oxygen mixtures has long been known and uti-

lized in certain diving operations by the American Navy. And of course, Hans Keller has demonstrated some amazing results in deep diving with secret mixtures of gases. Dr. Bond and Dr. Workman of the U. S. Navy, in a forerunner to our tests, demonstrated on animals that deep diving with helium-oxygen mixtures is possible for prolonged exposure up to several weeks with no detrimental effects on animals. But, of course with animals, it was impossible to check whether they suffered any mental retardation. Ours was the first experiment with humans to demonstrate that there is no loss of mental faculties. Nor have any other complications developed since. I feel this is a real break-through in diving techniques. ~

He ended the paper by summarizing his thoughts:

~ To conclude, I believe we have now reached the stage where deep underwater archeological recovery is practical, for man will be able at last to truly perform long hours of useful work at great depths. Furthermore, with the development of these techniques there is no end to the vast store-houses of the sea which will be at last available to man's use. ~

Stenuit later wrote an article for the April, 1965 *National Geographic* about his next deep dive orchestrated by Ed, in which he referred back to the 200-foot dive. First he told of his own excitement at Ed's initial attempt to dive in the SDC:

~ Two hundred people crowded the quay to observe the singular American who played in the water with a colossal tin can. The American dived and did not come back. The can sank. Then it shot out of the water like a torpedo, only to plunge again for the bottom. ~

Stenuit continued:

~ I watched these submergence and surfacing tests of the SDC with dif-ferent eyes. I knew what Ed had in mind: To live, eat, sleep, and work in depths so far unreachable by free divers, and in so doing to take a long step toward the conquest of the continental shelf. To me it was the most extraordinary adventure of which a diver might dream. My answer was ready when Ed asked me if I would like to spend a deep-down day or two in his shiny new can.
    The 200-foot Villefranche dive proved that Ed Link's cylinder and its occupant could function as planned. Then the long preparation for the 400- foot dive began. ~

When the excitement of Stenuit's 200-foot dive was over, it was time for a new project. Ed began planning a dive at a 400-foot depth, as well as tests with mice and a goat in the SDC. And in his mind he was designing an underwater habitat for the Man-In-Sea program using the SDC as an elevator to and from the bottom. But meanwhile he attempted to locate *Reef Diver*, searching first with the mud pinger with no results. Then John Margetis noticed an oil slick on the water just ahead of *Sea Diver's* bow that could possibly be coming up from *Reef Diver*. Ed went down the next day and verified that it indeed was from the little cruiser, then went back underwater in the chamber to observe as a scuba diver fastened a heavy line on the bow ring and *Reef Diver* was hauled to the surface, complete with five of the lost fifteen helium bottles still in the cockpit.

By September 14 *Sea Diver* was anchored in the middle of the harbor waiting for her winter berth at Monaco. A number of people were coming and going across her decks as usual. Marion commented that Mrs. Kaley, who stayed at their home in Binghamton, wrote that Clayton was safely home.

Marion and Ed were both tired out and they both succumbed to a flu virus. Visits to a doctor revealed that they were both suffering from high blood pressure. Still they continued making arrangements for their next season in the Mediterranean, which they hoped to extend to the waters around Bermuda.

*Sea Diver* was placed for the winter, looking very sturdy next to ex-King Farouk's old sailing ship (built originally for Kaiser Wilhelm) on one side and a sleek yacht on the other. Ed and Marion relaxed and toured the area. She wrote on September 30 that they were both feeling much better and were more rested but that Ed was still "far from achieving his usual self."

Still Ed was driven to accomplish all he had set out to do that year, which included carrying out tests in the chamber with three white mice in a small cage with a glass top. "They are to be at 400 feet, on helium- oxygen for 12 hours, then 24 hours in decompression," Marion wrote. Ed later wrote a paper called "Oceanology," a comprehensive look at where he thought mankind should be heading under the oceans. He stated in the paper after describing Stenuit's dive:

~ Emboldened by this success, we continued our experiments using mice and finally a goat at a simulated depth of 400 feet for periods of time long enough to insure complete saturation. The final test resulted in our keeping the goat at a 400 foot pressure depth for 13 hours. ...I next designed and built a tiny chamber in which tests could be conducted with small animals using various mixtures of gases up to a pressure equivalent to a 3,000 foot depth. In September aboard *Sea Diver* with the aid of Dr. Joan Membery, we conducted a [successful] series of tests with mice using helium- oxygen mixtures. ~

Ed's work with Caroline, a "very pretty," eight-month-old, brown and white spotted goat, was a first, described as a "major breakthrough" by the *London Evening Standard* on October 20, 1962. His work was hailed as being as significant as the space program, in another new frontier which was perhaps more relevant to the present needs of mankind. Until Ed had made his saturation dive, it was thought that no one could stay down more than a few minutes; now he further proved his theories with a goat, an animal whose respiratory system was close to that of man's. In the process of these experiments, he and Marion both grew attached to Caroline, and began treating her as a beloved pet.

Meanwhile he had discovered yet a another problem for which he would find a solution and earn another patent. This came about because, as he had written in his paper titled "Oceanology":

~ When Stenuit made his long, deep dive in the chamber, we found that one of the most difficult problems we faced was to provide sufficient heat to keep him comfortable, both in the chamber and outside. ...Whereas until then the common wet-type rubber scuba suit had proved satisfactory for all types of cold-water diving, we found it useless for such long exposure at depth. ~

After going into detail concerning various methods of combating the problem and defining all of their existing problems, he concluded:

~ I believe I have found in my work a satisfactory answer to this problem in a new type of material which I have developed with the assistance of US Rubber Co. In appearance exactly like the present wet suit, this garment is formed of sponge rubber cells joined in orderly rows running in the same direction and sandwiched between two thin coatings of rubber. The air in these cells is kept equalized with outside pressure by means of a regulator. ~

After a long season at sea Ed and Marion made their way to Binghamton by way of London where they attended the World Congress of Underwater Activities. Ed, said Marion, gave a talk on "Tools for Search," but everyone showed much greater interest in his recent diving experiments. Then she exclaimed with enthusiasm:

~ The Congress is really a great success! Everyone in the underwater world is here. I can't think of an exception. And the program is most stimulating. Ed is being treated like a hero, with radio and TV interviews, etc. In fact, our entire stay at Grosvenor House is as guests of M. Rossi of Martini and Rossi, along with Cousteau, Hans Hass, young Hans Keller, and Jacques Piccard of bathyscope fame. [Piccard is son of Belgian physicist Auguste Piccard, famed for his balloon ascents into the stratosphere and his bathyscaphe designs.] Ed and I were singled out to meet Lord Mountbatten, who opened the Congress. ...Ed gave his talk to a very attentive audience. ~

History was being made by those whose interests were concentrated on the oceans. All of the "names" in the underwater world came together and shared their experience and knowledge. Then at long last it was time to go home, just as history was also being made in foreign affairs. On October 23 Marion wrote: "The U.S. is warned of a ship blockade of Cuba today, and the world is very excited." On the 24th she continued: "We packed and took it easy this morning, leaving for the airport terminal about 1:00 p.m. ...Tension is high over the U.S. blockade of Cuba."

# CHAPTER XI

# 'OCEANOLOGY' AND THE NEED FOR SUBMERSIBLES

**1963–1966**

*Every movement will retain its course or rather every body*
*when moved will continue on its course as long as the power*
*of the impulse is maintained therein.*

— *Leonardo da Vinci*

hen the Link Foundation Board of Trustees presented scholarships to young engineering students in 1985 they hoped to give something of greater value than the award itself. As a source of inspiration, the scholarship package included a copy of the *National Academy of Engineering's Memorial Tribute to Ed* in which the author, Ed's friend and fellow inventor, Dr. Harold E. Edgerton, called attention to the late inventor's accomplishments. Edgerton pointed out that Ed made his contributions with more than mere mechanical skills, saying that he was essentially two men: "one with a tool box in his fist, the other with dreams in his head."

Taking it a step further, a Link Foundation board member prepared a written message for the scholarship package focusing on the character of the genius rather than on his inventions or his ability to dream. Spokesman Ralph E. Flexman, former Link employee and former director of Aviation at the University of Illinois, said in his introductory paragraph that in addition to the monetary gift, the board wanted to give something that would "provide a significant leverage to assuring an even more successful future" for the recipients. He went on to share with the scholarship winners insights and impressions of Ed, which he said "contributed to his successes in so many different fields of science and areas of human activity."

Flexman wrote of Ed's engineering expertise and sensitivity to problems, of how he accepted challenges and never found a problem that was insurmountable, and of how he used his ingenuity to find solutions "...often by borrowing from related and unrelated technologies," by discovering "useful relationships that the more narrow engineer or scientist might overlook." The document recognized Ed's ability to stay with a problem regardless of setbacks or obstructions until he came up with a workable idea, which was, according to Flexman, "perhaps because he never tackled a problem whose solutions would be trivial and not worth the effort or the sacrifices involved." Stressing these outstanding personal attributes and more, the message summarized what the board of trustees regarded as Ed's chief source of success:

> ~ Finally, if there is one characteristic of Ed Link's that we would like to see passed along, it is that of his faith. Ed had an immeasurable faith in himself and his ability to eventually solve a problem. He also had an unusual faith in his friends, that they would be a constant in his life. His faith in his associates was that they would do what they said they would do. He exhibited tremendous faith in his loved ones, that they would always understand and support him. However, his greatest faith was in his God who would give him a source of strength that could be relied on whenever it was needed. Without these dimensions of his faith he would certainly have settled for less rather than the ultimate, the very best that he could do. ~

Perhaps Flexman was referring in part to that era in which Ed's faith was taxed nearly to the limit. By 1963 it could already be said that the "dreamweaver" had displayed extraordinary faith in all of its dimensions throughout his career; it was like a magnetic compass by which he navigated his unlettered and uncharted course. It was the spirit in his bellows, the energy that kept him forever moving forward. In his mission to push the underwater frontier to the cutting edge he would continue to rely on faith to a remarkable degree, until, at the pinnacle of his successes, after designing the world's first lockout submersibles and assisting J. Seward Johnson, Sr. in founding an oceanographic institution in Florida, he would temporarily lose his bearings in the face of personal tragedy. For by 1963 his work was indirectly leading to an accident a decade later in which the deaths of his youngest son, Clayton, and a companion, Albert Stover, would sorely try his faith in himself and leave him and Marion to rely solely on their faith in God.

It was an irony of fate that at the end of the decade, during which Ed had pursued the safest means to keep men at work under the sea, the sea would claim the lives of two of four divers locked inside his submersible, entangled in the wreckage of a sunken ship off the coast of Key West, Florida.

Meanwhile, the next series of developments — the first lockout submersible, the Perry-Link *Deep Diver*; the *Johnson-Sea-Link* class submersibles; Harbor Branch Oceanographic Institution; and the ultimate heartbreak, the accident — had already been set in motion by 1963. Through a curious twist of events, Ed Link and J. Seward Johnson, who together would develop the *Johnson-Sea-Link* submersibles, were destined to meet one another at Woods Hole Oceanographic Institution because of an earlier, shocking submarine accident involving the U.S. Navy. Through his involvement with this accident, Ed made contacts with Woods Hole that brought him to the board of directors where he first met Johnson.

IT ALL BEGAN EARLY IN 1963 when Ed and Marion left their home in Binghamton once again for the French Riviera. On the way they stopped in Boston as guests of the Sea Rover's Club. Ed gave a presentation on his deep diving experiences before an audience of more than 1,000 people, including such other undersea notables as Pablo Bush and Stan Waterman. Next the Links stopped in London where Ed spoke to a committee of the House of Parliament on "Underwater Developments" and was guest of honor at a dinner afterward. Marion made a note in her journal that she was the only woman invited to the dinner and that she sat between "Sir John Maitland and Lord Taylor." Then she added with a modicum of pride, "Afterwards there were many phone calls for my popular husband."

But though he spoke before 1,000 Americans and addressed 75 members of the British Parliament, he never lost his perspective, his humbleness, or his sense of priorities. Once settled aboard *Sea Diver* at Monaco, he and Marion went straight to Villefranche to see a goat, their pet Caroline, now a resident of Cap Ferret Zoo. Marion wrote that they were both greatly pleased in the course of the reunion to learn that Caroline was not only doing perfectly well in the wake of her extraordinary deep diving experiences, she was also going to have a kid.

Marion had again taken up her record of their action-packed days. Ed had redesigned the ship, she wrote, adding nine feet to her bow. *Sea Diver* went on the ways at a local shipyard in Italy to have her rounded bow, which tended to plow in heavy seas, sliced off to be replaced with a sharper one, allowing her to cut through heavy seas and providing additional storage forward. At the same time new sinks and a laboratory were added in the stern. When all was accomplished the vessel slid back into the water on April 7, having gone from 91 to 100 feet in length.

However improved for Ed's work, *Sea Diver's* mission overseas was to come to an abrupt end because of the worst submarine disaster in US history: the tragic sinking of the nuclear powered submarine *USS Thresher* on April 10, 1963, somewhere in the North Atlantic with the loss of all 129 hands aboard. That day Marion made an entry in her journal about the arrival of an advance copy of *National Geographic* with a story on Ed's dives. At the end of the entry was the terse message: "(Thresher sunk.)"

Though Ed was following his own star, the illusion that something beyond himself was in control of its direction was heightened once again. And again he did not struggle against the tide, but went along with the events at hand. Though he had proceeded with his own work after first learning of the accident, his long-range plans were shattered by the disaster. He was soon asked to head the industrial and civilian aspects of the Navy's Deep Submergence Systems Review Group (DSSRG) to study the accident.

Later Ed summarized his work with the Navy in the manuscript he called "Oceanology", which appears to be a report on the DSSRG mission as well as a draft for lectures and a future article to be published by *National Geographic* magazine ("Tomorrow on the Deep Frontier," June, 1964). In his opening paragraphs of the draft he wrote:

> ~ I had just completed docking my research ship *Sea Diver* at her berth in Monaco Harbor after a two week trip to the waters off eastern Corsica where we had been testing a new type of proton magnetometer for search purposes when I saw my friend Admiral Robert Pierce, director of the International Hydrographic office in Monte Carlo. ...[Pierce] said, "Admiral [Edward] Stephan has been trying to reach you from Washington. He wants you to phone him right away."
>
> As I hurried to the phone I puzzled over why the retired head of the US Navy Oceanographic office should be calling me. I wondered if it might have something to do with the loss of the nuclear submarine *Thresher* the previous month, and the so far unsuccessful efforts to locate her in spite of a concentration of all available Navy and oceanographic ships and search equipment. ~

Ed's intense concern for human safety in perilous activities was due to come to the fore once again. As a young man he was motivated to build flight trainers because so many student pilots lost their lives while learning to fly. Now, deeply influenced by the *Thresher* tragedy, he would redouble his own efforts to improve man's capabilities for working under the sea for longer periods of time. He would dedicate himself to "safety in the seas," trying to anticipate and cover every possible underwater predicament. Meanwhile, he went on to write about Thresher:

> ~ Day by day reports heard on *Sea Diver's* radio while we were at sea had aroused the concern of all aboard, as well as constant speculation as to the chances of finding her at the extreme depth of 7,400 feet at which it was assumed she had disappeared.
>
> I was soon in contact with Rear Admiral E. G. Stephan, Ret.
>
> "Ed," the admiral said, "I need your help on a big job I've just been given." ~

During the course of their phone conversation Ed learned that Admiral Stephan had been appointed by the Secretary of the Navy to organize the group for review of the Navy's undersea capabilities as well as to set up a five year program for the search, rescue and recovery of lost submarines. The admiral wanted Ed Link to serve as a consultant and advisor, and asked that he come to Washington immediately.

Ed could not resist the challenge. "I wanted to help in any way possible," he wrote, "I was already planning to head for Bermuda within the next few weeks to carry on the program of experimental deep dives which I had begun in Villefranche the previous fall." However, it would take at least three weeks to cross the Atlantic with *Sea Diver*. The Navy preferred that he fly to Washington the next day to discuss the Admiral's plans.

Ed said in "Oceanology" that after meeting with DSSRG and understanding the importance and scope of the mission, he knew he must cancel his own research plans and arrange to join the group as soon as he could sail *Sea Diver* to a closer base, at Bermuda. In the same article he explained that the word "oceanology" was coined by Admiral Stephan to designate a two-part program consisting of oceanography, or the understanding of the oceans; and ocean engineering, the exploitation of the oceans. "It is this combination of research and development, augmented by man's mastery of the ability to exist in the sea," he projected, "which requires direction today."

He surely felt that the Navy's request was a natural outcome of his work, perhaps inevitable in some sense, and was particularly excited at the prospect because he saw it as a way to continue his research in collaboration with the best of the Navy's minds. Marion later wrote in *Windows In the Sea* that he felt the entire project was related to his Man-In-Sea program, to which she added: "He was aware that by working with experts in every field connected with the underwater world, he would undoubtedly learn more than he could ever hope to contribute." And he was certainly willing to contribute whatever he might have gained from his own extensive underwater experience.

By the time Ed flew to Washington Marion had already flown back home to undergo a series of hospital tests after coming down with serious digestive problems, which ultimately resulted in corrective surgery for what she said was a condition commonly known as "upside down stomach." Meanwhile *Sea Diver* and crew must await Ed's return to Monaco before sailing for Bermuda.

So it was that the Links were on the go once again. Before her surgery she flew to Bermuda to meet *Sea Diver* which, she wrote, arrived on June 11. Then Clayton, again a member of the crew, stayed on while Ed flew back to Washington and Marion went home to prepare for her hospital stay in Boston. Finally *Sea Diver* sailed for her homeland, to a new berth at the Washington Naval Yard on the Anacostia River for the duration of Ed's work with DSSRG, from late in June until the following January.

Ed was immediately occupied with the Navy investigations. He wrote that DSSRG meetings for the first month consisted largely of briefings by officers and scientists who were searching for *Thresher*. They told of frustrations and unanticipated problems encountered in the search, which, he said, illustrated the shortcomings of present equipment and pointed to the necessity for a future program to address deep water search and recovery equipment and methods. He wrote of how little had been done in oceanic technology:

> ~ Early in our investigations we became aware of how badly neglected had been the development of seas in relation to their importance to man. Diving, salvage and rescue techniques had scarcely changed in 25 years except in the development of nuclear-powered polaris submarines. These had completely outstripped our abilities in search and rescue.
>
> It was a startling revelation that if *Thresher* had sunk in less than its collapse depth, its crew could have lived on inside the hull for weeks. Yet we had never developed a means of operational rescue for more than 380 feet in depth.
>
> Better that *Thresher* was instantly demolished than that her crew might have lived on in a world helpless to save them from a long and hopeless wait. ~

It's apparent in Ed's early draft just where the events at hand were leading him, his ideas leaping from the submersible decompression chamber (SDC) he had tested so successfully the year before to the need for a submarine rescue system. The accident would further prompt him to go on in the direction he was taking, eventually to invent the first lockout submersible. However, at the time he continued to point out the difficulties they were facing in the *Thresher* search:

> ~ But even before rescue could be considered, it was necessary to locate the lost submarine. After many weeks of vain effort from vessels plying the surface in the area of the lost *Thresher*, [thought to be] at 7,400 feet below, with long cables, trailing magnetometers, cameras, and other locating gear, the three-man bathyscape *Trieste* had arrived to help with the search. Battling adverse currents and poor visibility, with inadequate navigational and search aides, it was startlingly apparent how hopeless was our effort. ~

*Trieste* was eventually able to pinpoint the accident site at 269 miles off the New England coast, actually at a depth of 8,400 feet. As reported in the June 1964 issue of *National Geographic* by James H. Wakelin, Jr., Assistant of the Navy for Research and Development:

> ~ Pictures of thousands of twisted and torn pieces of wreckage gave conclusive proof that *Thresher* had imploded from the sea's relentless pres-

sure. Although the sub's pressure hull was not sighted by *Trieste* in these dives, magnetic signals recorded in the area of the debris indicated it was probably still intact, though considerably ruptured. ~

Ed continued to write in detail of exploring the problems of detection underwater, dismissing towed search equipment as impractical, and making recommendations for future marker equipment for submarines. These included sonic markers similar to the surface radio direction finder and a distress buoy that could be floated to the surface, sending out long distance radio waves. He wrote that DSSRG recommended both, then continued:

~ After weeks of careful consideration, the Group has also reached the conclusion that given a choice of towing search equipment, or sending down a free, manned or unmanned vehicle for search, the most practical approach would be a submersible which could be easily maneuvered and accurately navigated on the bottom. ~

After exploring in his draft all other means of rescue at depth, once again he wrote: "It was apparent to the DSSRG that a free type, small rescue submarine with almost the same requirements as those already designated for search, is needed."

His writings go into further detail with pages of technical requirements for the proposed vehicle, including solutions to problems with underwater visibility. Then at one point he suddenly mentions, "The magnetometer offers the same broad coverage as sonar but only registers ferrous objects within its magnetic field and not brass or aluminum, *making it useless in searching for the nose cones of space vehicles.*"

It was as if Ed foresaw a specific mission of the *Johnson-Sea-Link* submersibles that took place nearly a quarter of a century later and five years after his death: the search for the wreckage of the downed space shuttle *Challenger*. Clearly, underwater searches for space vehicle parts were in his mind prior to the development of the free-swimming submersibles that would one day be critical to the *Challenger* undersea mission. Once again Ed Link was getting ahead of his time. He projected these future needs with precise accuracy, but would not live to see the day when his twin science submersibles would stun the world by efficiently locating *Challenger's* right-hand rocket booster and the burn-through section that caused the January, 28, 1986 accident.

At the Navy Yard Ed was provided with an office in one of the shore buildings near *Sea Diver's* dock where he spent his days working on the DSSRG project. At the same time he began working out his submersible designs on paper, already imagining how such a vehicle could be used for research and not just as an elevator to and from the ocean floor, particularly if he could take it a step further and, as he said, "put a man outside":

~ Granted, a small submarine such as we visualized, equipped with various types of actuators, would be invaluable to the oceanographer desirous of obtaining bottom samples or specimens of sea life, for the maintenance of oil lines and cables, or for mining valuable undersea minerals. Yet any of these tasks could be performed more efficiently and with greater success were it possible for man to emerge from the submarine and assist with his hands. ~

By then the seed for lockout submersibles was firmly planted in Ed's psyche. Meanwhile, Marion wrote on August 4: "I returned to *Sea Diver* with Ed today after a long absence. She has a beautiful berth in the Navy Yard on 'M' Street with wide views in every direction." On the 5th she wrote of Ed's latest activities:

~ Joan Membery [who had worked with Ed on his SDC animal experiments in Monaco] arrived today. She is going to act as ship's doctor and assist with animal diving experiments to be carried on aboard for the next two months. ~

Marion's records show that visitors once again began to arrive aboard *Sea Diver*. Bill and Julie Link came to Washington, bringing with them a load of gear for *Sea Diver* from Binghamton. Others included Barney Crile, who had recently lost his wife and diving companion, Jane, and Ed's old friend, business colleague, and barnstorming crony, Slim Emerson, who was there with his wife, Frances. Once again they connected with Navy doctor and underwater specialist Charles Aquadro, who had worked with them in the Sea of Galilee and the Mediterranean, and who now took them on a tour of the Navy's Underwater Research Center.

Ed continued to explore with the Navy all of the rescue systems that were currently under investigation, some turning out to be not as practical as others. At one point he wrote:

~ Recently Dr. George Bond, of the U. S. Navy Experimental Diving Unit, completed a buoyant free ascent from 320 feet using only a face mask and inflated life vest. He believes that this method might be extended to as much as 600 feet.
    Certainly such a method possesses the advantage of affording immediate escape, though on reaching the surface the swimmer is still faced with the problem of survival until a rescuing vessel reaches the scene. ~

Ed then offered a different solution:

> ~ Another system which I have proposed would overcome some of the difficulties. This is an escape system attached to the exterior of the submarine utilizing inflatable, balloon-like structures which would carry groups of the submariners to the surface at a carefully regulated decompression rate. Upon arrival at the surface, these rescue balloons could be converted into standard rubber life rafts offering shelter and security until rescue could arrive. Such a system would be available for immediate use and, furthermore, not [be] dependent on surface aid or weather. ~

This system demonstrates the streamlined manner in which Ed's mind worked. As so often pointed out by so many, he could see practical methods of using existing equipment in new and diverse ways, for first one purpose and then another. It was a simple idea, and as always, he had thought of every detail.

Again stressing his idea that man must be able in the future to work underwater for long periods of time, Ed was out to prove the viability of an underwater habitat. On August 9 he tried out his first "inflatable rubber underwater house" in the Potomac, and in spite of getting badly burned by sea nettles even though he wore a rubber suit, the launching was a great success.

His work with Dr. Membery continued. Ed had a small diving chamber ready for experiments with mice that could be pressurized to 4,000 feet. They carried out an experiment with two mice, putting them down to 1,400 feet successfully for 13 1/2 hours. The mice remained lively, eating and sleeping normally, then a slow decompression began. When it was over the experimental subjects were caged with four other mice, but there was no visible sign as to which ones had been in the chamber.

Then Ed and Marion took a break from the heat and pressures of Washington. Though little attention had been paid over the years to their rustic cabin in the Canadian wilderness, they had held on to it, and in August they went to the lodge for a family vacation with Clayton, Bill and Julie. Marion wrote of their pleasure at being all together again and out in the middle of the wilderness. She also mentioned their concern that the Quebec government was "slowly chiseling away" at their lease.

Back in Washington the mice were tested successfully to 2,000 and again to 3,000 feet. Ed knew then that he could continue with his plans for a 400 foot dive in an inflatable dwelling, and that his deep diving submersible ideas would one day be fulfilled.

He and Marion went home to Binghamton at the beginning of September. At that time he managed to begin a long-term project to rebuild the first of two great Link theatre organs, buying one from the old Capitol Theatre in Binghamton and locating and buying the other in Cleveland, Ohio. Eventually, with the help of John Cebula, a former Link maintenance worker and "born mechanic," and organ builders Al Emola and Paul Loomis, he rebuilt the instruments. The first he presented to Binghamton's Roberson Center — an arts and sciences museum holding a collection of his white papers and memorabilia, where a permanent, comprehensive Link biographical exhibition is housed — and the second to State University of New York (SUNY) at Binghamton, whose library also houses an impressive collection of Link white papers.

In September Ed and Marion went back to Washington. A new whirlwind of activities began, first with a conference between Ed, Dr. Membery and Senator Barry Goldwater, after which the Senator read Ed's experimental work into the Congressional Record. Typically, Marion kept up with her running notations: "Ed lunched with nine top-ranking admirals, trying to reach out and promote his underwater development program." "...Ed spoke at a dinner meeting of the Institute of Navigation, and afterward took nearly a hundred people through *Sea Diver*." "...He went to Quantico to carry out tests with "LID" (Link inflatable dwelling). "...Robert Stenuit arrived with his wife Annie." Robert was to take part in Ed's long- postponed deep diving program. At the height of these activities Marion recorded on October 1:

~ ...Ed had an interesting appointment yesterday with Teddy Kennedy, the young senator brother of the president. He has appointments with many high-level people in regard to the oceanographic problem. ~

By the end of the year the DSSRG project triggered by *Thresher* began to wind down for Ed and *Sea Diver*. Meanwhile, he had made contact with Seward Johnson through the oceanographic institution, Woods Hole. Ed was now a member and trustee of the corporation of Woods Hole, which had come about through new acquaintances made because one of the primary ships on the *Thresher* search mission had been the new research vessel operated by Woods Hole, *Atlantis II*. (*Atlantis II* had just finished sea trials when the investigations began.)

By 1963, Seward Johnson, retired Johnson & Johnson executive of Princeton, New Jersey, was already establishing a foundation he called Harbor Branch that would one day support his special interest in the oceans, an interest he had in common with Ed Link. Though perhaps the future cooperative endeavors of these two seafarers actually began long before, when Ed was a landlocked child dreaming of building a submarine in upstate New York and Seward was developing a lasting devotion for the oceans while serving as an officer on a submarine chaser during World War I.

Their meeting turned out to be nothing less than a broad stroke of luck for the ocean environment. Like Ed Link, Johnson was no ordinary man. He was J. Seward Johnson, Sr., yachtsman with an international reputation who had won numerous national and international trophies, active participant in the development of Woods Hole Oceanographic Institution, research chairman on the International Atlantic

Salmon Foundation, deeply concerned for the welfare of the planet ocean, and an heir to the Johnson and Johnson fortune.

Johnson was quick to recognize the unique capabilities of *Sea Diver* from his first tour of the vessel, and he immediately became an admirer and stanch supporter of Ed Link's genius. In the future he would take up scuba diving himself and from time to time catch up with Ed in his own 80-foot, all teak sailing yacht, *Ocean Pearl*, to observe, contribute ideas, and participate in the projects at sea. Ed in turn was impressed with Johnson's deep knowledge of the sea, his navigational skills, and his almost reverent respect for the world's oceans. Both men had already given much thought to how they could individually make their best contributions to the future of man in the sea, and a friendship was soon established in which Ed would eventually help Seward bring about one of the nation's leading oceanographic institutions.

\* \* \*

IT WAS A COLD AND BEAUTIFUL SUNNY DAY in January, 1964, when *Sea Diver* left the Washington Yard for Key West, Florida, grinding her way through ice floes in the Potomac according to Marion's records. Marion also prepared a cryptic list, sometimes giving single names only, of those aboard: "Eden, Woods, Logan, Margetis, Price, Vernon Weihe, Marilyn, Ed, and myself; Frank Sastwell, to make final changes in *Geographic* article [May, 1963] on DSSRG," to which she added: "Chief Price of Honey Fitz loaned to us to help with piloting...." But even with expert advice they went aground in the dark the first night out and were finally conducted to an anchorage by a river police boat. The lovely weather went sour during the night.

So began a new era for Ed and his underwater work. (NOTE: photo on pg. 175, #12). He headed toward the Intracoastal Waterway. Before putting to sea, his sister Marilyn went ashore to return to her duties as a sales manager at Mohawk Airlines. The vessel sailed on through sleet, rain, snow and ice. The deck became coated with ice. Icicles hung from the pilot house. They anchored for the night and listened to reports of heavy storms all up and down the Seaboard. But like the oriental sage observed: "Squalls do not last the morning, nor downpours the day." The next day all was clear. *Sea Diver* left Morehead City on the outside, heading for Nassau in the Bahamas.

After conducting preliminary tests in the Bahamas the divers went on to Key West and a greater rush of activities. One evening Ed and Marion had dinner in Miami with the Jenkinsons from Port Royal, contacts from their former surveys of the old sunken city. Marion made a brief reference in her journal to plans the Jenkinsons had for Port Royal: "They want Ed's help and advice in developing Port Royal like a miniature Williamsburg. Of course they would like him to bring *Sea Diver* back and do some more explorative diving there, also." But Ed was not interested in tourism, and would have no time for more explorations of Port Royal. He was in fact organizing a new underwater company, Ocean Systems, Inc., and was planning to continue his research and development program with the Navy.

Once again the Links went home to Binghamton, this time to catch up with the family. Marion wrote:

> ~ Clayton came down from Colgate... . Bill came east to interview at Corning Glass and arrived this evening. He will also interview at IBM tomorrow before returning to Tucson. It is so good to see both of the boys again and to talk over their ambitions and plans for the future. Bill is interested in programming computers, accounting, etc. with the idea of going into Link eventually. And Clayton is taking O.C.S. exams next week with the hope of getting into the Navy — perhaps eventually working into the underwater company which Ed is forming. ~

Meanwhile she flew back to Key West, and on February 26 reported:

> ~ Plans are underway for a new organization to develop and produce underwater gear and equipment, and contract for undersea jobs. Ed had meetings in Washington and New York with General Precision Equipment and Union Carbide officials, as well as Navy associates to plan same. ~

Ocean Systems, Inc. would engage in the commercial development of a broad range of underwater services and supporting systems. Ed became a board director, marine consultant, and a minority stock holder, but did not take a position with OSI in order to maintain a greater degree of autonomy. Marion thought about the far reaching potential for his plans, and wrote: "So he is going to be in the midst of another big deal, as earth-shaking as aviation was forty years ago." The conclusion was that if private companies took the initiative, the government might also be stimulated to become involved and create undersea programs that could make a major contribution to society.

Her words could have been prophetic, had the government had the foresight to invest as significantly in the oceans as it did in outer space. Ed was pushing for this, believing that the nation should develop "oceanology" just as they were developing the space program, but for more immediately practical reasons. He saw the oceans as the only hope of human survival because of the population explosion, and he foresaw an all new industry that could help to raise the standard of living for people the world over as a result of new oceanic programs.

He saw the future heading in a new direction, which is yet to be realized today, and he certainly saw more present hope for mankind in the oceans than in outer space. He saw a need for a special government agency to pull it all together, saying: "It is imperative that an organization for ocean engineering be considered immediately by both the executive branch and the legislative branch of our government."

Perhaps in 1964 he foresaw the vast implications of overpopulation, even as we see it today in our inner cities, in third world countries, in world-wide economic woes, in wars and threats of wars, and in wholesale environmental destruction. With apparent clarity of vision he went on to write:

~ The successful development of the seas can proceed only with international cooperation, or there will be one point of conflict after another. But the United States will be unable to play its role unless we can present a thorough national oceanology program.

We must also develop a national policy within our own agencies with respect to international law in this field. It is easy to see many differences between the military outlook and the civilian unless these efforts are coordinated. ~

Ed was a man of great hope. He foresaw oceanology tapping into fresh water rivers flowing beneath the sea, and economical ways to convert salt water to fresh while simultaneously extracting other minerals and salts for commercial use. He wrote of developing new methods and machinery for garnering fish as well as utilizing the nutritive plant life of the oceans. And he turned a compassionate heart to world-wide suffering:

~ With unlimited fresh water available in any part of the world, and with food equally plentiful, the hardship countries will have a new chance. Health will improve, and a rejuvenated people will set to work with the vigor of pioneers, simultaneously demanding the education that will spark the political and economic development of their countries. ~

In the same vein he wrote for the June 1964 issue of *National Geographic*:

~ It is commonplace of fourth-grade geography that almost three-quarters of our planet lies beneath the oceans. And yet, phrased another way, the fact is startling: almost three-quarters of our planet is virtually unexplored; almost three-quarters of our planet is virtually unused. And this in a world afflicted with poverty and overpopulation. ~

If Ed's enthusiasm for oceanic development had been more contagious with national leaders when he wrote his paper in 1964, perhaps the world would not be on the verge of the disastrous economical and environmental crisis it faces today. Again he stressed:

~ However, to maintain America's place in the accomplishment of these things, a national program is needed to direct, coordinate and fund their development. ~

And yet again he tried to inspire the bureaucracy:

~ With approximately a quarter of the land mass of the world made available by man's ability to exploit the continental shelf, we would hope that with so much wealth to be shared, national selfishness would be forestalled and a peaceful development of these resources ensue.

However it is accomplished, the United States, if it would maintain its place in the conquest of the oceans, must commence immediately developing a coordinated, dedicated oceanology effort backed by the military, the agencies of government, and the people. With the findings of the Deep Submergence Systems Review Group as a basis, it should not be difficult to build an all-encompassing oceanology program wherein each department can expand to its ultimate growth because of a national plan which utilizes and makes available the best of each for all. ~

Ed had a vision. He reported it to the government through the DSSRG. Then he took it up himself, plodding on, making his own contributions even though he was unable to turn the tide of governmental thinking from the still unproductive reaches of outer space to the rich resources held within man's own environment. Surely he saw it as senseless that so much of humanity should suffer massive starvation while the necessary technology to safely and sensibly tap the ocean's resources was already coming into view. He saw the land eroding away, plants and animals becoming extinct, while this great nation concentrated its monetary resources on curiosity about space rather than on developing the ocean technology at hand.

Ed therefore went on with his work, dedicating himself to ocean engineering. In February, 1964 he was ready to try out his underwater tent, *Igloo,* and see it through its primary failures, about which Marion wrote:

~ [*Igloo*] is finally overboard alongside *Sea Diver* and they are having the usual problems that go with a new development. It gets full of air, then tips slightly, spilling the surplus and setting up a chain reaction which causes it to dump all of its air with a great surging rush of white water to the surface, and then sinks to the bottom again. ~

As always, he plugged away until he made it work. Meanwhile, he and Marion went back home again where he spent time researching and developing submersibles and working on the theatre organ, and again as always, his classical music played in the background. On June 4 he went to Des Moines, Iowa, spoke to the graduating class of the College of Osteopathy and Surgery, and received an honorary degree, Doctor of Engineering. Next they visited Colgate for Clayton's graduation. Marion was most pleased when she wrote on June 6:

> ~ Ed and Marilyn arrived from New York this morning and we headed for Colgate after lunch.
>
> We went to the President's reception and cocktails at the Lambda Chi house. After dinner, which also included [George] Theron and Virginia [Ed's brother and wife], we went to see the Torchlight Ceremony by the lake on campus.
>
> Then we drove to a motel in Utica for the night.
>
> Today is our 33rd wedding anniversary. ~

She continued on June 7:

> ~ Today was a real cause for celebration. Clayton got his BA from Colgate, and Edwin received an honorary degree from Hamilton College. Of course, they were both slated at exactly the same time. ...Marilyn and I drove to Colgate for Clayton's commencement while Virginia and Theron attended Edwin's. ~

After the festivities Clayton flew back with Ed and Marion to Florida and *Sea Diver* at her dock at the Key West Naval Station. A new expedition was to begin. This time the vessel carried SPID (submersible portable inflatable dwelling). Marion wrote that their old *Sea Diver*, now renamed *Sea Hunter*, manned with photographers, reporters, TV cameramen and other observers, was to accompany them.

Ed's full crew included the University of Pennsylvania's Dr. Christian Lambertsen, an authority on hyperbaric physiology; his assistant, Dr. Jim Dicksen; and Dr. Joe MacInnis, described by Marion in *Windows-In-the-Sea* as:

> ~ ...a young Canadian medico, studying to become a full-time life support specialist for the Man-In-Sea program. He would be a permanent replacement for the trained Navy doctors like Dr. Bornmann, who had been made available only on a temporary basis. ~

Jon Lindbergh, oldest son of Charles Lindbergh, joined the diving mission. He was an ex-Navy diver and a current associate of California's Offshore Divers, Inc.

On June 13 three doctors monitored Stenuit and Lindbergh as they did a simulated dive on deck to 420 feet, and all went well.

Marion made a side trip the next day to see her friend, Florida's famous writer and conservationist, Marjorie Stoneman Douglas, who brought her together with a representative from the University of Miami Press to discuss the reprint of her book, *Sea Diver*.

Clayton left on June 14 to represent Ed in Mexico City at the Underwater Conference of America, taking his father's place in a symposium on Manned Undersea Stations. On June 16 they anchored in Bimini to clear customs then cruised on to Great Stirrup Cay. On June 17 the Navy ship, *Nahant,* arrived. Now the press also arrived in numbers.

Meanwhile the June issue of *National Geographic* came out, which included the oceanic overview written by Ed titled, "Tomorrow on the Deep Frontier." He had evidently prepared for this comprehensive article with his "Oceanology" thesis, covering among other things all of the latest developments in sea technology including his own *Igloo* as well as his rubber inflatable submarine escape tent that could be turned into a raft.

Marion began day-by-day accounts of the buildup to the world's longest, deepest dive, to be made by Robert Stenuit and Jon Lindbergh in the Bahamas via the submersible decompression chamber to SPID on the bottom. Seward Johnson, who had a good sense of the general area and had already written a letter to Ed advising where to look for the most appropriate dive site, joined them. Ed and Marion then spent more than a week aboard his lovely teak yacht, *Ocean Pearl*, seeking the perfect site. Then *Sea Hunter*, now owned and operated by John Perry (maker of a small sub called Cubmarine, and other submersibles) out of Riviera Beach, and *Nahant*, under the command of Lieutenant Leon Mills, rendezvoused with *Sea Diver* and *Ocean Pearl* at the Great Stirrup Key site. Meanwhile Clayton returned from Mexico, elated and feeling that Ed's work was well received at the conference, where he had delivered a talk along with Dr. George Bond, and with Jim Dugan representing Jacques Cousteau.

Years later a handwritten draft by Ed turned up in the Link Foundation files, titled "Man In Sea," in which he described the necessary preparations for the dive and wrote in detail of the need to find the perfect location for this sort of experiment. He credited the Navy's Capt. Ken Wilson, out of the Key West Naval Base, and *Nahant's* skipper, Lt. Mills, as well as Johnson for helping to find the best dive site. It was at a depth of 432 feet.

Ed posed and answered questions in his draft.

"How deep is this?" he asked.

"If New York City were covered with this much water, only a few of its tallest buildings would be sticking out!" he answered.

He pointed out that the location of the dive site was critical. He said it could not be on the edge of an underwater cliff where the cabled, inflatable rubber dwelling could accidentally drop off into the sapphire abyss, and added: "There are enough hazards to a first dive of this kind without inviting that one."

He said that a dive to that depth and length of time was not easy to achieve. He referred to deeper dives made by others, but within submarines, and longer dives outside, but at lesser depths. He explained that a dive of 430 feet represented over 200 pounds of pressure per square inch on the human body, which no human had yet tried to endure for as long as two days. He spoke of gaining experience in their previous deep dives, but said that he worried anyway about the dangers and possible "booby traps" they could come across. He said they had learned many things from the 200 foot dive in the Mediterranean, but then he asked with hesitation, "Was it everything?"

He said ordinary scuba equipment was impossible to use at this depth because breathing tanks on the divers' backs would have to be as big as a railroad car to supply enough air at that pressure for even a shorter length of time. He told of how the minds of diverse disciplines had come together and pooled their talents to overcome undersea obstacles. For instance, they had to design and invent a system whereby divers could reuse their air over and over. He wrote of overcoming other problems one by one; of finding the proper mixture of helium and oxygen, which had to be different at every depth; of creating reliable instruments to tell divers of the condition of the gas they were to breathe at all times, and of needing two sets of these in case one failed; of providing a dry place for the divers to live where the inside gas would equal the pressure of the water outside.

He said ordinary clothing would not do, as the pressure of 200 pounds per square inch would squeeze such articles as flat as a piece of paper, adding, "though the human body will stand any pressure if it is allowed to absorb gas slowly." He continued: "Correspondingly, [the gas] must be bled off the body slowly or the dreaded divers bends will occur with instant death if not arrested."

The problems were met one by one. He said the clothing problem was met by developing a material that could be inflated to the same pressure as the outside. The bends problem was taken care of by the SDC, his chamber that could be submerged and brought to pressure, and then locked onto a decompression chamber on the deck of the ship after the dive, where the pressure could be bled slowly enough to avoid any damage to the body.

Other problems were cited, with possible nitrogen narcosis, with communications, of monitoring the physical condition of the divers, of developing the best types of cables, and on and on, "too many to mention," he said after mentioning all of these. Large problems and small problems were met and overcome, any of which left unaddressed could cause death.

Eventually Ed described the record dive for the April 1965 issue of *National Geographic* in an article titled, "Outpost Under the Ocean." He said in his opening paragraphs:

~ Call it the deepest dive. Call it the longest deep dive. Both definitions describe our goal beneath the bright water of the Bahamas.

With the support of the National Geographic Society, including substantial grant funds through its Committee for Research and Exploration, we had come to put two men a long way down for a long time — more than 400 feet for more than 48 hours.

Why? To prove that men can live and work in the untried depths that cover the vast unexplored part of the earth called the continental shelf. For that they must go deep and stay there — for days, weeks, even months. And they must do it not as surface dwellers sheltered in the steel cocoon of a submarine, but as creatures of the deep, exposed to pressures many times greater than man was meant to endure.

We had spent more than a year, working closely with a medical life-science team from the University of Pennsylvania, to extend our Man-In-Sea Project further into unknown reaches of the ocean, yet with complete safety to the divers. Now, as our ship *Sea Diver* rode the swells off Great Stirrup Cay, 140 miles east of Miami, the long wait was ending. ~

Marion later described the submersible, portable, inflatable dwelling, SPID, in *Windows In the Sea*:

~ It was composed chiefly of a heavy iron frame to hold the lead ballast, and a heavy duty rubber balloon shaped like a sausage, which when inflated would float above the ballast frame. The shelter was entered through an open hatch in the bottom, and would receive air either from the surface or by means of tanks of gas strapped to the frame. It had undergone preliminary tests twice that fall, and Ed was satisfied that it would fill their needs. ~

She wrote of the participants — Robert Stenuit, who had been preparing for the project since early fall; Dr. Joe MacInnis, who had completed his studies in hyperbaric medicine at the University of Pennsylvania and now found himself "immersed in studies of relative pressures, decompression schedules, oxygen analyzers, and the like"; Lieutenant Commander Edward Wardwell, submarine officer and engineer and former executive secretary of the DSSRG, only recently retired, who assisted Ed in managing the operation; Dan Eden, who had been with them as engineer since their underwater archeological work in Israel; and John Margetis from their diving days in Greece, who continued to "keep everyone happy with an unfailing combination of good humor and quantities of good food." There were others, too, she said, "hardworking young men with a sense of adventure...." Then she wrote of the Captain:

~ Over all, constantly spurring them on by his own example, was the originator of the program. Ed was concerned that so much time had been lost by the mission in Washington and was eager to get on with the dive. Often after the long work day, he would call the group together in the lounge of *Sea Diver*, and far into the night they would go over the many phases of preparations. ~

On June 30, 1964, SPID rested at a depth of 432 feet — the height of a four-story building, Marion said — connected to *Sea Diver* by three cables, a braided nontwist safety line, a coaxial cable for TV, a cable for electric power and communications, and the essential air hose that kept the tent inflated and provided breathing gas to the divers. Divers Stenuit and Lindbergh were lowered in the SDC to their underwater home. Ed joined them briefly and they overcame obstacles as the experiment proceeded. Stenuit and Lindbergh began passing in and out of the rubber house, carrying out chores, making unexpected repairs, warming themselves by the heater, eating and sleeping comfortably then returning to the surface again via the SDC 48 hours later, on July 2. The experiment was a success, and much new information was gleaned for future work.

Ed was pleased but also already convinced that there was a better way of doing things. Eliminating the cables and three-part system (underwater house, SDC, and a ship/deck decompression chamber (DDC)), he saw that what he needed was a self-contained vehicle in which divers could descend, lock out and do their work, return to the pressurized submarine and return to the surface under pressure to slowly decompress or pass into a decompression chamber on the deck.

Though new technologies would come out of these initial developments, his rudimentary systems — the SDC, the inflatable tents and gear — were already becoming obsolete in his mind. And in fact, when he finished with them, *Igloo*, SPID, etc. would disintegrate badly in storage. The SDC would go to the Smithsonian and eventually be loaned for exhibit at Planet Ocean in Miami, then end up years later on display at the Harbor Branch Visitors Center where it remains to this day.

Meanwhile the divers were brought back to the decks of *Sea Diver* and transferred to a deck decompression chamber, finally to emerge like Rip Van Winkle — having endured eons of uncertainty — to a waiting world 80 hours later in Miami. After press conferences, much excitement and confusion, Marion wrote on July 6, 1964: "The divers are fine. I wonder if everyone will ever get caught up on sleep"!

In Ed's "Man-In-Sea" draft, published in part in the April, 1965 issue of

*National Geographic*, he refers to an article written by Robert Stenuit, "The Deepest Days," that was published in the same issue. He said Stenuit wrote about how it feels to live in what Ed called "this new unexplored world, ...Not the moon, but more important to us, it is the ocean here on our own earth, where we can take home its resources and use them when needed."

Stenuit had begun his own article with a comment from within the deck chamber where he and Lindbergh spent four days in decompression:

> ~ I am sitting on a bunk, eating steak. My wife stands three feet away, watching me. I wave. She smiles. A sun I cannot feel brightens her hair. A sea breeze I cannot savor ruffles it. I wish I could join her, for I have returned from a strange journey into an alien world. ~

On finally emerging from the chamber Stenuit stated: "Project Man-in-Sea goes well. Ed Link has triumphed again."

Ed had reached a creative high point, the momentum building from the development of the submersible decompression chamber to the orchestration of the world's longest, deepest dive with the SDC and SPID.

At that point, his creative energies appear to have gone dormant. He slipped into a strangely barren era, for him, wandering around Florida's waters with Marion aboard *Sea Diver*, again becoming involved in the elusive, intellectually unproductive business of salvaging treasure. But he was blindly searching for more than treasure, perhaps intuitively groping for his future while vague ideas began to take shape in his head. Still, he was accomplishing things. The company Ocean Systems was thriving and growing, and occupied some of Ed's time as part owner and director. (Union Carbide and Singer were the other stockholders.)

Salvaging activities began in January, 1965, when the Links returned to *Sea Diver* at her winter dock at the Miami Ship Yard. First they cleared John Margetis and his new Greek wife, Anna (who was expecting their first child) with US Immigration. Next they were joined by their friend Justin Havee, formerly with Pan American Airlines, now retired and heading up the South Florida Historical Association, and his friends, the Tietze family, who, like so many others before them, had become Ed and Marion's friends for life.

Chris Tietze, son of Nan and Rob Tietze, was a young diver with a potential for engineering genius who had already identified with Ed's work and become enamored of *Sea Diver* and her specialized abilities. He first met the Links prior to their missions in Israel and Greece, had once heard Ed speak at his high school, and had been invited then to see *Sea Diver* for the first time. He looked up to Ed from the beginning as his mentor. Now he began to appear at the Miami Ship Yard nearly every day, scrubbing the ship's decks, painting and scraping, sand-blasting, making himself useful in any

way he could just to be around until he eventually found himself on the payroll as a
deck hand for the summer. He later joined them again as crew member until, drafted
during the Vietnam war, he joined the Naval Training Squad in California and worked
with aircraft. Eventually he returned to Florida, attended Florida Atlantic University,
then rejoined Ed's operations. At this writing he is still at Harbor Branch. Originally
under Ed's tutelage, Chris has since been awarded several patents and has now
become clearly one of Harbor Branch's most innovative engineers.

Years later Chris discussed Ed's management style:

~ He would take an infinite amount of time to talk to you about what you
wanted to do and why you wanted to do it. If it seemed right, he'd say "do
it." Or he'd say to you, "I want a flare gun there. Do it." If he liked what
you came up with, he'd use it. When he gave you a job, he let you do it,
let you work on it, and then either accepted it or encouraged you to make
it right. If you made a mistake, that was okay. Ed would always let you
make one mistake, but if you made the same mistake twice, then you were
in trouble. And if you ever screwed up and didn't tell him, you were really
in trouble, especially if it related to human safety. He'd get annoyed at
goof-ups, but nothing like if you didn't tell him. And he couldn't bear
lying. People lost their jobs if he found out they were lying. ~

Meanwhile, more visitors poured across the ship's decks, including the
Smithsonian's Mendel Peterson and the famous navigator Van Weems who came to
visit with his wife, Margaret.

Marion then wrote of a move to the Keys that brought them in regular contact
with a famous treasure salvager:

~ Sunday, January 24, 1965 - I spent a quiet day with the exception of
having many visitors, including Mel Fisher and his party who have been
salvaging the rich wreck at Vero Beach. They gave us a beautiful gold
coin from the wreck. ~

The Links continued with their expeditions and countless other activities: In
1965 Ed was presented with the Elisha Kent Kane Medal by the Philadelphia
Geographic Society for Eminent Geographical Research. He and Marion sailed to
the Dry Tortugas and back to Key West. Entertaining continued aboard *Sea Diver*.
Ed, in the meantime, was in demand for lectures. He gave a talk in California, then
another at the Smithsonian in Washington. The last edition of Marion's book *Sea
Diver* was reprinted, this time in paperback by the University of Miami Press. She
signed autographs at Waverly bookstore in Vero Beach.

Marion recorded on Monday, March 5: "Clayton received his Navy Commission as an Ensign to be assigned to Newport." Shortly afterward he visited his parents in Florida. Ed continued to conduct tests aboard *Sea Diver*. Marion wrote that they went to the Tongue of the Ocean in the Bahamas, at Young Sound below Fresh Creek, that they found it to be "amazingly steep" there, and different from the way it was depicted on the charts. This was an ideal spot for future dives. She wrote that the Coral Harbor Yacht Club was being considered as a base for Woods Hole's experiments with the Navy's new submersible, *Alvin*.

Ed was sidetracked temporarily by salvaging, but the fallow period was coming to a close after a few more stabs at treasure diving. More significant accomplishments were ahead, as was a future home. Marion wrote on March 26, 1965, that they left the Miami Ship Yard for Fort Pierce, Florida, with Nan, Rob, and Chris Tietze aboard, and added:

> ~ Ed has made a deal with a group of businessmen (Salvage Research Corp.) to help them look for some of the lost treasure of the Spanish Plate Fleet of 1715. There are several groups with leases from the State about to search these waters where a million dollar wreck was discovered last year. We arrived just at dark and tied up at the Gulf Dock where we will be located for a while. Ed and Mary Boots came over from Vero Beach to welcome us. He is a friend of Casey Jones [first promoter of the the Link Trainer] and was responsible for getting Ed involved in this. ~

Ed made a trip to Florida State University at Boca Raton to instruct congressmen in the Florida oceanographic program. On his return Marion wrote of their first day of salvage diving, which included mention of another key player in their future:

> ~ Sunday, April 4 - The sea is rather rough. Our first day on location off Vero Beach, just beyond the three mile limit.... A port boat assisted by towing the magnetometer over the area and placing buoys, with Carl Wild (sand man) directing. ~

Carl Wild was part owner of a sand mining company surrounding a deep water channel in Fort Pierce, sister city to Vero Beach.

Meanwhile an underwater film team showed up, and several "names" in oceanography were suddenly on the scene. Marion wrote on Monday, April 12:

> ~ *Sea Diver* was a busy place today with a film crew aboard, and John Perry, Jacques Piccard, Captain and Mrs. Nichlas, etc. They took pictures all day, inside and out, using Ed, Jacques and Perry as chief characters. ~

John Perry, who had stood by for Ed's longest, deepest dive with the old *Sea Diver*, now *Sea Hunter,* was to be yet another key player in the future. To paraphrase the Desiderata, events in Ed's life were no doubt unfolding as they should.

At one point Ed and Marion went to Cape Canaveral to "check on" the Woods Hole-operated Navy submarine, *Alvin*, and its catamaran tender. Ed was on the Woods Hole advisory board for the newly developing system of tender-barge, *Lulu*, and submarine, *Alvin*, and was not happy with what he found at the Cape. He was, says Marion, "very disappointed that the catamaran had not been designed to provide spring when joining to *Alvin*." She explained in her journal:

~ He said it would be impossible to pick up *Alvin* in even the smallest seas. He had warned them of this last year at Woods Hole. Now he says he refuses to take part in testing *Alvin* at sea until this is remedied. ~

There was more contact with Mel Fisher. He told of a wreck off Fort Pierce's South Beach where he claimed to have picked up 150 coins, but when they dove with him on the site they found nothing. Fisher offered Ed a share in his salvaging interests but Ed declined, having decided that a true commitment to treasure diving would be much more trouble than it was worth. (According to an August, 1992 Knight-Tribune News Service report, Stephen Shouppe, a Mel Fisher sub contractor, discovered a gold coin in the mud off [Sebastian-Vero Beach]. After digging "'like a hound dog,'" they said he "ultimately came up with an estimated $1 million in gold dubloons, silver coins and various ornate objects from a Spanish treasure ship," which was probably "one of a Spanish fleet of 11 ships heading back to Spain from Cuba in July 1715"). Then Ed became acquainted with Wes Knight, a Vero Beach grove owner and prospective salvager, whose son, Pete, would eventually become another of his permanent admirers as well as a *Sea Diver* devotee and crew member to this day. (Pete is now the ship's highly capable chief engineer.) Wes told of pulling up four brass cannons from a wreck several years before, and said he wanted to do business with the Salvage Research Corporation.

In a seemingly aimless way Ed and Marion went back to Miami to attend a historical meeting where the Smithsonian's Mendel Peterson was the guest speaker. Then Ed went to New York. They both returned to Vero Beach, again with Chris Tietze who was now joining *Sea Diver* as a regular crew member. Though it remained essentially a non-creative time for Ed — whose true vocation was still mining his own ingenuity — he was silently drifting toward significant future developments.

On their return to Fort Pierce Marion wrote: "*Sea Diver* was left in Carl Wild's sand pit while we were gone, a very good hurricane shelter in time of trouble." The right contact had been made. Ed had unknowingly found the place for his future home and where a future oceanographic institution was to materialize. Now the salvage business was to indirectly lead him to a resurgence of creativity.

For some time Ed had wanted a hydraulic crane to place on *Sea Diver's* stern for raising heavy objects out of the sea. He picked up a Bucyrus-Erie crane north of Miami that was supposedly used for CIA work in the past, and, he was told, had been sunk in the Bay of Pigs invasion. It was badly corroded and appeared to be falling apart, but Ed docked *Sea Diver* at Riviera Beach and began to perform his magic on it, eventually turning it into a truly innovative crane. He designed articulated parts, including wrist and elbow joints, experimented with hydraulic brakes from airplanes, and then finally worked disc brakes into the system. At last it became a remarkable tool that could be used for launch and recovery. Moreover, the project itself had evidently reinspired him to go on with designing and building the submersibles that were to be handled by the crane.

Marion wrote in her journal that he had increasingly needed the crane as he handled more diving equipment, then she remarked: "But oh, what it is doing for the looks of our beautiful boat. It'll really be 'tug boat Annie' from now on." Again she showed concern for *Sea Diver's* graceful lines, saying: "The hydraulic crane is installed on the aft deck, and we really look like a work boat now." [Late in 1992 *Sea Diver* gained another 14 feet and a Harbor Branch Crane modeled after Ed's original design was installed on the stern to handle a new submersible.]

Ed had modified the crane until it became his own design which would become a prototype for a new crane that was so efficient it could pick up a nine ton submersible and place it in its cradle on the aft deck within a matter of seconds. He worked on it for hours at a stretch. "There were times," Chris Tietze says, "when fellow engineer Bill Launius and I had to drag him out from under the crane." Chris had a hand in the modifications, which would lead him to one day develop an ingenious, hydraulic "drop-lock" system to attach to the submersible from the mouth of the crane for safely lifting it into or out of the water, and which earned Chris a patent. (NOTE: photo on pg. 178, #19).

Ocean engineering was now taking precedence over salvaging with Ed. In the spring of 1965 he rendezvoused with Woods Hole's two-man submarine, *Alvin*, and her catamaran tender barge, *Lulu*, off the coast of Cape Canaveral from where *Sea Diver* was to tow the system to the Bahamas for sea trials. Marion made a brief comment in her journal: "We are close to the weird and clumsy looking 'cat,' *Lulu*. ...*Alvin* is a winsome little white sub."

Several days before the next space shot the Link party was given a VIP tour of the Missile Base. Compared to preparations for a dive into "inner space," Marion wrote that they found the scope of preparations for the shot to be "fascinating and completely unbelievable." "They are preparing for a two-man *Gemini* shot on June 3rd," she reported, "and the astronauts have been training in the simulator," produced by the Link Company.

While the crews prepared for *Alvin's* experiments and Marion shopped for *Sea Diver* provisions, Ed took the opportunity to tear down and refurbish his new crane while he had a Navy crane nearby to assist. At last *Sea Diver* towed *Lulu* and *Alvin* to their diving test site near Coral Harbor in the Bahamas. Ed's new crane worked like a charm. Though *Alvin* developed plumbing problems and held up sea trials, Ed was not dismayed because he was enjoying something else: "Ed," Marion observed, "has had more fun using his new crane to lift *Cubmarine* and *Reef Diver* aboard."

Yet another contact was to keep him on course. On June 7 *Sea Diver* sailed for Andros Island and a Navy installation just south of French Creek where Ocean Systems, Inc. had been contracted to carry out surveying work with John Perry's *Cubmarine,* at a depth of 600 feet. At one point Marion wrote that Perry's vessel *Sea Hunter* was carrying on board four Navy divers, a biologist and an oceanographer, and she observed: "It is an important contact for Ocean Systems, as it is the first of its kind." Ed watched the little sub at work, which led shortly thereafter to a partnership with John Perry to build an all new sub.

Throughout much of the following year the experimental work continued. Ed experimented with a heliox voice unscrambler. In 1966 he and Marion worked with the crew and various other interested parties in the Bahamas, they made a brief flight to Port Royal, Ed went to New York and California, they entertained as always aboard *Sea Diver*, and on June 4 Ed received an honorary doctorate degree from Syracuse University while Marion became an Alumni Trustee there for five years. The Link Engineering Building at Syracuse University was named in Ed's honor. Two days later Marilyn, Bill and Julie Link gave a 35th wedding anniversary party for Ed and Marion in Binghamton.

Ed was becoming more and more involved with his submersible designs, concentrating in particular on the problems of breathing underwater. Through Ocean Systems he also conducted experiments with rebreathers for a Norway diving project in the North Sea. Then once again extenuating circumstances prompted him to move, as was noted in Marion's journal on June 23:

~ Ed is interested in relocating *Sea Diver's* headquarters, as Miami Ship Yard has an expansion program and wants our dock space. It would be better for all if we could get permanently located. We plan to leave at 3:00 a.m. for Palm Beach where John Perry has a place for *Sea Diver* at his new submarine plant. ~

After that it was only a matter of time until Ed collaborated with John Perry and developed the world's first lockout submersible, *Deep Diver*. But meanwhile, Ed and Marion flew to London for an underwater conference where Ed shared the agenda with, among others, Jacques Cousteau.

# CHAPTER XII

# DEEP DIVER, JOHNSON-SEA-LINK SUBMERSIBLES, A TRAGEDY AT SEA & THE FINAL YEARS OF A DREAMWEAVER

**1967–1981**

*It is the heart that reaches the goal.*
*Follow the heart, for a pure heart seeks beyond*
*the intellect — it gets inspired.*

— *Sri Sathya Sai Baba*

By January, 1967, Ed's creative endeavors and other activities had again picked up full momentum. His enthusiasm for oceanic work continuously mounted. He served on government committees and wrote papers on oceanology. That year he published with RAdm. P. Gallery, USN (Ret.), "Deep Submergence and the Navy." From January until the end of June he tried out the Perry-Link (PL-4) submersible, *Deep Diver*; acquired a partly new crew on *Sea Diver*; refurbished the SDC to be used by the Smithsonian; carried out another series of experiments with all of his submersibles, including the still operable rubber dwellings; made a trip to Hawaii for his younger son Clayton's wedding; did a story with *Life* magazine; made a film with Union Carbide; worked with *National Geographic*; took Werner Von Braun on a lockout dive; and set new records with the PL-4 *Deep Diver*. *Deep Diver* had the capability of diving to 1,250 feet, carried a pilot and one observer in the forward compartment, and two pressurized divers in the aft chamber who could lock out through a hatchway on the bottom.

*Sea Diver* was in Palm Beach that January when Ed and Marion flew in with Seward Johnson in what she describes as his "beautiful Johnson & Johnson Jet Star." They found their ship in top shape with her latest crew, now consisting of engineers Bill Launius and Pete Knight as well as John Margetis, "a good crew," Marion observed in her journal, "along with Denny Breese who lives on his own boat with his wife, Willa." Seward Johnson was now aboard *Ocean Pearl* preparing to participate in the next project.

Just as Ed's early acquaintances became part and parcel of his simulator industry, many who now came and went would eventually be a part of Johnson's future Harbor Branch just as he would, including Dr. Gene Wallen, who came from the Smithsonian.

The pace continued to gather momentum. Ed went to a meeting at Woods Hole in January. Clayton wrote to say he was planning to be married on March 11 at the Submarine Memorial Chapel in Pearl Harbor. His fiance was Maurine Muzzy, an airline stewardess from Seattle. The Link team became involved with Florida's Governor Claude Kirk on an oceanographic project. Then *Deep Diver*, now owned by Ocean Systems, was suddenly ready for sea trials.

They were in the Bahamas in February when Marion wrote:

~ The sea was rough this morning but they launched *Deep Diver* again and this time took pictures of Ed and Denny locking in and out on the bottom. Seward Johnson's *Ocean Pearl* joined us later and acted as platform to photograph *Deep Diver* being raised and lowered in the water from the stern of *Sea Diver*. ~

Ed and Marion flew to Hawaii for Clayton and Maurine's wedding. On their return Marion wrote of their latest project to the interested bride and groom:

~ Both SPID and *Igloo* were on the bottom. *Deep Diver* was in operation along with our new rubber boat [an inflatable dingy] and *Reef Diver*. *Sea Hunter* was anchored near us as a base of operations for the photographers and some of the divers. The sea was rough, and everything was done with great effort, but the whole operation was most successful. You never saw so many photographers! There was a team of eight from Young & Rubicon making a film for Union Carbide; Jerry Greenburg for *National Geographic*; Bernie Campaii, a diver photographer who now works for OSI (Ocean Systems, Inc.), and the two *Time-Life* reporters who were friends of Jon Lindbergh.

Of course we always have a quota of visitors, this time they included Werner Von Braun who came back a second day and did a lockout dive from the submarine, and an AT&T vice president to observe *Deep Diver* in operation, following a cable and repairing it. ~

Later Marion made her first deep sea dive in *Deep Diver*, and said that the water was too murky, due to rain the night before, to see anything, but that it was thrilling just the same. *Deep Diver* was then flown to Los Angeles for its debut at an oil show in Long Beach. There Ed signed up to do a show with CBS, and that March the entire entourage went to the Bahamas, including *Sea Diver*, *Ocean Pearl*, and *Sea Hunter* with *Deep Diver*, *Igloo*, SPID, and the SDC. Walter Cronkite covered the expedition on "21st Century," sponsored by Union Carbide. "A blast of publicity followed in magazines and newspapers," Marion noted in *Windows in the Sea.*

Then one day Ed insisted that Marion make a lockout dive. She had come a long way from the early treasure diving days when she feared going underwater and didn't even like to swim. He went down with her and supervised compression, opening the hatch and generally looking after her. "I wore a face mask, weight belt and flippers," she reported, "but no air." She described the event:

> ~ I slipped out of the hatch to the outside where I could see SPID on the bottom. I hung on to a line from inside as I was not weighted heavily enough, and came back in rather soon without additional air. It was a real thrill. I guess I am the third woman to do this, following Joyce Grab and Joan Membery. ~

Joan Membery had joined them once again to continue working with Ed on pressure tests. Joyce Grab was a scuba instructor, teaching Seward Johnson to dive as well as Marion, who had until then only snorkeled and worked at depth with air hoses. (Joyce was to marry another friend of Ed's and Seward's, astronaut Scott MacLeod, who joined their missions from time to time as an observer.) Although it's not recorded at what depth Marion made her first lockout dive, her next excursion in *Deep Diver* was a two hour dive at 120 feet.

On Monday, April 17, she recorded a tragedy that took them both home for funeral services: "There was a terrible accident! The Link Company Beech [aircraft] landing at Tri-Cities [airport] in bad weather hit a hill top and crashed." The same Pete Dougherty Ed had stopped to see at Los Angeles when they were on their way to Japan in 1936, who since became a company pilot, was killed in the accident with two of his companions, while a third passenger survived.

In June, 1967, Ed was hospitalized with diverticulitis, an intestinal disorder that also became a problem for Marion in her later years. He was in the hospital in West Palm Beach when they marked their 36th wedding anniversary with a small celebration.

By now Ed's opinions were highly regarded in many important circles. A June 1, 1967 letter found in his files, on US Embassy, Office of the Defense Attache, London letterhead, from one US Navy rear admiral to another, recommended Ed's views on a Manual then in circulation for review:

> ~ ...Because of my appreciation of what Mr. Link had done and is doing in ocean engineering, I feel we should give serious consideration to his views. ...If I did not know Mr. Link so well and wasn't aware of his accomplishments and contributions to the scientific oceanographic field, I would not be making this request... ~

Marine scientists from the Smithsonian were now lining up to take advantage of *Deep Diver*. George Bezak was one of the early pilots, as was Ex-Navy frogman Roger Cook. They were both destined to be among the first *Johnson-Sea-Link* submersible pilots, and Roger was to become the first director of Marine Operations at the future Harbor Branch. Mike Adams, at this writing a Harbor Branch submersible pilot, worked then for Ocean Systems and was one of the first lockout submersible pilots. On June 14 *Deep Diver* made a record dive to 1,000 feet.

Joe MacInnis flew in for dives to follow. It was a memorable time for all concerned. One day Marion wrote that they had a picnic on a sandy beach at the end of a good afternoon's diving sessions. Pete Knight caught a five-pound hog snapper, John grilled it, and Marion appreciated it, saying, "It was delicious." The series of exciting experimental dives went on, the team only half conscious that they were making underwater history.

Meanwhile Marion kept up with current events, saying that along with her routine of daily swimming she had developed the habit of listening to the United Nations discussing the Israeli-Arab problems. She also kept her wonderful, reliable journals going. Longer dives and night dives were tested. Pete Knight kept up the fresh fish larder, spearing — in one afternoon — a huge grouper and five hog snappers.

On June 26 *Deep Diver* supported the deepest yet lockout dive, conducted by Ken MacLeish of *National Geographic* and Denny Breese, at 400 feet for fifteen minutes. Navy representatives arrived and *Deep Diver* went through her paces in a series of eight lockout dives within an hour. "It went off like clockwork," Marion wrote, "and made quite an impression."

The little undersea vehicle, painted yellow, sporting a conning tower with viewports all around, had proven itself. Much more experimentation ensued in the Coral Harbor area off Nassau. Seward Johnson participated in the projects. Roger Cook beat the 400-foot record and set a new, still unbroken world's lockout dive record at a depth of 700 feet. However, Ed was beginning to wonder about the viability of such dives and called a halt to deep lockout diving for no other purpose than record-setting. Since then it was generally considered that any outside diving deeper than 300 feet was unsafe, though with new technologies that may be subject to change today.

Seward Johnson and the Smithsonian Institution became more and more involved in the work. Smithsonian scientists saw the practicality of conducting marine research from beneath the surface rather than by the traditional method of throwing nets overboard and then guessing about the relative depths and relationships of sea life hauled up to the surface, with plants and animals often damaged in the process. Deep Diver continued diving to new depths. Bill and Julie Link joined the mission for a visit.

Later in 1967 Ed began a series of experiments with oceanographers and the Navy at Duke University, where they could utilize Duke's new hyperbaric facilities, including a pressure chamber allowing experimental "dives" to 1,000 feet. Other milestones transpired: That year Link Group, which had been the Link Division of General Precision, became a subsidiary of The Singer Company. Another month's expedition transpired in the Bahamas.

Marion wrote on January 29, 1968 — from *Sea Diver*, anchored off Coral Harbor for a new season — that they had just received the disturbing news that the Navy might want *Deep Diver* right away for an emergency, which would have upset their plans for a Smithsonian expedition. The *Pueblo* had been captured by North Korea, and the Navy was considering a mission, possibly to recover secret documents with the submersible. However, the mission never transpired. Then on January 31 she wrote that Seward had to leave because of the death of his brother, General Robert Wood Johnson. By the time he returned word was getting around that their science missions were a great success. Marine botanist Dr. Sylvia Earle joined the expedition. She would go on to become a well-known advocate and user of the deep diving submersibles herself, and would credit her experience with Ed Link as a great source of inspiration for her work. Dr. Paul Fye, director and President of Woods Hole, was another visitor on the scene.

In May, a second American nuclear submarine, the *Scorpion*, sank. The Navy commandeered *Deep Diver* and Ed's crane and shipped them to the Azores for a search and recovery mission. The Navy submarine was reported missing somewhere between the Azores and Norfolk. There was speculation that it might have hit a sea mount 300 miles from the Azores at a depth of between 600 and 1,000 feet. If so, there was on off chance that it might still be intact with its 99-man crew alive but disabled and unable to come to the surface. However, no trace was ever found of *Scorpion* and *Deep Diver* was returned to her operators.

June 6 was a quiet day. Ed continued to experiment with the magnetometer, he and his bride had a pleasant day on deck and went swimming, and that evening they celebrated their 37th wedding anniversary with champagne for dinner. Then after three more weeks of underwater work they went home for the summer.

At the beginning of the next dive season, on January 8, 1969, Ed and Marion became grandparents for the first time when Mary Catherine Link was born to their older son Bill and his wife Julie. Ed had to attend meetings regarding their next mission, so Marion flew alone to Denver to see the baby and visit with the young couple at their new mountainside home.

Back in Binghamton she left with Ed for a three-month cruise starting at the Florida Keys and including the Dry Tortugas, Cozumel, Chichen Itza and Belize, British Honduras, where they rendezvoused with *Ocean Pearl* and a number of scientists and other visitors. At one point they supported a shark hunt with underwater photography conducted from the SDC. Ed began to have sugar problems again and at times did not feel well. Their friend, Dr. Barney Crile, came with his new wife Helga for several weeks. Ed flew to Washington to give a Smithsonian lecture and attend to Ocean Systems business.

In March Marion wrote that Ed was having problems with Ocean Systems over not being allowed to build a second sub for his own use. "He is very upset at being restricted on his own creation which he has shared with OSI," she wrote. Ed called from New York and told her that he was not having any luck convincing one of the members to go along with his wishes, and added that he might have to pull out of OSI (which some time later he did). He returned very discouraged, but feeling better physically. Meanwhile, he had made arrangements to build a submersible to be used by the Smithsonian Institution that would be strictly for scientific use.

On the way home from British Honduras they stopped for a short visit at Port Royal near the end of March, and though Marion reported visiting again with the Jenkinsons, there was no mention of the yacht club owners' future plans to develop the old sunken city area for tourism. By April they were in the Bahamas and Ed was attending to the business of trying to withdraw from OSI. Chet Smith, a fellow OSI member, joined *Sea Diver* to sail back with them to West Palm Beach.

Ed and his party arrived at the Perry dock on April 19, but not to stay, for a new home was on the horizon. An entry in Marion's journal reads: "Ed and Chet and Bill Launius went to Fort Pierce this afternoon to look at Carl Wild's property as a possible future site for *Sea Diver* and OSI." On April 23 she wrote from *Sea Diver*: "We had a visiting delegation from NASA to see the crane, including Werner Von Braun."

Again the stars appeared to align themselves in such a way as to work a unique coincidence in Ed's life. This time he and Marion had been invited by NASA to witness the take off of Apollo 11 on July 16 for the first moon landing on July 20, 1969. They were on their way to a new and permanent dockage for *Sea Diver* at the time where Ed and Marion had bought land. After the takeoff they left Cape Canaveral, stopped to dive near Sebastian, then when the astronauts landed on the moon, they arrived at Carl Wild's sand pit channel at Fort Pierce on July 20 for their own new beginning. "We celebrated," John Margetis reports, "at the time of man's first step on the moon." They watched television from the after deck of *Sea Diver* as astronauts Neil A. Armstrong and Edwin E. "Buzz" Aldrin touched down with their lunar module *Eagle* and became the first men to walk on the moon. In spite of finding themselves on a channel in the thick of Australian pines and mangroves in an alligator-ridden, mosquito-infested site, the crew had chosen to sit outside that night, under the light of the moon.

Though they still maintained the house in Binghamton, which had originally been built by Ed's now deceased mother, this Fort Pierce location was to be a new home site where Ed spent much of his time in his final years and Marion made her permanent home after his death. Ed designed and built a charming and modest ranch style home along the channel, which they named Link Port (now known as the Harbor Branch channel). At first *Sea Diver* served as home as well as headquarters, temporary office and theatre of operations for the development of a marine science center. So it was that the aquanauts arrived at their permanent dock to help promote the exploration of inner space just as the astronauts were walking on the moon. On either side of the channel, beyond swamps and ponds, saltwort, wax myrtles and mangroves, the surrounding sand pit reflected the moonlight on slopes as barren as the moon.

Tietze now says he couldn't believe Ed would choose such a site in the wilderness after leaving "beautiful Riviera Beach." "There were gnats, millions of ants, mosquitoes, huge gators in the back swamp, and even cougars running around, which ate a couple of John the Greek's goats."

Clearing began immediately, though the environmentally concerned developers determined to leave the area as pristine as possible. Ed had negotiated first with Carl Wild's partner, buying out 51% of Indian River Minerals company, then later 9% of Wild's interest. Seward personally and also Harbor Branch acquired more of the surrounding property, including an adjacent grapefruit grove. Years later his son, J. Seward Johnson, Jr., now chairman of the board, bought property as did Harbor Branch under his direction. The total now held by Harbor Branch is more than 485 acres.

Seward Johnson, Sr. also built a stunning house on site, designed along the lines of a ship. A screened dome over a large round swimming pool behind the house replicates the northern hemisphere, its frames marking the lines of latitude and longitude and its reflection in the round pool completing the formation of the globe, as seen from the second floor teak deck. The Smithsonian earlier had established "The Marine Science Center" on site, a corporation which dissolved upon Ed's death and which had become less active when the senior Johnson began a major contribution to marine science by developing on site what eventually became the full-fledged oceanographic institution. Today Seward's Harbor Branch Oceanographic Institution includes fully equipped marine science and ocean engineering research laboratories, a marine railway, welding and machine shops, sophisticated computer facilities, three research vessels and three manned submersibles. A small boat marina and a fleet of small boats were later acquired, and visitor, education and conference facilities have recently been added to the institution. The newest building is appropriately named the "J. Seward Johnson Education and Conference Center."

In 1970 Ed received Syracuse University's "1870-1970 Centennial Medal." That year The *Pilot Maker*, describing the history of simulators, by Lloyd L. Kelly as told to Robert B. Parke, editor of *Flying* magazine, was published. By 1970 Ed had already designed for construction the newest submersible, with an aluminum alloy hull and an acrylic "bubble" sphere, at his home workshop in Binghamton. (NOTE: photo on pg. 175, #14). Then he took the project to Florida, where he and Seward Johnson had agreed to develop for use by Smithsonian scientists an all new lockout submersible for scientific research. Johnson would finance further development of the submersibles, but Ed had already invested $400,000 in the design and construction of the first one. Before he ever started on the project, Ed had made a model to scale which is on exhibit at Harbor Branch today. (Tietze reports that Ed was a great believer in working out his ideas with models before building finished products.)

Both Seward and Ed were excited and enthusiastic about the project. The submersible was designed with a forward acrylic sphere to provide panoramic visibility underwater for a pilot and one scientist/observer. Sphere occupants would enter from a hatch at the top and remain at one atmosphere, breathing ordinary air. In the after chamber two more divers could make observations through port holes and have the capability of locking out and decompressing through a hatch. The submersible was to be all in one, as Ed had dreamed of after joining the DSSRG — not an elevator to and from a rubber underwater dwelling, or a small and uncomfortable submersible with poor visibility like *Deep Diver*. Marine scientists could use it as an underwater laboratory. It would have scrubbers and rebreathers. It would be battery operated from a pod beneath the vehicle, forward of the after hatch. It would be made from an aluminum alloy, remaining unpainted and therefore easier to maintain. It would not have a "skin," or casing around it, leaving various parts, including breathing gas tanks, easier to remove and replace. It would be able to rest on the bottom. It would have vertical and horizontal propellers, allowing it to move in any direction or to hover like a hummingbird along underwater cliffs.

Ed would go over and over the designs, thinking of everything yet possible to think of. What he didn't include would be left for engineers and submersible crews to create and install over the following years. Because it would be so easy to dismantle, it would be free to evolve into a more and more sophisticated machine, having its outdated parts removed and new equipment constantly added. Unintentionally, it would look like a cross between an underwater helicopter and something dreamed up by the combined minds of Jules Verne and Isaac Asimov. Intentionally, it could be taken apart for regular maintenance and put back together again.

One day its parts would be interchangeable with its future twin, *Johnson-Sea-Link II*. Finally, it would be loaded with manipulator arms with intricate "hands;" suction devices that could pick up samples from the outside and deposit them into rotating "lazy-susan" type acrylic jars; still and broadcast quality video cameras; laser beam depth of field focusing devices; Harbor Branch (Tietze) developed xenon arc lights that could approximate sunlight in the darkest seas, illuminating underwater scenes in true color; and whatever other technology the engineers at Harbor Branch could devise over the coming years. Eventually it would not even need to be used for lockout dives. Today, from inside the acrylic sphere, a well-trained pilot can skillfully use tools that have evolved to do just about anything on the outside that human hands once did in lockout dives. The subs are now certified by the American Bureau of Shipping to dive to a depth of 3,000 feet, more than half a mile beneath the surface of the ocean. (NOTE: photo on pg. 177, #18).

Ed and his team, including Dr. Jerry Stachiew and Dr. William McLean, after a prolonged search located a California sculptor, Bruce Beasley, who also had considerable background and expertise in acrylic, to create the 66-inch diameter, four-inch thick acrylic sphere. All done, the submersible was 23 feet in length and weighed nine tons. It was then certified to dive to 1,000 feet. As compared to the Navy's DSRV-1, built at a cost of $41,000,000 (now out of commission), and *Alvin*, built for $2,000,000, it was relatively inexpensive to build at approximately $400,000. With all the sophisticated navigation and operating equipment it now has, it would cost more than a million dollars to build today.

Although Ed achieved a number of patents for other inventions, and other people made important contributions to the deep-diving vehicle, he was the designer and orchestrator of *Johnson-Sea-Link* class submersibles. To many, this was ultimately his greatest expression of genius. It was also his greatest labor of love. The earlier Link Trainer was created out of compulsion and need early in his career, when he had a passion for flying and a desire to make aviation a safer occupation for all concerned. The submersibles resulted from a logical series of developments that took place within the context of his growing familiarity with and respect for the vast and mysterious underwater world, and from the need to place man in the sea to work and to discover new undersea plants and animals. From submarine disasters such as the *Thresher* accident, he also knew how great a need there was for advances in underwater technology. Thus all of his talent and accumulated experience, his desire to make a contribution to the betterment of mankind, his appreciation of the oceans, his childhood dreams of building a submarine, and his intense desire to at last see all of it materialize were poured into the making of this remarkable vehicle. As was his habit, he often worked all night long, ignoring sleep, perhaps gaining some measure of relaxation from his ever-present music playing in the background. For inspiration he had Marion, whose faith in him was constant. Seward Johnson, Sr., with his own ardent desire to place scientists directly within the laboratory of the ocean, also supported, motivated, prompted and encouraged him with ideas and endless enthusiasm.

* * *

ON THE FIRST OF JANUARY, 1971, Marion wrote in Binghamton that they celebrated son Bill's birthday with a venison dinner, "courtesy of John Cebula," with friends and family before leaving the next day for Florida. Bill, Julie and young Mary Catherine saw them off. They were met in West Palm Beach by Charles Aquadro. It was a Saturday and Ed was anxious to check over the progress on the sub construction before work started again on Monday in preparation for the official launch scheduled with the Smithsonian for January 29.

The first trial launch in the home channel was a failure. There was more work to do. The second, on January 19, was a success. Ed ran *Johnson-Sea-Link* under its own power on the surface then dove 14 feet to the bottom. All went well and he was elated at the success. Seward was delighted. Marion, John Margetis, Pete Knight, Chris Tietze, Bill Launius and other hardworking contributors cheered him on. A number of people again started arriving on the scene. Joe MacInnis arrived in his sailboat, *Apollo*. Chet Smith and others came for dinner on *Sea Diver* that night. More work was needed to ready all systems.

The commissioning of *Johnson-Sea-Link* to the Smithsonian "to be available to universities and scientific institutions for marine research" took place on Friday, January 29. About 350 people attended. Tom Adams, then Lieut. Governor of Florida, took the first "ride" with pilot John Fike. Seward's youngest daughter, Jennifer, christened the submersible. The Smithsonian's Dr. S. Dillon Ripley and Dr. I. E. (Gene) Wallen were the speakers. Ed and Seward were each presented with the Smithsonian Institution's first Matthew Maury Award for their contributions in the field of ocean science, a gold medal with a raised representation of *Johnson-Sea-Link* on the back.

With that launching an endless love affair between *Johnson-Sea-Link* and the news media began. Reporters who would never get to go near the water in the submersible still found it irresistible. Just standing before it was an awesome experience. It was futuristic, pure science fiction. They compared it to a rotorless helicopter, a wingless dragonfly. As in the early days when the government did not yet appreciate the Link Trainer and the press saw it as a vital tool for aviation, the media now saw the submersible, not to be recognized by the military until the *Challenger* mission, as the beginning of a new era of man's in-situ exploration of the ocean floor. It was, in fact, reporters who called Harbor Branch first, before the military or NASA, to ask if the submersibles would be used for undersea exploration when *Challenger* went down. They wrote endless descriptions of the vehicle. They were careful to explain to the public the difference between a submarine, which leaves shore on its own volition, and a submersible, which is carried to its dive site to be launched and recovered by a tender vessel, or "mother ship."(NOTE: photo on pg. 177, #17).

The submersible was dedicated and donated by Ed to the Smithsonian Institution. At that point Harbor Branch was still a trust, not an operating approved 501(c)3 organization. However, after the 1969 Tax Reform Act, a series of organizational changes, and the passing of time, Harbor Branch became the owner and operator of the submersibles.

Although he had begun his initiatives the year before, the senior Johnson officially established Harbor Branch Foundation as a private operating foundation in Fort Pierce, Florida in November, 1971. He then saw to the construction of new buildings while Ed, his crews, and science investigators went to the Bahamas for a series of dives during which marine research and ocean engineering deep diving experiments continued. *Ocean Pearl* sometimes joined them. *Sea Diver* returned to Harbor Branch in April. Testing, improvements, and media coverage, now including *Popular Science* magazine and such exotics as *Playboy* magazine, continued.

Again in the Bahamas, Ed orchestrated a 190-foot lockout dive on Tuesday, May 11, 1971. Two days later, on May 13, he and Marion learned that they were grandparents for the second time, when Thomas Edwin Link was born to Bill and Julie. The next day Arthur Godfrey flew in to see *Johnson-Sea-Link*. Marion said John cooked a "fine musaka and rum pie dinner," then continued:

~ Arthur came over to make a dive but the weather was very uncooperative so we came up to the harbor at West End, then towed the sub to sea with *Reef Diver*. Ed was the pilot with Godfrey up front and Bob Wicklund and I in the diving chamber - my first trip in the diving chamber. ~

A new era in oceanographic work had begun just as yet other milestone in the family history was being made. On the following January 15th, Stephen Clayton Link was born to Clayton and Maurine. As young Stephen grew from a toddler to a bright school student, he learned that his paternal grandparents were most unusual people. Nearly two weeks after his arrival, Marion, a grandmother now for the third time, sat aboard *Sea Diver* in Florida and documented the progress at Seward's Foundation:

~ Saturday, January 29, 1972 - An estimated eight hundred to a thousand people visited today for the dedication of the new Harbor Branch Johnson Science Laboratory. The weather was perfect and everyone was impressed at the many additions since the sub launching just a year ago. ~

The additions included docks, two ships, and such other installations on site as a mobile unit belonging to the Florida Institute of Technology (FIT), and a diving academy (no longer there) out of Fort Lauderdale. Seward was now traveling in the company of his new wife, Barbara (more commonly known by her Polish nickname, Basia), and Marion wrote that they stayed in one of the new apartments in the Science building across the channel from his developing million dollar house. She also mentioned that Basia's brothers, who came for the dedication, stayed aboard *Ocean Pearl*. At that time an informal relationship was established between Harbor Branch and FIT, and the Links and Johnsons went together for a tour of the FIT Jensen Beach campus. (Eventually the main FIT campus at Melbourne, Florida, which has a collection of Link papers in their library, also dedicated the Link Engineering Building in Ed's name.)

More honors came in 1972. Ed was named Director Emeritus, USAir. He was elected by the OX 5 Aviation Pioneers to the OX 5 Aviation Hall of Fame. Meanwhile work continued as usual in the Bahamas. Marion wrote on May 11 that Clayton was with them, now in his new position as Director of Diving for the Smithsonian after a stint with Ocean Systems and after a recent discharge from the Navy where he had served as a diving officer aboard a submarine rescue vessel. More history was being made. On May 24, a 250-foot lockout dive was conducted near Great Harbour Key. On May 25, the first night dive was a success. The only hitch that day was that Marion got into trouble with Ed. She wrote: "Ed is mad at me because I swam too far from *Reef Diver* this morning on the reef." There were always perils to diving. On the next day she nearly got into trouble with sharks:

> ~ Ed and Clay went down in the sub this afternoon for a lockout. I went to a point in the middle of Bond Cay with Jim [Parrish, a crew member] and Pete to explore the bottom by skin diving, and I got chased back into *Reef Diver* by three small, three-to-four foot sharks in one spot. Otherwise, I enjoyed the trip.
>
> There is a tropical storm off the Carolinas drifting southward but the weather is beautiful here so far. ~

Early that fall Ed and Marion took a break from the constant experimental work with the sub and flew to the South Seas for a vacation with their friends Hugh and Ginny O'Brien. She wrote pages of descriptions in her journal of reef diving and sightseeing, and said they were particularly taken with Western Samoa and "Aggy Gray's hotel in Apia." They spent nearly a month in the South Seas then arrived late in October in the Hawaiian Islands. Ed was scheduled to give several lectures on the mainland, but these had to be canceled due to a serious foot infection he had contracted in Samoa.

Clayton met them in Miami on October 25, and on the 26th Marion commented:

> ~ Seward Johnson arrived today to spend a few days checking the Smithsonian-Harbor Branch setup, so Ed will have little time to catch up on things otherwise. There is a move on to separate the two organizations with separate directors. ~

The Smithsonian then came under the direction of scientist Dr. Mary Rice, a well-known and highly regarded marine ecologist who specializes in part in sipunculans, the environmentally important reef-building worms. The Smithsonian research effort became a marine science station that remained on the Harbor Branch complex, operating in an office and lab in the Johnson Science Laboratory and out of a floating barge, although they now have plans to erect an impressive permanent facility on the grounds.

Seward Johnson, Sr. continued developing Harbor Branch into a progressive research facility while Ed worked on his advanced engineering concepts. It was a climate of excitement, cooperation, and dedication. And sadly, it was the willingness of all concerned to experiment at the cutting edge of what they knew so well to be a hostile atmosphere that eventually led to a heartbreaking tragedy, taking two lives and nearly permanently costing Ed his peace of mind.

It was early in the morning on a beautiful, sunny day; Father's Day, June 17, 1973. The submersible was working on the bottom. Word of trouble from below reached the wheelhouse. Ed and Marion were both aboard *Sea Diver* when *Johnson-Sea-Link* glided toward a man-made, artificial reef consisting of old tires and two scuttled World War II Navy vessels, *USS Wilkes Barre* and *USS Berry*. They were 15 miles off the coast of Key West in the Florida Keys. The sub, at a depth of 362 feet, was heading for a fish trap that had been left on the *Berry* by researchers who had begun reef population studies the previous day, when suddenly the pilot reported, at 10:13 a.m., that he was snagged in what was later described by a rescue diver as "a lot of spaghetti" consisting of cables, wires and antennae.

On board *Johnson-Sea-Link* in the forward acrylic sphere were 30-year old pilot Archibald (Jock) Menzies and 27-year old marine biologist Robert Meek. In the lock-out chamber were 51-year old Albert D. Stover and 31-year old Edwin Clayton Link.

If ever it appears that events just seem to work themselves out according to an irrational plan that remains completely beyond human understanding, this was just such an event. Although there was an official declaration of fault when it was all over, circumstance alone seemed to have the ultimate rule when two of the four men came to the limit of their days. An uncanny series of events combined to make the accident turn out the way it did, for each happening on its own would probably not have resulted in the loss of life. To begin with, Clayton and Stover were not adequately equipped for long term survival under water because this was intended to be a short dive in which no lockouts were planned. For another thing, Menzies had reported to the ship prior to the entanglement that the Gulf Stream current at that depth was far stronger than any they had ever encountered before, and no one yet knew what this could mean. (Chris Tietze would later describe it as "a terrific, terrific current.") How were they to know that that same current would prevent divers from holding course long enough to rescue them in an entanglement that no one ever expected to occur?

And the tragic chain of events played out. Ed immediately radioed the Key West Naval base for help, with complete faith in the results. *The USS Tringa*, a submarine rescue ship, was at once ordered to get underway, but most of the crew was off on liberty and it was two o'clock in the afternoon before she left the dock. At

11:10 a.m. the Baralyme "scrubber" in the sub, which absorbed carbon dioxide, had broken down. As the carbon dioxide increased, Menzies and Meeks extracted the Baralyme from the scrubber and put it in the fan in the air conditioner, which gave them time and very likely helped to save their lives.

Since they knew that help was on the way, all occupants aboard the submersible decided against a desperate attempt to save themselves by leaving the sub and trying to detach the vehicle; they knew they had a limited amount of air in their tanks, they had no idea what they would encounter, and they had no wetsuits to protect them from the 40-degree water. Clayton and Stover agreed not to pressurize and leave the compartment to surface because the navy was on the way and their gear seemed inadequate to make what would have then been the longest free ascent in marine history. Ed would later blame himself for respecting their decision. He took the side of caution in part because he too knew that the Navy was on the way, and in part because he feared the dangerous current, temperatures, further entanglement, and other unforeseen possibilities. Meanwhile the *Tringa* arrived at four o'clock in the afternoon, but somehow could not get properly anchored with its diving platform in a precise position for helmeted divers to work down to the dive site until a maddening five hours later.

Time and temperature became the true enemies. Those in the forward sphere were insulated by its four-inch thick acrylic, which kept them reasonably warm and helped to save their lives, but the aft chamber occupants were threatened by the cold temperature of the water that the aluminum housing had taken on, which reduced the effectiveness of the Baralyme, in turn causing them to breathe in deadly carbon dioxide. Clayton and Stover tried rubbing the Baralyme over their bodies in an attempt to increase its effectiveness with their body heat.

Help was on the way from all directions. Alcoa's *Seaprobe* was underway. Perry Submarine sent out two subs. A commercial salvage vessel, *A. B. Wood*, chartered by the Navy Ordnance Laboratory, had responded to the Mayday call and was underway. Meanwhile several teams of helmeted divers went down but were unable to get close enough to help because they were swept away by the current. Then a diving bell flown in by the Navy from San Diego, California, arrived at dawn the next morning with four top Navy divers, but they could go no lower than 300 feet and they were unable to get through the debris entangling the sub. John Perry's mini-sub arrived on the scene at two o'clock that afternoon, but it too was unable to penetrate the debris or withstand the strong currents. Meanwhile the divers reported no signs of life in the after chamber and two obviously weakened occupants in the acrylic sphere. Chris Tietze arrived also at two o'clock, to hear Ed say as he leaned on the rail of *Sea Diver*, "I'm afraid you're too late, they are already dead."

It was a twist of irony that the Navy, which Ed had worked with so diligently on the problem of rescuing the occupants of submarines, was now unable to rescue the downed submersible. Instead, it was skipper Hugh Bowen, who arrived on the scene aboard *A. B. Wood II*, 23 hours after he got underway, who would end the agonizing ordeal. To the surprise of the many professionals on the scene, who for the most part were skeptical of his rig, he managed to free the sub within an hour and a half with a tethered tow sled, an underwater camera, a grappling hook and a lifting crane on the boat. Menzies and Meek in the forward sphere were still alive, but after 32 hours in the sub it was too late for Clayton and Al Stover.

Ed and Marion had suffered quiet desperation as the tension mounted during the dreadful 32-hour ordeal, but they remained outwardly calm and focused their attentions on the rescue effort. Though badly shaken, Marion made a heroic effort to keep a log and man the radios, relaying messages. Ed had originally gone aboard *Tringa* to work with the Navy team. Excerpts from an article titled "He Wasn't Just Standing By," Tuesday, January 19, 1972, in the *Binghamton Sun-Bulletin*, describe the scene:

...The tension was electric. ...Mr. Link had looked often at his watch, and he had looked often at the sea, spending long moments alone at the *Tringa's* rail, staring into the floodlighted waters from beneath the long brim on his cap. ...Sleepless and tightlipped, the aging inventor had clutched the walkie-talkie throughout the night and following morning, clenching and unclenching his fists as he coordinated the painfully slow-moving rescue efforts with the *Tringa's* officers and the team of Navy experts flown in from San Diego. ...Mr. Link had been an integral part of the rescue efforts, not just a father standing helplessly by waiting for news of his son. ...Yesterday he had squatted on the *Tringa's* deck with two divers from the Navy team. He explained how to reach the after-hatch....His face was grim and glistened with sweat under his cap.

There were so many "if onlys" when it was over. If only the current hadn't been so strong. If only the Navy's *Amberjack*, which carried the Perry mini-subs, had gotten there sooner and done more. If only Bowen had been closer when he heard the distress call. If only the water hadn't been so cold. If only the occupants had carried extra gear. If only they had done things differently. If only stormy weather had scrubbed the dive. If only that day had never been. But whatever has power over life and death let the circumstances pile up, and the sea claimed her own. Ed nearly had a breakdown; perhaps he did indeed have a breakdown. Chris Tietze claims that for some time Ed became a recluse. He would ask himself over and over again what the outcome might have been if only he had done things differently.

But Ed and Marion had to carry on. Marion told the reporters: "We are going to learn as much from this as we can — and then just go forward."

When all was over John Margetis came across Ed and Marion as they stood in their stateroom just beyond the open door, holding tightly to one another and crying their hearts out. When they realized John was nearby they reached out for him and the three mariners wept together. By the time Clayton's brother Bill arrived it was all over. Clayton's wife Maurine was at home in Vero Beach when the ordeal began, then she later went to Miami to meet Marilyn, who flew in from New York.

When Ed began to recuperate he charged into the development of an unmanned submersible which he called CORD for cabled observation and rescue device, the only tethered vehicle in existence even today (though CORD I and its follow-up, CORD II, are presently out of commission) which can withstand the strong currents of the Gulf Stream. He also pushed his campaign to increase public and governmental awareness of the need to establish and fund a comprehensive national underwater program to improve rescue capabilities. He wrote a letter to the officer in charge of the Coast Guard investigation in which he stated:

> ~ The tragedy of the situation is that with an adequate undersea rescue system and equipment, this loss need never have occurred. Had it been a modern nuclear submarine with 100 men entrapped, the result could not have been the same. The Navy and Coast Guard have recognized the problem for years, but with inadequate funds have not been able to develop such a system. It is inevitable that as man continues to invade the ocean depths, similar accidents are bound to occur in spite of every precaution. The sole remedy — rapid, effective submarine rescue systems — must be developed and kept in strategic locations. The technical knowledge of such a system has been available since the loss of the nuclear submarine *Thresher* ten years ago, but it has not been implemented. ~

Al Stover was survived by his wife Lucy and seven sons (an eighth son was killed earlier while training to be a paratrooper). The highly popular seafarer had retired from the Navy in 1959, where he had taught diving physiology. He had become involved with civilian diving, had become a chief pilot of mini-submarines, and had worked as operations manager for Perry Submarines. He knew the risks involved in underwater work. He had only recently joined Harbor Branch, where he was slated to become the captain of the newly commissioned *R/V Johnson*, a former coast guard cutter that was being transformed into a submersible tender ship and research vessel (which has since been replaced by the all new *R/V Seward Johnson*).

Clayton had lived a full and happy life in his allotted years, doing what he loved most. He too knew the risks. He was a top diving professional like his father, and like his father he had an inborn love for the sea. He was an expert Navy diver in life support systems and underwater safety. He had joined his parents during the diving seasons and taken part in at least a part of almost every expedition they had undertaken. He had enjoyed a loving, if short, marriage and a good family life. He had received two bachelors degrees, one in psychology from Colgate and one in marine biology from the University of Washington, Seattle. He had also done graduate work in marine biology. He worked for Ocean Systems after leaving the Navy and before joining the Smithsonian. He had spent the greater part of his life in oceanic endeavors, making his contributions to oceanography at the cutting edge of "Man-In-Sea." Those who knew him agree that he would have asked no more, except to call attention to the greater need for Man-In-Sea programs and for safety in the seas.

The tragedy in fact led to the creation of "Safety in the Seas," an annual award that is now presented to worthy, conscientious seafarers by Compass Publications, publishers of the popular international technical magazine, *Sea Technology.* Seward Johnson's son, the famed sculptor J. Seward Johnson, Jr., Harbor Branch board chairman and founder of the bronze- casting Atelier in Princeton, New Jersey, would sculpt a four-piece ensemble of giant-sized busts depicting Al Stover and Clayton, cast in stainless steel to symbolize their eternal youth, and his father and Edwin Link, cast in bronze to represent the aging men in their maturity. The grouping, dedicated to "Safety In the Seas," is now installed on the park like grounds of Harbor Branch Oceanographic Institution, facing the Link Engineering Laboratory, which was itself dedicated in 1974. (NOTE: photo on pg. 178, #20).

But even more to the point, the government panel that probed the accident made recommendations for the future, including new regulations to beef the life-support system of research submersibles, to require equipment on board aimed at facilitating rescue operations and to require that rescue ships or airborne rescue units be equipped with underwater television cameras or other equipment designed for deep sea rescue operations.

The team of Coast Guard and National Transportation Safety Board officials conducting the investigation ruled on March 12 that the accident was due to the error of the pilot, Archibald Menzies. The official government report said the accident "was the fault of the submersible pilot for his failure to ensure that the intended maneuvering area ... was free from obstruction." Perhaps it seemed to the shorebound that the diving enthusiasts had grown too complacent after so many years of experience. The report further said: "The submersible pilot and the two occupants of the divers compartment displayed an incredible casualness in their preparations for the dive, considering the inherent hazards of their operations." Still, if only there had not been that incredible convergence of coincidences, the loss might never have occurred.

Afterwards, Ed, continuing his concentration on the rescue device CORD, also developed with Harbor Branch engineer Bob Dolan an aluminum alloy mother ship, *Sea Guardian,* as part of its operations system. Chris Tietze was Ed's partner on CORD from the start, eventually taking over the entire project. CORD was a four-part system: the vehicle itself with underwater TV and still cameras, a half-inch coaxial cable that allowed it to work in swift currents without blowing off course, a control panel on the ship, and a "klunk," or heavy weight that helped to guide it and hold it in position.

When the Harbor Branch research vessel *Seward Johnson* with *Johnson-Sea-Link II* first went to Cape Canaveral February 12, 1986, to participate in the *Challenger* search and recovery mission, CORD II was the first vehicle to successfully function underwater in the strong currents of the Gulf Stream. Other unmanned subs belonging to the Navy tried and failed because their oversized cables tended to act as sails, dragging them off course in the current. CORD, on the other hand, sat directly on station and faithfully relayed to the surface all the data needed prior to sending down the manned submersible. (Coincidentally, just before the ship left home port for Cape Canaveral — on Valentine's day — Marion Link and the narrating author had given Marion's very special guests, their Majesties King Michael and Queen Anne of Rumania, a complete tour of the ship.)

At first neither NASA nor the Navy had realized how great a contribution the Harbor Branch submersibles could make to their mission, expecting the Navy's own 100-foot submarine, the NR-1, to take over on its pending arrival on site. Although the science research ship and sub had already proven themselves by the time the NR-1 arrived, the Navy, thinking the Harbor Branch vehicles were no longer needed, sent *R/V Seward Johnson* on its way back home to Fort Pierce. However, they soon placed a call to Harbor Branch, even before the captain at the helm turned his ship back into its home channel, asking that it please return to the search area. They had since learned that the Navy submarine was too large and cumbersome to do the same job that the highly maneuverable little sub had done. It was particularly valuable to them with its specialized mechanical apparatus that enabled the pilot to do work outside the sub from within the forward sphere. Not long afterward, the Navy requested that *R/V Edwin Link* with *Johnson-Sea-Link I* also join the mission. During the search operation, surface vessels were used to scan the water with sonar, pin-pointing objects on the sea floor. Then the submersibles took NASA and Naval personnel under water for "ground-truthing" (identifying exactly what the objects were). In this way the two submersibles found first the right-hand rocket booster and later the burned-through section that caused the accident. The Navy was to proclaim afterward that *Johnson-Sea-Link I & II* played a key role in bringing the three-month mission to a successful conclusion.

Meanwhile, the year 1973 marked a milestone for Marion when, though overshadowed by the submersible accident in which she lost her youngest son, her second book, *Windows in the Sea*, describing historic underwater events and the development of underwater equipment was published by the Smithsonian Institution Press in Washington.

In 1974, Ed was the recipient of the International Oceanographic Foundation, *HMS Challenger* 1872-1876 "Pioneer in Exploration" award. That year the second deepest lockout dive on record was made from *Johnson-Sea-Link* by Jeffrey Prentice and Steven Nelson to test the recently developed Harbor Branch decompression tables at a depth of 500 feet. In 1975 Ed was named Trustee and Vice President of Harbor Branch. That same year *Johnson-Sea-Link II* was commissioned.

In 1976, on July 24, an honor was "Awarded to Edwin Albert Link For Outstanding Contributions to Aviation," when he was elected to the Aviation Hall of Fame.

Now Ed slipped into a routine that endured throughout his remaining years. He was content to live for the most part at his home adjacent to the Harbor Branch complex with Marion and to go regularly to Binghamton in the summer. On their 45th wedding anniversary, when Ed was 72 and Marion was 69, he presented his bride with a booklet, "Especially for Marion," titled, "It Must be Love." Inside he had drawn a railway ticket, dated June 6, 1976, which read: "To ... Anyplace. From ... Here. Good until used. Agent: Edwin A. Link." It was signed, "I love you, Edwin." In the upper right-hand corner he had penciled the words "Ireland or Ceylon," but his reason for doing so remains a mystery to this day.

Harbor Branch continued to grow. As long as his health held out, at age 72 Ed was content over the remaining years to focus his interests in the engineering division, hands on whenever possible. He acted in an advisory capacity as vice president, while the senior Seward, president and chairman of the board, concentrated his attention primarily on the sciences. Ed and Marion continued to take cruises on *Sea Diver* from time to time, though the ship was also dedicated to marine science research work and submersible operations, along with *R/V Johnson*. Ed also remained involved with CORD and the crane operations on both ships. He and Seward actively participated in NOAA's (National Oceanographic and Atmospheric Administration) initial dives on the *USS Monitor*, with both ships and both submersibles serving as platforms for operations. Underwater cinematographer Al Giddings ("For Your Eyes Only," "Mysteries of the Sea," "Ocean Symphony," etc.) joined the mission and obtained classic footage of Ed and Seward for posterity, including an interview with Ed from within *Sea Diver's* salty wheelhouse.

Ed remained on government panels, and took an active part in the Navy's undersea habitat program. Among others, he was a member of the Research & Development Board of the United States Government and Chairman of the Testing and Training Section of the Guided Missiles Committee of this important board. He also took up a number of avocations, including rebuilding the second theatre organ at his home in Binghamton and becoming involved in energy studies. He experimented with steam and built his own steamboat. In 1980 he and Marion established the Link Antique Steam Foundation for research and education relating to energy resources and their conservation. He built two steam driven trains and took them out on tracks adjacent to Harbor Branch through the mangroves to the Indian River lagoon and back for tours by Harbor Branch personnel and their families, friends, and school groups. He set up other steam driven experiments for children at the Link Steam Foundation building and brought in Vero Beach resident Eleanor Sexton to organize tours and serve as guide and teacher.

In 1980 Ed was presented the Lindbergh Award before 500 dinner guests at the American Museum of Natural History in New York.

In May, 1981, at the SUNY-Binghamton Commencement Exercises, Edwin A. Link was presented with the honorary degree, honoris cause. Though not his first honorary degree, it was the first such award ever conferred by the State University of New York, which was yet another first for Ed.

Gradually his health failed. He constantly battled with diabetes, a heart condition had resulted in his wearing a pacemaker, and he had developed cancer. Still he rode around Harbor Branch on his golf cart with the last of several dogs he had loved over the years, little fluffy Sherpa, the Tibetan terrier. And still he listened to his classical music.

In May, 1981 he was proud to survey with Seward Johnson the extensive exhibits set up in the high bay area in celebration of Harbor Branch's first decade. More than 4,500 people attended. His younger sister Marilyn, an education and business administration major who had most recently been with the Smithsonian Institution in Washington and an airline public relations manager in New York City, was now Managing Director of Harbor Branch.

Ed had encouraged Marilyn, as had Seward, to "take charge" because of her loyalties to both men and to the organization, and because she could bring her much needed and well established organizational skills to their operations.

That July, at age 77, Ed flew to London with Marion for the 50th Anniversary Celebration of the Link Trainer and fulfilled another lifelong dream. (NOTE: photo on pg. 176, #15). Just as he had gone around Europe as a teenager visiting all of the important concert organs, he drove around the United Kingdom visiting the major trains and railway stations. He and Marion wrote a summary of their tour in the UK, which in spite of Ed's failing health was as action-packed as any of his other missions:

~ During a period of 29 days, traveled over 2900 miles of roads in England, Wales and Scotland, using 140 gallons of fuel at 20.7 m.p.g.; visited 21 active and mostly restored Narrow Gauge steam railways; visited 25 railway, ship and other industrial museums, preserved viaducts, aquaducts, canal locks of historic importance, water pumping stations and two folk museums; visited five active water mills; inspected one restored static windmill; visited a unique ecological community complex;

traveled on two lake paddle steamers and inspected a third paddle steamer (Loch Katrine); crossed a sea loch by ferry; traveled across the longest single-span road bridge in the World, the day after its official opening by Queen Elizabeth [just missing yet another first]; endured the variable standards of 16 different hotels; entertained and were entertained, and were honored guests on three occasions; visited the top of the highest mountain in Wales - Snowden; had close-up views of the highest mountain in the UK - Ben Nevis, 4406 ft.; sailed on the largest stretch of inland water in Britain, Loch Lomand, 24 miles long; and failed to see the Loch Ness Monster. ~

After returning home Ed's health continued to degenerate. He was in and out of the hospital. On one occasion, two weeks before the end, he declared his wheelchair to be poorly constructed and set out to redesign it. His attitude toward work had never changed. Looking back over his many years of intensive labor, he still liked to say that he had never worked a day in his life. He was at home in Binghamton when he took his final rest on Labor Day, September 7, 1981.

At Ed's death the news media called Harbor Branch from the world over, and arrived at the institution in numbers from regional newspapers and television stations. Marilyn Link was Managing Director when he died. She told the staff of approximately 127 people that, in keeping with Ed's wishes, it would be "work as usual." Those who knew Ed understood; he saw work as a way of overcoming difficulties and achieving peace of mind. A memorial service was held in Binghamton. In a moving performance Searle Wright played a concert on Ed's rebuilt Link Theatre Organ at Roberson Center. The last tribute to a man who loved great music all his life was a program of Ed's favorite classical pieces, organ music by the automatic player mechanism, and a medley of his favorite Victor Herbert tunes: "Ah, Sweet Mystery of Life," "Indian Summer," and "Kiss in the Dark."

# AFTERWORD

**E**d's death turned out to be the most sensational media event this biographer, then the Public Affairs Director at Harbor Branch, had ever dealt with, except possibly handling the extensive news coverage of the ships and submersibles throughout their prolonged *Challenger* mission with NASA and the US Navy. Seward Johnson survived Ed by almost two years, then he also died of cancer, at age 87. Seward was an extraordinarily generous man who gave in countless ways, particularly to what many see as the greatest love of his life, the oceans. He was also a modest and private man, and in keeping with his wishes, his passing was as quiet as could be for a man of his stature. A simple but moving service was held outdoors at Harbor Branch for friends, family and Harbor Branch personnel.

Coincidentally, at around the same time that *Challenger* went down, there was also intensive news coverage from another quarter: Harbor Branch and the Johnson children were parties in a sensational Will Contest with Seward Johnson's widow, Barbara Johnson, in which the institution and the children won by settlement an inheritance from Johnson.

Thanks to Seward Johnson's generosity and other sources of outside funding, the science and engineering programs and the ship's operations at Harbor Branch have continued to grow. In addition to basic science, a new biomedical marine research division was formed and new aquaculture programs were undertaken. To help increase public awareness of the needs of the marine environment and oceanic possibilities, a visitor's center was opened in 1989, and in 1991 the new Seward Johnson Marine Education and Conference Center was established.

*Johnson-Sea-Link I & II* are now operated from the aft decks of the all-new, 176-foot *R/V Seward Johnson*, captained by Dan Schwartz, and the recently purchased and renovated, 168-foot *R/V Edwin Link*, captained by Chris Vogel. And the sturdy little *R/V Sea Diver*, with another extension of 14 feet supervised by her captain, Ralph van Hoek, still proudly supports science and engineering. Ed's design of a hydraulic, articulated crane has been returned to *Sea Diver* for launch and recovery of a new little yellow submarine, recently purchased from a private company. This "PC-1204" is a four-man Perry Cub with a conning tower, not entirely unlike Ed's and Perry's *Deep Diver* but without a lockout facility and with the added advantage of a small acrylic dome forward for better visibility, named *Clelia* for Seward Johnson's granddaughter.

* * *

DURING THE LAST YEARS OF ED'S LIFE there were many disasters at sea. It must not be forgotten that while he spent much of that time in the ocean, in oceanographic meetings, writing about oceanic possibilities, or in machine shops devising new underwater instruments, he was helping to push back new frontiers. He said himself that accidents would occur, just as they did in the early flying days and just as they are bound to occur as mankind races to the reaches of outer space. He too knew the risks. He was navigating a new realm, and just as he derived so much pleasure from it and had so much to give to it, the sea dealt him a measure of pain. He responded with yet another rescue system. He responded by putting more pressure on the government, and succeeded to some extent, though it is certain that he wanted to see his government go much further and initiate an undersea program counterpart to the space program such as he described in his "Oceanology" draft.

(After a lengthy interview with Ed for the Sunday edition of the June 16, 1974 *Miami Herald*, Anne Wilder and Phil Long of the Fort Pierce bureau had written a feature story about Ed in which they claimed to denote a "residual of bitterness over what he regards as a lack of public interest in undersea and submarine safety.")

Looking back over his career, it is possible to see a hidden refrain of coincidence, synchronicity and circumstance playing endlessly in Ed Link's life. Perhaps the same is true in all our lives, but less noticeable in ordinary circumstances, obscured by the demands of day to day living. There were relationships with Ed between sky and sea, planes and boats, deep space and deep sea exploration. Even his name suggests an interface, perhaps between sky and sea. It was yet another coincidence that his own work would ultimately make a major contribution to the doomed space shuttle *Challenger* mission, in inner space where he thought man's direction should be, before outer space.

Ed was many faceted, and his friends and admirers often saw him very differently. Marion was perhaps attracted to him even before they met, when his friend Gilbert Giles told her of Ed's flight school while traveling on a train from her home in Illion to her first job in Binghamton. Eventually she came to know Ed as no one else did. To her he was as an adventurer who followed a wandering star but never got lost in the process, a beloved husband and father, a persistent genius with a mission to make safety a factor in man's more daring adventures, to which she could give of her talents wholeheartedly. Ed's sons saw him as a father to be extremely proud of, to admire and respect with awe. His younger sister Marilyn saw him as a man who, no matter what he did, "whether it was taking pictures as a photographer or sailing a sailboat or owning and operating *Sea Diver* or starting a hobby with a steam train," would turn it into a productive enterprise then turn it over to the professionals and go on to the next thing. The narrating author, privileged to know him for only a short while, saw him as a "right-brained," intuitive genius who thought like an artist, seeing endless correspondences, and who could in some ways be compared to Leonardo da Vinci. The world saw him as an inventor. John Margetis knew him as a "humble millionaire." Joe MacInnis perceived him as a brilliant engineer and a dreamweaver; Chris Tietze as "a damn clever guy," someone to look up to, a wise mentor, a man who got things done and demanded respect, and who never asked anything of anyone that he wouldn't do himself. Mike Adams considered him an admirable "hardass" who nevertheless could be made to listen. Al Giddings portrayed him as an underwater photographer and an incredible engineer at the cutting edge of oceanography. Tim Askew, engineer and early submersible pilot who worked closely with Ed developing *Johnson-Sea-Link II,* now Harbor Branch Director of Marine Operations, says: "Ed Link was a dreamer who had the unique ability to turn his dreams into reality. His ideas and inventions have enabled mankind to conquer the last frontier—the ocean." Many people at Harbor Branch admired his stature from afar, and yet felt drawn to him with affection, as to a venerated relative. There were others, too far removed from him, who regarded him as old-fashioned, perhaps authoritarian, a fossil from another generation. Ed called himself a navigator.

Joe MacInnis also had this to say:

~ Some of us were fortunate enough to work for him. Whatever the task, he would bend his back to it, toiling alongside us...he made us feel like we were young men on a young frontier. Looking back, decades later, it was an apprenticeship to genius. ~

But oddly enough, in spite of all the diversity of opinion about Ed, when he died and the letters of condolence came pouring in to Marion from all over the world, the different Ed Links seemed to merge into one simple man. As a good friend put it, Ed was: "...quiet, modest, hard working. He will be missed as a great American of our time," and another: "His sense of humor and humility masked his unparalleled ability to solve problems and overcome road blocks."

He was a man of endless ideas, many of which came to him in his dreams. "I can't tell you the number of times that Ed woke me in the middle of the night to tell me about new ideas," says Marion, who shared all of his adventures and who at the age of 85 continues to live in the home they built together at Harbor Branch.

And yet, perhaps he was after all "an enigma," as a reporter once claimed, "whom few people really got to know." How did he do so much in one lifetime? Ed Link had no college degree, no apparent continuity in his wanderings, was without specific goals, never had a map for the future, and yet his life had a strong, unwavering undercurrent of continuity. He began his career with musical instruments, moved to improving the safety and training factors for aviation and ended with the design of undersea vehicles. At one point he took up rebuilding musical instruments, and he continued throughout his life to play his classical music as background to all of his other activities. He almost always had a dog. His interest in trains and the field of energy and its optimum usage continued to the last.

Ed Link the navigator sought new realms, and perhaps now he has found them. Vincent van Gogh once wrote in a letter to his brother Theo that death is a train ride to other realms of the universe.

When Ed's days were done a friend named Barney sent the bereaved Marion this excerpt from Leo Rosen's *The Astonishing Talmud*:

> ~ In a harbor, two ships sailed: one setting forth on a voyage, the other coming home to port. Everyone cheered the ship going out, but the ship coming in was hardly noticed. To this a wise man said: "Do not rejoice over a ship setting out to sea, for you cannot tell what terrible storms it may encounter, and what fearful dangers it may have to endure. Rejoice rather over the ship that has safely reached port and brings its passengers home in peace."
>
> And this is the way of the world: When a child is born, all rejoice; when someone dies, all weep. We should do the opposite. For no one can tell what trials and travails await a newborn child; but when a mortal dies in peace, we should rejoice, for he has completed a long journey, and there is no greater boon than to leave this world with the imperishable crown of a good name. ~

POSTSCRIPT: The surviving Link family members were recently been informed that Edwin A. Link was elected an honoree of the International Aerospace Hall of Fame. His sister Marilyn, grandson Stephen Link, and other relatives and friends attended the induction in formal ceremonies at San Diego, California on September 19, 1992.

# WORKS CITED

Aller, Fran. "If It Didn't Exist, He Invented It." *Science Outlook*. SUNY Binghamton (Oct. 1980).

Bach, Richard. *Illusions*. New York: Delacorte Press, 1977.

Bach, Richard. *Johnathan Livingston Seagull*. New York: Macmillan, 1970.

Bach, Richard. *Nothing by Chance*. New York: Macmillan, 1969.

Baigent, Michael; Richard Leigh. *The Dead Sea Scrolls Deception*. New York: Summit Books, Simon and Schuster, 1991.

Bowers, David; Murray Clark; Harvey Roehl. "An Interview With Ed Link." *Link Piano Company, Inc.* Binghamton. Roehl, 1965.

Cawley, Tom. "Ed Link's vision reached as far as the sea." *Binghamton Press* (1981).

Clark, Martha. "Edwin A. Link." SUNY, Binghamton.

Collins, Larry; Dominique Lapierre. *O Jerusalem*. New York: Simon and Schuster, 1972.

Devine, Reverend. "The Truest and Largest Account of the Late Earthquake in Jamaica." London Library Archives (c. 1692).

Edwards, Betty. *Drawing on the Artist Within*. New York: Simon and Schuster, 1986.

Edwards, Betty. *Drawing on the Right Side of the Brain*. Los Angeles: J.P. Tarcher, 1979.

Ferguson, Marilyn. *The Aquarian Conspiracy*. Los Angeles: J.P. Tarcher, 1980.

Freedburg, Sydney P. "Fisher's Atocha discovery is not all glitter." *The Miami Herald* (Sunday, July 19, 1987).

Furbay, John. Taped personal interview with Edwin A. Link, 1966.

Gilbert, Frank M. *History of the City of Evansville and Vanderberg County Indiana*. Chicago: Pioneer Publishing, 1910.

Hammerschlag, Carl A. *The Dancing Healers*. New York: Harper & Row, 1989.

Hauser, Hillary. *The Adventurous Aquanaut*. Flagstaff, AZ: Best Publishing, 1990.

Hauser, Hillary. *Call to Adventure*. Longmont, Colorado: Bookmakers Guild, 1987.

"He Wasn't Just Standing By." *Binghamton Sun-Bulletin* (Jan. 19, 1972).

Herzog, Arthur. "Explorer of the Underwater Frontier." *True*, (Dec. 1964).

Johnson, Paul. *A History of the Jews*. New York: Harper & Row, 1987.

Kelly, Lloyd L.; Robert B. Parke. *The Pilot Maker*. New York: Grosset & Dunlop, 1970.

Kilbracken, Lord. "The Long, Deep Dive." *National Geographic* (May 1963).

Killgore, James L. "The Planes That Never Leave the Ground." *American Heritage* (Winter 1989).

LeShan, Lawrence: Henry Morgenau. *Einstein's Space & Van Gogh's Sky*. New York: Macmillan, 1982.

Link, Edwin Clayton. "Lost in the Canadian Wilds." *Boys Life* (1949-50).

Link, Edwin A. "Toward Better Air Traffic Control." *Flying Magazine* (1961).

Link, Edwin A. "Our Man-in-Sea Project." *National Geographic* (May 1963).

Link, Edwin A. "Tomorrow on the Deep Frontier." *National Geographic* (June 1964).

Link, Edwin A. "Oceanology." Unpublished Paper, n.d.

Link, Edwin A. "Outpost Under the Ocean." *National Geographic* (April 1965).

Link, Edwin A.; Marion C. Link. *A New Theory on Columbus's Voyage Through the Bahamas*. Washington, DC: Smithsonian Institution (Jan. 20), 1958.

Link, Marion Clayton. *Sea Diver*. 1958. Coral Gables, FL.: University of Miami Press, 1964.

Link, Marion C. "Exploring the Drowned City of Port Royal." *National Geographic* (Ieb. 1960).

Link, Marion Clayton. *Windows in the Sea*. Washington, D.C.: Smithsonian Institution Press, 1973.

Link, Marion Clayton. "An Airman Goes to Sea." *Rudder* (Fawcett Publications), (Dec. 1947).

*Link, The Story of the Link Orchestral Organ*. Binghamton, NY: The Roberson Museum and Science Center, n.d.

Lovelock, James. *The Ages of Gaia*. 1988. New York: Bantam Books — Doubleday, 1990.

MacInnis, Dr. Joseph. "The Dreamweaver." *Sea Technology* (Jan. 1982).

MacLeish, Kenneth. "A Taxi for the Deep Frontier." *National Geographic* (Jan. 1968).

MacLeish, Kenneth. "Sea Search into History at Caesarea." *Life* (1961).

Marx, Robert F. *Port Royal Rediscovered*. New York: Doubleday, 1973.

Morison, Rear Admiral Samuel. *Admiral of the Ocean Sea*. Boston, Little, Brown (1942, 1991).

Peczenki, Fannie. "Antenati." *Fellowship in Prayer*. (April), 1992.

Petersen, Mendel. *History Under the Sea*. Washington D.C.; Smithsonian Institution Press, 1965.

Roehl, Harvey. "Ed Link 1904-1981." Unidentified publication.

Rosen, Leo. *The Astonishing Talmud*. Unidentified publication.

Spall, Juliet R. "Edwin A. Link." Unpublished Paper, 1986.

Stenuit, Robert. "The Deepest Days." *National Geographic*. (April, 1964).

Verhoog, Captain Pieter. *Guanahani Again*. Amsterdam: C. De Boer, Jr. (1947).

Wakelin. James H. Jr. "Lesson and Challenge." *National Geographic*. (June, 1964).

Wilder, Anne; Phil Long. "Pushed by Personal Tragedy, He Invents Sea Rescue Device." *Miami Herald* (June 16, 1974).

Wood, Wanda. (Radio - Community College) Interview Transcription. Binghamton, NY: Oral History Program, Action for Older Persons, Inc., Broome County Oral History Project.

Zukav, Gary. *The Dancing Wu Li Masters*. 1979. (William Morrow) New York: Bantam Books, 1984.

# PERMISSIONS